S0-AUD-627

HIGH PRESSURE
PHYSICS
and CHEMISTRY

Volume 2

High Pressure
Physics
and Chemistry

Edited by

R. S. BRADLEY

Department of Inorganic and Structural Chemistry
The University, Leeds, England

VOLUME 2

ACADEMIC PRESS · LONDON and NEW YORK · 1963

ACADEMIC PRESS INC. (LONDON) LTD.
BERKELEY SQUARE HOUSE
LONDON, W.1

U.S. Edition published by
ACADEMIC PRESS INC.
111 FIFTH AVENUE, NEW YORK 3, NEW YORK

Copyright © 1963 by Academic Press Inc. (London) Ltd.

All rights reserved

NO PART OF THIS BOOK MAY BE PRODUCED IN ANY FORM, BY PHOTOSTAT, MICROFLIM, OR ANY OTHER MEANS, WITHOUT WRITTEN PERMISSION FROM THE PUBLISHER

Library of Congress Catalog Card Number: 63–21395

Printed in Great Britain by
Robert MacLehose & Co., Ltd, The University Press, Glasgow

PREFACE

Following the pioneer work of Bridgman and the successful synthesis of diamond there has been in recent years a rapid development in the study of systems at high pressures, mostly in the ultra-high pressure range. There are several useful symposia and review articles in this field, but most of the monographs deal mainly with experimental techniques. In this book a group of international workers have combined to write a comprehensive and advanced study covering most major aspects of this field, and including both theoretical and experimental work and static and dynamic pressures.

The dangers of such a combined effort are well known, but it is hoped that they are offset by the advantages of an authoritative presentation and comparatively speedy publication. Some degree of overlap has been allowed between different authors, but it is hoped that this will not detract from the book and will in fact enhance the value of the chapters considered separately. An attempt has been made to fill in some of the background of the subject and to present it in a planned frame-work in a manner which would be inappropriate in a collection of papers for a symposium. Although the selection of topics and the balance between them may not suit all readers, it is hoped that research workers will be stimulated to read for further information in the extensive lists of references, on topics not considered in detail.

Most authors deal with pressures greater than 1000 atm. A unified spelling has been adopted but it has not seemed desirable to unify the symbols from chapter to chapter, except those applying to the common thermodynamic functions.

It is hoped that this book will appeal not only to workers in the field but also to those who have a general interest in the states of matter.

June 1963   R. S. BRADLEY

CONTRIBUTORS TO VOLUME 2

R. S. BRADLEY, *School of Chemistry, University of Leeds, England*

BARNETT F. DODGE, *Chemical Engineering Department, Yale University, New Haven, Connecticut, U.S.A.*

G. E. DUVALL, *Poulter Laboratories, Stanford Research Institute, Menlo Park, California, U.S.A.*

G. R. FOWLES, *Poulter Laboratories, Stanford Research Institute, Menlo Park, California, U.S.A.*

S. D. HAMANN, *Commonwealth Scientific and Industrial Research Organisation Division of Physical Chemistry, Melbourne, Victoria, Australia*

D. C. MUNRO, *School of Chemistry, University of Leeds, England*

J. A. S. SMITH, *School of Chemistry, University of Leeds, England*

P. J. WYLLIE, *Department of Mineralogy, The Pennsylvania State University, University Park, Pennsylvania, U.S.A.*

CONTENTS

6. Applications of High Pressure Studies to the Earth Sciences

PETER J. WYLLIE

7.i. Chemical Equilibria in Gases

BARNETT F. DODGE

7.ii. Chemical Equilibria in Condensed Systems

S. D. HAMANN

CONTENTS OF VOLUME I

5.v. Superconductivity of Solids.

D. H. Bowen

5.vi. High Pressure Spectroscopy of Solids.

S. E. Babb, Jr. and W. W. Robertson

5.vii. Diffusion in Solids under Pressure.

A. W. Lawson

Chapter 6

APPLICATIONS OF HIGH PRESSURE STUDIES TO THE EARTH SCIENCES†

PETER J. WYLLIE

*Department of Geochemistry and Mineralogy,
The Pennsylvania State University
University Park, Pennsylvania, U.S.A.*

† Mineral Industries Experiment Station Contribution No. 62–20.

I. INTRODUCTION

THE earth is a giant high pressure laboratory, so it is inevitable that in any book dealing with high pressure chemistry and physics attention should eventually be focused upon the earth. From the surface of the earth to its centre, the pressure increases from 1 bar to 3 640 kb, and the temperature increases simultaneously. This chapter is concerned only with the outer part of the earth, to a depth of approximately 1 000 km, comprising the crust and the upper mantle. The preceding chapters have been concerned largely with the effects of high pressures on homogeneous systems consisting of solids, of liquids, or of gases, but the important processes occurring in the outer part of the earth usually involve heterogeneous equilibria. Within the earth's mantle, solid-solid phase changes may account for seismic and density discontinuities. Many magmas are believed to originate in the mantle, and their development involves solid-liquid, and perhaps solid-liquid-vapour reactions. Within the earth's crust, solid-liquid-vapour, solid-solid, and solid-vapour equilibria are involved in igneous and metamorphic processes. The deformation and folding of rocks during orogeny is a mechanical process, but interstitial gases or solutions may have a profound effect.

It would be impossible in a chapter this size to present a comprehensive survey of the application of high pressure studies to the earth sciences, and no attempt has been made to compile a complete bibliography. References have been selected with the intention of illustrating methods and approaches, and the selection is biased towards the author's own interests. Topics which have been discussed in recent reviews are described briefly, and readers are referred to the publications concerned for details.

The chapter divides conveniently into four parts. Sections I, II, and III are introductory, giving an outline of the range of pressures, temperatures, and compositions encountered in the earth, and the extent to which these conditions can be reproduced experimentally. The author trusts that geological readers will excuse the geological introduction, and hopes that physicists and chemists will welcome it. The second part, Section IV, indicates the wide range of experimental data now available, and only passing reference is made to their applications. In the third part, Sections V, VI, and VII, three specific topics are considered in more detail as examples to illustrate the experimental approach to some geological and geophysical problems. These are: (i) a solid state problem concerning the nature of seismic discontinuities within the earth, (ii) an igneous problem concerning the origin of granite and related rocks, most of which crystallized from melts, and (iii) a metamorphic problem concerning the conditions under which rocks recrystallize in the earth's crust. The fourth part, Section VIII, is a brief statement of the present position, and of the lines of future research which appear to be most promising.

A. *The Earth Sciences*

The classical earth science is geology. It is on and just below the surface of the earth that man cultivates or seeks the food, water, and raw materials necessary for his existence and for the manufacture of the accoutrements of his civilization. Geologists' first interest is therefore in the rocks exposed at the surface. However, when geologists attempt to unravel the processes whereby surface rocks attained their present composition, mineralogical constitution, and position, they are forced to extrapolate to considerable depths within the earth. Only recently has it become possible to test rival hypotheses by experimental measurement of the properties of minerals and rocks at the high pressures and temperatures to which they had been subjected within the earth's crust. Geological time cannot be reclaimed, and evaluation of its effect remains difficult.

The history and evolution of the earth as a whole has long been a favourite topic for physicists, chemists, astronomers, and philosophers, as well as for geologists; and the geologists have benefited in no small measure from the cogitations of these scientists. The earth sciences embrace many disciplines, most of them overlapping to a greater or lesser extent, usually greater, and this overlap makes definition and delineation rather difficult. The most vigorous branches at the present time are geophysics and geochemistry. These sciences have been defined as the physics and chemistry of the earth, respectively. However, such broad definitions leave little for the geologist, and it is perhaps more appropriate to define geophysics and geochemistry as those branches of the earth sciences in which the principles and practices of physics and chemistry, respectively, are used to study the earth. It is with the experimental approach to geochemistry that this chapter is mainly concerned, but the structure and composition of the earth, and the processes operating within it, can only be established from the combined data of geology, geophysics and geochemistry.

B. *Historical*

With a few notable exceptions, it is only since 1949 that high pressure-high temperature studies aimed at solving problems in the earth sciences have been successfully accomplished. Excellent historical reviews of work in this field have been presented by Morey and Niggli (1913), Morey and Ingerson (1937), Christensen and Roedder (1952), Loewinson-Lessing (1954), Eitel (1954), Roy and Tuttle (1956), and Ellis and Fyfe (1957).

II. THE EARTH

In order to plan experimental work designed to elucidate the processes occurring at various depths within the earth, some knowledge of the composition and physical state, and of the temperatures and pressures of the earth's interior is required. Details supplementing the brief outline which follows can be found in several textbooks (e.g. Mason, 1958; Jacobs *et al.*, 1959; Howell, 1959).

A. *Physical Properties*

1. *Seismic Discontinuities*

Analysis of earthquake waves shows that there are two major or first-order discontinuities in the earth at depths of about 35 km (in continental regions), and 2 900 km. These divide the earth into three parts: the crust, extending down to the Mohorovicic discontinuity (henceforth referred to as the M discontinuity); the mantle, extending from M to the Wiechert-Gutenberg discontinuity; and the core, extending from this level to the centre of the earth. Second-order discontinuities have been recognized in all three parts of the earth, and

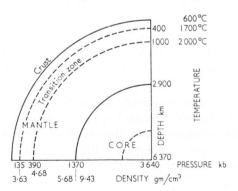

Fig. 1. Section through the earth.

the existence of a transition zone in the mantle between two second-order discontinuities at depths of approximately 400 km and 1 000 km appears to be well-established.   These features are summarized in Fig. 1.   Between M and the beginning of this transition zone there is a low-velocity layer, with the minimum wave velocity occurring at a depth of about 150 km.

2. *Density Distribution*

Bullen (1936) computed the density distribution within the earth, and he reported an abrupt density increase across the mantle-core boundary, and a nearly discontinuous change in density at a depth of 300–400 km. Some density values are shown in Fig. 1.

3. *Pressure Distribution*

From his density data, Bullen also calculated the pressure distribution within the earth.   At the M discontinuity, there is considerable variation in pressure because the thickness of the crust varies from place to place. A mean value for continental areas is 10 kb.   The pressure distribution

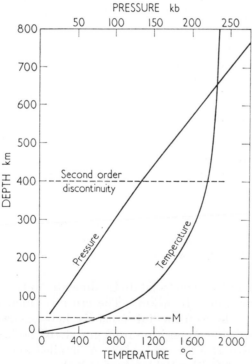

FIG. 2. Geothermal gradient (reproduced with permission from Howell, 1959) and pressure gradient (reproduced with permission from Bullen, 1936) in the earth.

to a depth of 800 km is shown in Fig. 2 along with an estimate of the geothermal gradient.   Other pressures are shown in Fig. 1.

4. *Temperature Distribution*

Estimates of the temperature distribution within the earth are subject to large uncertainties.   An estimate by Howell (1959) is shown in Fig. 2. The temperature at the base of the continental crust is probably in the range 500–600° C.

5. *Internal Structure*

Several earth models have been proposed, and one of those generally accepted is illustrated in Fig. 1.   Estimated densities, pressures, and temperatures at critical depths are shown.   Experiments so far completed at high pressures and temperatures have applications only to processes occurring in the crust and upper mantle (Section III, C). The compositions of these parts of the earth are discussed in the following sections.

B. *The Earth's Crust*

The earth's crust is variable in thickness and in composition.   The stable continental shields and ocean floors are crossed by narrow zones of greater activity, the young orogenic belts (fold mountains and island arcs) and the mid-oceanic ridges.   The continental crust averages 35 to 40 km in thickness, increasing to as much as 60 km in mountainous regions (see Fig. 3).   The oceanic crust averages about 5 km in thickness,

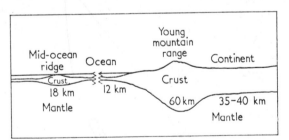

FIG. 3. Section through the earth's crust.

and this is overlain by unconsolidated sediments and sea-water with a combined thickness of 6 to 8 km.   The crust is thicker beneath the oceanic ridges.   The continental crust is heterogeneous, probably grading downwards in composition from granite to gabbro, whereas the oceanic crust is basaltic (or gabbroic).   A detailed symposium on the earth's crust was edited by Poldervaart (1955).

The continental crust is composed of igneous, sedimentary, and metamorphic rocks. Igneous rocks are those which crystallized from a silicate melt (magma) containing small, but influential proportions of dissolved volatile components. Sedimentary rocks are fragmental or chemical deposits produced by the breakdown of pre-existing rocks, followed by deposition in water or on land. Metamorphic rocks are those which have recrystallized in response to high temperatures and high pressures (normally in the presence of dilute solutions) within the crust. Although about 75% of the surface of the earth is covered by a thin veneer of sedimentary rocks, these make up only 5% of the outer 16 km of the crust. The remaining 95% is composed of rocks of igneous origin. The origin and behaviour of igneous rocks is thus of prime importance for an understanding of the evolution of the crust.

The average composition of the earth's crust is close to the average composition of igneous rocks. An estimate is given in Table I. It is

TABLE I. The Commoner Chemical Elements in the Earth's Crust
(Table 10 in Mason, 1958)

	Weight per cent	Atom per cent	Radius (Å)	Volume per cent
O	46·60	62·55	1·40	93·77
Si	27·72	21·22	0·42	0·86
Al	8·13	6·47	0·51	0·47
Fe	5·00	1·92	0·74	0·43
Mg	2·09	1·84	0·66	0·29
Ca	3·63	1·94	0·99	1·03
Na	2·83	2·64	0·97	1·32
K	2·59	1·42	1·33	1·83

TABLE II. Analytical Data on Kilauea Gases
(Table 22 in Mason, 1958)

	Minimum and maximum volume percentages at 1 200° and 760 mm	Average analysis in volume per cent	Average analysis in weight per cent
H_2O	17·97–97·09	67·68	45·12
CO_2	1·42–47·68	12·71	20·71
CO	0·00– 3·92	0·67	0·69
H_2	0·00– 4·22	0·75	0·06
N_2	0·68–37·84	7·65	7·93
A	0·00– 0·56	0·20	0·30
SO_2	0·00–29·83	7·03	16·67
S_2	0·00– 8·61	1·04	2·47
SO_3	0·00– 5·51	1·86	5·51
Cl_2	0·00– 4·08	0·41	0·54

interesting to note that only 8 elements are present in amounts exceeding 1%, and these together make up over 98% of the earth's crust. The influence of volatile components in igneous magmas has been mentioned. Some indication of the proportions of volatile components in magmas may be obtained from chemical analyses of gases emitted from volcanoes. Table II shows that water is the dominant volatile component, with CO_2 the next most abundant.

1. *Igneous Minerals and Rocks*

The average chemical composition of the igneous rocks is given in Table I. The elements are combined in seven principal mineral groups: The silica minerals, feldspars, feldspathoids, micas, amphiboles, pyroxenes, and olivine. The average mineralogical composition of igneous rocks is quartz 12·0%, feldspars 59·5%, pyroxene and hornblende 16·8%, biotite 3·8%, accessory minerals 7·9%. Igneous rocks may be classified on the basis of their chemical composition, but their mineralogical composition is more often used. Figure 4 gives the

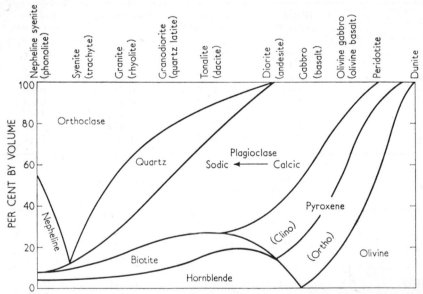

FIG. 4. Approximate mineralogical composition of the commoner igneous rocks (lavas in brackets). (Reproduced with permission from Mason 1958, p. 96.)

mineralogical composition of the common types of igneous rocks. Of these, field observations show that granite (acid) and basalt (basic) are the most abundant rocks. Granite intrusions are generally associated with mountain building and metamorphism, and basalt forms 98% of the world's lava flows.

2. *Sedimentary Minerals and Rocks*

Since sediments are formed at the surface of the earth, they are not subjects for high pressure studies. However, they become metamorphosed when buried and folded, and it is helpful to know the nature of the rocks before metamorphism. The chemical composition of sedimentary rocks is very varied but only a few minerals can be considered as abundant constituents. These are quartz, feldspars, calcite, dolomite, and the clay minerals. In mineralogy, therefore, the sediments may be contrasted with igneous rocks in their abundance of hydrated and carbonated minerals.

3. *Metamorphic Minerals and Rocks*

The chemical composition of a metamorphic rock may correspond to that of any pre-existing rock, igneous or sedimentary. Because of this, and the fact that they may develop under a wide range of temperatures and pressures, metamorphic rocks contain a wide variety of minerals. Quartz, feldspars, pyroxenes, amphiboles, chlorite and micas are abundant, the inosilicates and the phyllosilicates being especially characteristic of metamorphic rocks. Typical metamorphic minerals which are rare or absent in igneous and sedimentary rocks, include garnets, epidote, staurolite, kyanite, sillimanite, andalusite, and cordierite. Calcite and dolomite persist in metamorphosed limestones, and reaction between carbonates and silicates produces calc-silicate minerals such as wollastonite. The influence of pressure in the formation of metamorphic rocks is illustrated by the orientation of platy and prismatic minerals, producing foliation and lineation in the rocks.

C. *The Earth's Mantle*

The mantle is marked everywhere by a sudden increase in the velocities of seismic waves. Of rocks known at the surface, only dunite (olivine), peridotite (olivine + pyroxene + minor plagioclase), or eclogite (jadeitic pyroxene + pyrope-rich garnet) have the properties required to satisfy the available geophysical data. Until the Mohole deep-drilling project is successfully accomplished (Hess, 1960), there are no direct observations on its composition. Indirect evidence for the mantle composition is provided by analogy with meteorites, on the assumption that these represent fragments from a disrupted planet with composition and structure similar to that of the earth. Unfortunately, there are divided opinions about interpretation of the analogy (e.g. Lovering, 1958; MacDonald, 1959; Harris and Rowell, 1960).

If the upper mantle is composed of dunite or peridotite, the M discontinuity is caused by a chemical change from gabbro to peridotite, but if it is composed of eclogite, the discontinuity may be simply a mineralogical phase change, with the gabbro of the crust undergoing a transition to eclogite, its denser chemical equivalent. This is an important problem which may be resolvable by high pressure studies (Section V, B).

The transitional zone between the second-order discontinuities in the mantle may similarly be caused by a gradual change in composition, or by a phase change. The composition change invoked involves the appearance of disseminated nickel-iron. The phase change hypothesis involves a transition from olivine and other minerals to a complex spinel solid solution (Section V, A).

The essential rigidity of the earth's mantle confirms that it is composed of crystalline material, yet the formation of magmas within the mantle indicates that mantle temperatures are not far below melting temperatures. Limits for the geothermal gradient at depth may therefore be provided by high pressure melting experiments on various minerals and rock samples (Section IV).

D. *Geological Processes*

Much of the impetus for high pressure, high temperature studies has come from attempts to understand the origin of igneous and meta-morphic rocks. These rocks provide fossil records of the processes which are involved in the development of mountain ranges and the formation of the continents, processes which are merely surface manifestations of changes proceeding within the mantle. An understanding of the origin of igneous and metamorphic rocks will therefore lead to a better understanding of the evolution of the earth as a whole.

1. *Igneous Processes*

(a) *Basic Magmas.* There is good evidence to support Bowen's (1928) contention that basaltic magmas originate by partial fusion of ultrabasic mantle material. Some may be formed at depths as great as 700 km, in the transition zone of the mantle, where deep focus earthquakes occur. The composition of the melt produced will depend not only upon the composition of the mantle, but also upon its mineralogical constitution at the depth of fusion. Experimental studies on high pressure polymorphs of silicate minerals may therefore have considerable bearing on the origin of magmas. Once a magma has developed it migrates upwards, being lighter than the surrounding rocks, and it may crystallize in a region of high pressure within the earth's crust, or it may be erupted at the surface as a lava. The effect of volatile components on the crystallization and differentiation of the magma may be estimated from experimental data.

(b) *Acid and Intermediate Magmas.* Granites and granodiorites are concentrated in enormous batholiths in the roots of fold mountain chains. The origin of these rocks has been the subject of heated controversy (Section VI). It has been maintained that they represent differentiation products of a basaltic magma, that they are primary magmas developed by partial fusion of crustal material where the crust has been forced downwards into hotter regions, or that they formed by recrystallization in the solid state without the intervention of a liquid phase. Investigation of the solid-liquid-vapour and solid-vapour phase relationships of natural rocks and related synthetic systems at high pressures has yielded much information about the feasibility of the various theories proposed.

2. *Metamorphic Processes*

Detailed accounts of metamorphic processes can be found in Ramberg (1952), Fyfe *et al.* (1958), and Turner and Verhoogen (1960). An excellent, shorter account is contained in Mason (1958, Chapter 10). Metamorphic processes differ from those which control the formation of sedimentary and igneous rocks. Recrystallization proceeds in the solid state, with temperature increasing, and the important reactions involve solid-solid, or solid-vapour equilibria.

Metamorphic rocks are of several types. Dislocation or dynamic metamorphism is produced by high shearing stress at moderate temperatures; the process is destructive. Thermal, or contact metamorphism is produced in rocks baked by an igneous intrusion, usually with low to moderate pressure conditions. Regional metamorphism is restricted to the elongated orogenic belts which border the continents. The burial of sediments in a geosynclinal trough is accompanied by increasing temperature and pressure, and reactions are promoted by the influence of shear stress, which accompanies the folding and deformation of the rocks, as well as by the circulation of pore fluids. In the highest grades of metamorphism, metamorphic and igneous processes converge, and the rocks eventually undergo partial fusion with the formation of magmas. The possible formation of granites in the solid state has already been mentioned. The relative positions of metamorphic facies are illustrated in Fig. 5. The pressure and temperature scales are not well-defined.

Progressive metamorphism, either thermal or regional, results in a series of dehydration and decarbonation reactions, and other reactions involving no release of volatile components (solid-solid reactions). Water and carbon dioxide are thus progressively expelled from the rocks. About this there appears to be general agreement, but there are significant differences of opinion concerning the composition, mobility,

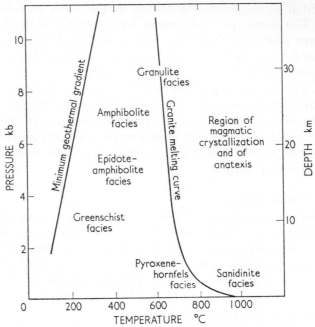

Fig. 5. The principal metamorphic facies with estimates of temperature and pressure. (Reproduced with permission from Mason, 1958, p. 256.)

and the pressure of the pore fluid during metamorphism. These differences of opinion lead to very different estimates of metamorphic temperatures, using as a basis the available experimental data. An understanding of metamorphic processes is thus a prerequisite for the successful application of experimental data to metamorphic reactions.

Some of the important variables to be evaluated include the influence on mineral reactions of bulk composition, pore fluid composition (vapour phase composition in experimental studies), temperature, hydrostatic pressure, and shearing stress.

3. *Formation of Ore Deposits*

An ore deposit is a concentration of minerals from which one or more metals can be profitably extracted. The minerals may be concentrated directly from an igneous magma during crystallization: they may become concentrated in the silicate fractions which crystallize late, such as pegmatites: or they may be precipitated from the gas or liquid (aqueous solution) remaining after crystallization of the silicate minerals from the magma, or expelled from a magma during crystallization. There is evidence to support the view that the formation of many ore deposits is genetically related to magmatic processes, but the deposition may occur under conditions which are related to metamorphic processes, and this includes reaction of gases or solutions with the country rocks.

There has been a great deal of discussion about the nature of the ore-forming fluids, especially with respect to their compositions, the temperature and pressure conditions during precipitation of various minerals, their acidity or alkalinity, and whether they are gaseous or liquid. Experimentally, it is desirable to obtain reliable data on the solubilities of metallic compounds and silicates in dilute solutions of various compositions at various temperatures and pressures. Measurement of the PT stability fields of sulphide minerals may also yield important information about the conditions of formation of ore deposits (Kullerud, 1959). Some of the problems are clearly stated in a recent paper by Barnes and Kullerud (1961), which deals with equilibria in sulphur-containing aqueous solutions, based on work in the system Fe–S–O, and which provides a comprehensive review of the thermodynamic requirements on the chemistry of the formation of ore deposits.

III. EQUIPMENT AND METHODS

Equipment for high pressure research has already been dealt with in Chapter 2. However, it is perhaps worth while to draw attention to the types of equipment which have proved most useful in studies applicable to the earth sciences, where high temperatures are required, as well as high pressures. The types of apparatus may be divided into four categories (Dachille and Roy, 1960a) depending upon whether the applied pressure is hydrostatic or uniaxial, and whether the heating is external or internal to the pressure vessel.

A. *Hydrostatic Pressure Vessels*

1. *Externally Heated*

One of the first vessels used for systematic investigation of heterogeneous equilibria in silicate systems at high pressures and temperatures was the " Morey bomb ", (Morey, 1953). Since the whole vessel is placed in a furnace, its pressure-temperature range is limited. This range was extended in the pressure vessel designed by Tuttle (1949), an extremely simple device, which is familiarly known as the " Tuttle bomb " or the " test-tube bomb ". Because of its simplicity of operation and its adaptability, the Tuttle bomb has provided more data of geological interest than any other type of high pressure apparatus.

The fact that it is relatively inexpensive makes it popular as well as useful.

2. *Internally Heated*

The temperature which can be attained by the Tuttle bomb is limited by the hot strength of the alloy used. In order to reach higher temperatures, a small furnace is placed inside of a larger vessel whose outer wall is cooled by circulating water (Smyth and Adams, 1923; Goranson, 1931; Yoder, 1950a; Clark *et al.*, 1957; Baker, 1961).

This type of apparatus is usually rather cumbersome. Modifications by Griggs and Kennedy (Kennedy, 1960) promise to make measurements much simpler by permitting fast sample interchange. One of these has been described in detail by Goldsmith and Heard (1961).

B. *Uniaxial Devices*

1. *Externally Heated*

The simplest type in this class is Bridgman's " simple squeezer ". A modification to permit the study of mineral reactions at high pressures and temperatures was described by Griggs and Kennedy (1956). Dachille and Roy (1960b) have described a simple squeezer in which the lower piston rotates continuously back and forth through a 2° arc, adding a shearing component to the hydrostatic pressure.

2. *Internally Heated*

An internally heated version of the uniaxial device was first described by Coes (1953). Many variants have been developed, and some of these are described in Chapter 2. The design of Boyd and England (1960a) has yielded data of considerable geological and geophysical significance.

C. *Extent of Experimental Probe*

Figure 6 illustrates the experimental limits of the four types of apparatus described above. A geothermal gradient illustrates the extent of the experimental probe within the depths of the earth attainable by the use of these devices. In order to reproduce conditions within the earth, samples of selected compositions have to be subjected to pressures and temperatures corresponding to points on the geothermal gradient.

The hydrostatic pressure vessels provide an experimental probe through the earth's crust. Conditions corresponding to a depth of 20 km, or about halfway to M on the continents, can readily be attained in Tuttle cold-seal pressure vessels, and Tuttle (personal communication) has recently extended this range to 40 km. Theoretically, the internally heated gas vessels can reproduce conditions within the earth's mantle, but most results obtained so far have been limited to 10 kb, corresponding approximately to the M discontinuity in continental regions.

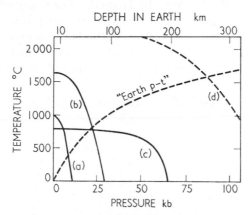

FIG. 6. Approximate experimental limits of various types of apparatus. (Reproduced with permission from Dachille and Roy, 1960a.) (a) Tuttle test-tube pressure vessel; (b) Internally-heated, hydrostatic pressure vessel; (c) Simple squeezer, externally heated; (d) Internally-heated piston and cylinder devices.

Although pressures corresponding to a depth of 300 km can be attained with uniaxial devices, the high temperatures in the mantle at this depth are beyond experimental limits. The internally heated uniaxial devices are theoretically capable of probing conditions to depths of 250 km or more, but little systematic work has been reported under the extreme conditions.

It can be seen from Fig. 6 that, despite the recent advances in equipment design, the extent of the experimental probe within the earth is still very limited. It does not extend as far as the second-order discontinuity in the upper mantle.

D. Experimental Method

Most available data have been obtained using an adaption of the quenching technique which has been so successful in the study of silicate melts at atmospheric pressure. Small samples (normally 5–50 mg) of known bulk composition are held at the required temperature and pressure for a length of time believed to be sufficient for attainment of equilibrium. The reaction is then quenched, by rapid cooling and release of pressure. The phases thus preserved are examined and identified by X-ray techniques, the petrographic microscope, differential analysis, infra-red absorption spectroscopy, and any other analytical techniques which prove useful in particular systems.   Methods for differential thermal analysis at high pressures have been developed by Smyth and Adams (1923), Yoder (1950a, 1952a), and Baker (1961), but the approach has not yet been widely used.   For many silicate systems, homogeneous glasses prepared by repeated fusion of suitable components are satisfactory starting materials.   Methods of preparation have been reviewed by Schairer (1959).   For other systems, gels may be more suitable;   their preparation has been described by Roy (1956).

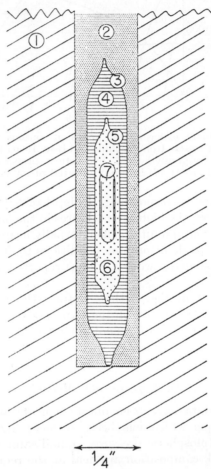

Fig. 7. Sketch of assembly for controlling oxygen fugacity at high temperatures and water vapour pressures.   (Reproduced with permission from Eugster and Wones, 1962.)   (1) pressure vessel;   (2) pressure medium, H_2O;   (3) sealed gold capsule;   (4) oxygen buffer;   (5) sealed platinum capsule;   (6) charge;   (7) open silver capsule.

Mechanical mixtures of oxides, or of carbonates or hydroxides, may also be employed (Yoder and Eugster, 1954; Wyllie and Tuttle, 1960a), although these are homogeneous only on a coarser scale than glasses or gels. Natural minerals and natural rocks, crushed to fine powders, have also been used as starting materials.

In the hydrostatic pressure vessels, two experimental approaches may be employed. In the first, the crystalline or amorphous sample is contained in a gold foil crucible, and the required pressure is imparted to the sample by a gas of known composition; water, carbon dioxide, argon, or a mixture of gases may be used. The other approach involves the use of a sealed gold or platinum capsule. In one method, water, or a stable hydrous solution of a second volatile component, is weighed into a capsule together with solid components. In another method, H_2O and crystalline materials containing carbonate are sealed within a capsule. Under appropriate experimental conditions carbon dioxide is released from the crystalline components and mixes with the water vapour. Pressure is transmitted to the sample inside the capsule by collapse of the walls in response to the pressure applied within the vessel by any hydrostatic pressure medium.

An ingenious technique for controlling the fugacity of oxygen at a very low level while an iron-bearing sample is subjected to high pressures of water vapour at high temperatures, has been developed by Eugster (1957a). The experimental method was described in detail by Eugster and Wones (1962). It involves the use of a buffered mixture separated from the sample by platinum, through which hydrogen diffuses to keep the oxygen fugacity within the sample at the level demanded by the buffer (Fig. 7).

E. *Equilibrium Problems*

The attainment and recognition of stable equilibrium are among the most difficult problems involved in high pressure studies relevant to the earth sciences. Equilibrium in silicate systems has been discussed by Christensen and Roedder (1952), Goldsmith (1953), Roedder (1959), Schairer (1959), and Fyfe (1960), among many others.

Fyfe (1960) recently published a searching review of the synthetic, quenching method, with specific reference to equilibrium problems. The influence of starting materials on results obtained received special attention. The problem is that the most reactive materials are likely to produce metastable phases, whereas the most desirable materials are likely to be so low in free energy that they do not react in a reasonable time.

Proof of equilibrium in the experimental determination of phase diagrams is often difficult, and in some silicate systems it may be practically impossible to avoid metastable equilibrium. Despite these problems, as Fyfe was careful to point out, the experimental data already obtained at high pressures and temperatures have been and continue to be of great usefulness and applicability to the earth sciences.

IV. The Range of Available Data

A. *Introduction*

Much of the early interest in high pressure studies stemmed from the effort to synthesize minerals and, as indicated in other chapters, much of the recent interest lies in the effort to synthesize new materials and to grow large crystals for use in an advancing technology. Synthesis alone does not provide data with useful applications to the earth sciences. Rocks formed under a range of pressures and temperatures, and a knowledge of the pressure-temperature stability fields of minerals and mineral assemblages is required.

Most phase equilibrium studies applicable to the earth sciences involve silicate minerals or carbonates, and volatile components may be added at high pressures. It is known that volatile components have played a most important role in the genesis of rocks. These volatile components may be essential in that they take part in the reactions, or they may act as catalysts promoting solid-solid transitions without combining with the crystalline phases. Some of the severe kinetic problems encountered in the study of silicate reactions are greatly eased by the presence of a volatile component under high pressures. Water, the most abundant volatile in the earth's crust, is especially effective.

It is convenient to consider the experimental studies in two groups: those without volatile components, and those including volatile components. The former group includes measurements of the physical properties of minerals and rocks, studies of solid-solid phase changes, and studies of the melting curves of minerals. In the latter group, a vapour or gaseous phase is usually present, and the various types of reactions include solid-solid phase changes, with a vapour phase present as a catalyst; dissociation reactions, in which the volatile component enters both crystalline and vapour phases; liquid-vapour or solid-liquid-vapour equilibria, where the volatile component may be distributed between all phases; measurements of the solubility of the volatile components in the liquid phase, and of the crystalline phases in the dense gaseous phase. In the following outline, the range of available high temperature-high pressure data is divided initially in terms of composition. Systems are considered on the basis of the volatile components present, and each division is subdivided according to the type of reaction, e.g. solid-solid, solid-vapour, solid-liquid, and solid-liquid-vapour. Solubility measurements are described together at the end of this review.

B. *Physical Properties of Minerals and Rocks*

An excellent information source for the physical properties of minerals and rocks is the Special Paper published by the Geological Society of America (Birch *et al.*, 1942). More recent measurements at high pressures and temperatures have been reviewed in several papers, and these will not be discussed in detail here. It is a fact that rapid advances have been made in this field, as in other high pressure fields, only since the design of specialized equipment.

1. *Flow, Fracture, and Strength*

Rocks appear to be strong and brittle, yet there is abundant evidence that they are extremely weak on a large scale over long periods of time. Experimental studies on the flow, fracture, and strength of rocks are necessary for an understanding of the mechanics of deformation of rocks in the earth. Petrofabric analysis of crystallographic orientations in deformed rocks has produced a great number of objective data, but interpretation has lagged behind. Investigation of the crystal fabric of specimens deformed under known conditions should lead to more precise interpretations of these data.

In one of the pioneering publications in this field, Griggs (1940) concluded that five environmental factors should be investigated experimentally: confining pressure, shear stress, temperature, time, and the effect of solutions. His results indicated that pressure alone is inadequate to explain the natural behaviour of rocks. From reconnaissance work in the presence of solutions, he concluded that solution and recrystallization may play an important role in rock deformation. Much more recently, Handin (1960) stated that, prior to 1957, only the effect of confining pressure had been adequately investigated in rocks other than carbonates. Since then, considerable progress has been made as indicated by Handin's (1960) review for the period 1957–1960.

A memoir edited by Griggs and Handin (1960) contains papers covering most of the recent work completed on experimental rock deformation. Griggs and Handin (1960) tabulate experimental data suggesting that all materials will pass from a brittle to a ductile state if the temperature, or pressure, or both are raised high enough. For example, ordinary limestone can be deformed more than 1 000% at 5 kb pressure and temperatures in the range 600° C to 800° C. The memoir contains a comprehensive bibliography.

2. *Elastic Constants of Rocks*

In order to interpret seismic velocities in terms of materials, the effect of pressure and temperature on the elastic constants or the velocities of elastic waves in rocks must be known. There are now many published measurements. Birch has been active in this field, and in 1960 he presented data for the velocity of compressional waves in many rocks up to 10 kb pressure. In a later paper (Birch, 1961), he discussed the results obtained. At pressures above a few kilobars, the velocity depends mainly upon density and mean atomic weight. Examples of measured wave velocities in km/sec at 1 kb and at 10 kb pressure are: granite, 6·00 and 6·42; gabbro, 6·95 and 7·11; eclogite, 7·56 and 7·92; dunite, 7·65 and 7·87. Further details, together with extensive bibliographies, can be found in these two papers by Birch (1960, 1961).

C. *Systems without Volatile Components*

Reactions of this type have been treated in some detail in Chapter 5. They are particularly important in geological processes because the positions of the reactions on a pressure-temperature projection are independent of any volatile components present in the rocks (so long as the volatile components do not react with the crystalline phases). Furthermore, when the phases concerned are of constant composition, the transition is independent of bulk composition. They thus offer good prospects for estimating the pressures and temperatures attained during various geological processes.

1. *Solid-Solid*

Measured curves for solid-solid transitions are plotted in Fig. 8. The quartz-coesite transition has already been discussed (Chapter 5). The effect of shearing stress on the kinetics of this reaction has been reported by Dachille and Roy (1960b), who found that the reaction rate was increased by two to three orders of magnitude.

Al_2SiO_5 exists in three polymorphic modifications, andalusite, kyanite and sillimanite, and all three occur in metamorphic rocks. Determination of their stability fields would provide extremely useful fixed reference lines on a PT projection. Clark *et al.* (1957) and Clark (1961) studied the equilibrium between kyanite and sillimanite.

Most natural reactions are likely to involve not two, but several phases. Data on complex reactions are still scarce, but the phase relationships between nepheline, albite, quartz, and jadeite (dense phase) have received considerable attention, both theoretical (Yoder, 1950b) and experimental. Robertson *et al.* (1957) located the position of the univariant curve for the reaction albite + nepheline⇌jadeite. The shear apparatus permitted its study at lower temperatures, in the range 300° C to 600° C (Dachille and Roy, 1962). Birch and LeComte (1960)

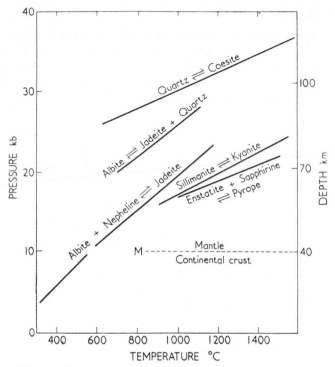

FIG. 8. Some high pressure transitions in minerals.

studied the reaction albite⇌jadeite + quartz. Kennedy (1960) reported complications caused by the solid solution which occurs among these phases. Boyd and England (1959) determined the stability field of pyrope, bounded on its low-pressure side by less dense crystalline phases, and on its high-temperature side by a melting curve.

Boyd and England (1960b) have measured the solubility of alumina in enstatite ($MgSiO_3$) at 1 400° C and 18·2 kb pressure. They found that at least 14 and perhaps 19 weight % Al_2O_3 can be dissolved in $MgSiO_3$. Enstatites found in rocks believed to have formed at high pressures are characteristically rich in alumina compared to enstatites in rocks from low-pressure environments, and further experimental data may yield a means of estimating the pressure of formation of rocks containing enstatite. Unfortunately, the solubility of Al_2O_3 in enstatite depends not only upon pressure but also upon its availability, that is, upon the bulk composition of the rock. Clark and Neufville (1962) reported continuous solid solution between $CaMgSi_2O_6$ (diopside) and $CaAl_2SiO_6$

B   H.P.P. 2

at 20 kb pressure. The behaviour of alumina in dense, high pressure mineralogy is clearly important.

2. *Solid-Liquid*

The experimental measurement of melting curves of silicate minerals at high pressures provides upper temperature limits for the geothermal gradient, as well as estimates of the temperatures of basaltic magmas in the region of their origin. Several melting point curves are illustrated in Fig. 9. The mean slopes of the melting curves for albite (Birch and

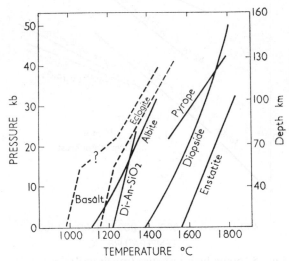

FIG. 9. Melting curves of minerals, mineral systems, and rocks. Compare Figs. 11 and 21.

LeComte, 1960; Boyd and England, 1961), enstatite (Boyd and England, 1961), diopside (Yoder, 1952a; Boyd and England, 1961), and pyrope (Boyd and England, 1959), in the pressure range 10 to 30 kb are 9°, 9·5°, 9°, and 14° C/kb, respectively. Neufville *et al.* (1962) have reported preliminary work in the system $CaMgSi_2O_6$ (Di)–$CaAl_2Si_2O_8$ (An)–SiO_2 at 20 kb. The slope for the solidus in this more complex system is about 5° C/kb.

D. *Systems with Water as a Volatile Component*

The effects of volatile components on phase diagrams differ only in degree from those of other components (Christensen and Roedder, 1952, p. 185). The main difference is that changes in pressure have a great effect on the concentration of a volatile component such as water in a silicate melt, and on the concentration of the " non-volatile " components in a gaseous phase. Furthermore, because of the low molecular weight of water compared to most other components of silicate systems, a small change in concentration of the dissolved water produces a large change in both solidus and liquidus temperatures.

The effect of water vapour under pressure on those physical properties of silicate materials involving rate processes (viscosity, nucleation, crystallization, melting, etc.) is very great. This has made possible the study of silicate systems which have persistently defied experimenters in the " dry " way. Buerger (1948) explained the rate effects in terms of reduction of the number of Si–O–Si bridges in polymerized silicate liquids when O is replaced by (OH). For sub-solidus reactions, Donnay et al. (1959) have proposed that changes in Al–Si distribution occur when tetrahedra are pried open and closed by diffusing protons and hydroxyl ions.

1. Solid-Solid

Many sub-solidus reactions involving silicates are extremely sluggish, but in the presence of water vapour under pressure the reaction rate is greatly increased. One of the best available examples remains the first system to be studied in this way, $KAlSi_3O_8$–$NaAlSi_3O_8$–H_2O (Bowen and Tuttle, 1950). From petrographic studies it appeared that at high temperatures the alkali feldspars form a complete isomorphous series which unmix into two phases at lower temperatures. Attempts to locate a solvus in the system in the dry way were unsuccessful. Schairer (1950) obtained only partial crystallization of glasses when they were held for several years at optimum conditions for crystallization. Using the same samples in the presence of water vapour under pressure, Bowen and Tuttle (1950) obtained complete crystallization in a few hours, and located the position of a solvus. The compositions of the two feldspars in equilibrium at any temperature were obtained.

Natural feldspars occur in different structural states, probably referable to the degree of order of silicon and aluminium in tetrahedral sites. It is a simple matter to convert a " low " feldspar to a " high " feldspar (order→disorder) by heating, but no feldspar with low structural state has yet been synthesized. In the presence of water vapour under pressure, Mackenzie (1957) succeeded in converting high albite to an albite with properties intermediate between the high and low forms, but even in runs of three months duration the structural state of low albite could not be reproduced.

2. Solid-Vapour

Several of the important mineral groups are hydrated, e.g. the clay minerals, micas, amphiboles, zeolites, etc. Knowledge of the stability fields of such minerals has important applications for metamorphic and igneous processes. The first study of this type to be completed will serve as an example. A comprehensive review of work up to 1956 has been presented by Roy and Tuttle (1956), and another summary is given by Ellis and Fyfe (1957).

The univariant curves measured by Bowen and Tuttle (1949) in the system $MgO–SiO_2–H_2O$ are illustrated in Fig. 10. The figure illustrates

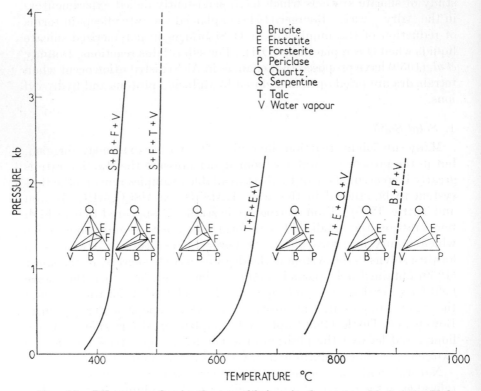

FIG. 10. PT curves of univariant equilibrium in the system $MgO–SiO_2–H_2O$.
(Reproduced with permission from Bowen and Tuttle, 1949.)

the general shape of the dehydration curves, and the compositions of the phases reacting along each univariant curve are given by the diagrams (triangles for a ternary system) between the curves. Results in more complex systems are conveniently represented in the same way. Some of these curves have been relocated in subsequent work, and stable fields for additional phases have been established, e.g. anthophyllite (Fyfe, 1962). The equilibrium problems involved in this type of study have been discussed by Roy and Roy (1957), with particular reference to the reaction: $Mg(OH)_2 \rightleftharpoons MgO + H_2O$. Fyfe (1960) discussed equilibrium problems in a more general way, using several simple dehydration reactions as examples. In particular, he compared the various experimental curves for the dissociation of brucite with those calculated thermodynamically by MacDonald (1955). To these may be added the recent determination by Barnes and Ernst (1960).

Thus far, dehydration studies have been completed only in the presence of excess vapour, with the confining pressure equal to the pressure on the gaseous phase. Greenwood (1960) reported preliminary experiments in the system $MgO-H_2O$ with the pressure on the vapour phase less than that on the crystalline phases. Yoder (1952b) and Roy and Roy (1955) discussed the " water-deficient " region of the system $MgO-Al_2O_3-SiO_2-H_2O$, the region which cannot be investigated with this experimental approach. A detailed discussion of water-deficient regions has been given by Roy (1953; quoted by Roy and Roy, 1955).

Oxygen isotope fractionation between minerals and water vapour has been investigated at high pressures and temperatures. Clayton (1959) measured the oxygen isotope fractionation between calcite and water up to 750° C, using the sealed capsule technique in cold-seal pressure vessels. The pressure in all runs was 1 kb. The equilibrium constant for the exchange reaction:

$$\tfrac{1}{3}CaC^{16}O_3 + H_2{}^{18}O = \tfrac{1}{3}CaC^{18}O_3 + H_2{}^{16}O$$

is

$$K_{CW} = \frac{(^{18}O/^{16}O)_{carbonate}}{(^{18}O/^{16}O)_{water}}$$

and has the value 1·03187 at 25° C (Epstein et al., 1953; Clayton, 1959), and its temperature behaviour over the range 0° C to infinite temperature can be described by the equation

$$\ln K_{CW} = 2725T^{-2} \quad \text{(Clayton, 1959)}$$

O'Neil and Clayton (1962), using similar experimental techniques, have measured equilibrium constants for the isotope exchange reaction between quartz and water between 380° C and 700° C (at a confining pressure of 1 kb) and they obtained the equation:

$$\ln K_{QW} = 3629T^{-2} - 0·00256$$

Combination of these results with the calcite-water exchange reaction gives an experimental determination of the oxygen isotope fractionation between quartz and calcite:

$$\ln K_{QC} = 899T^{-2}$$

This equation can be used to give quartz-calcite " isotopic paleotemperatures '' for rocks in which these two minerals were crystallized together at equilibrium.

3. *Solid-Liquid-Vapour*

Goranson (1931, 1932, 1938) was the first to complete systematic hydrothermal studies using rocks and rock-forming minerals. His work in the systems granite–H_2O, $NaAlSi_3O_8$–H_2O, and $KAlSi_3O_8$–H_2O, at pressures up to 4 kb, was not followed up for some years, until Bowen and Tuttle (1950) investigated the ternary system $NaAlSi_3O_8$–$KAlSi_3O_8$–H_2O. They confirmed Goranson's data for albite and orthoclase, and obtained additional data for the isomorphous alkali feldspar series. The phase relationships in more complex systems involving the alkali feldspars are illustrated in Section VI.

Yoder (1954a) studied the effect of water under pressure on the system $CaAl_2Si_2O_8$ (anorthite)–$CaMgSiO_3$ (diopside), where the crystalline phases are completely immiscible. In the binary system, the eutectic temperature is 1 270° C and the liquid contains 43 weight % of $CaAl_2Si_2O_8$. In the ternary system, at 5 kb pressure, the eutectic temperature is lowered to 1 095° C, and the eutectic liquid (expressed in terms of the anhydrous components only) contains 73 weight % $CaAl_2Si_2O_8$. This is a remarkable shift in both the temperature and composition of the eutectic, and it demonstrates the extent to which the

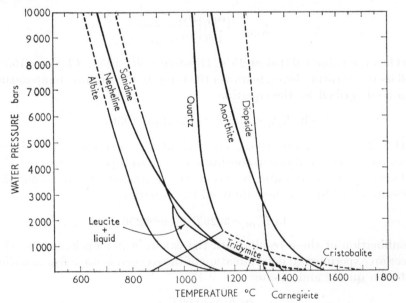

FIG. 11. Projection of univariant solid-liquid-vapour equilibria in silicate–water systems for the silicate minerals labelled. (Compilation by, and reproduced with permission from Yoder, 1958.)

" dry " silicate phase diagrams may be modified by the addition of volatile components under pressure.

The effect of water vapour under pressure on the melting temperatures of many silicate minerals has now been determined. Yoder (1958) summarized the available data in a diagram reproduced here as Fig. 11. At water vapour pressures corresponding to a depth of about 20 km (5 kb), melting temperatures may be depressed by 100° C ($CaMgSi_2O_6$–H_2O) or by as much as 700° C ($NaAlSiO_4$–H_2O, SiO_2–H_2O). PT projections do not provide a complete picture of the phase relationships. TX and PX projections are required in addition in order to illustrate the compositions of the three phases solid, liquid, and vapour co-existing along a univariant curve. These data are now available for the system SiO_2–H_2O (Fig. 25; Section IV, J).

Complete graphical representation of the phase relationships in multicomponent systems is impossible in three dimensions, but much useful information can be obtained by the use of suitable sections and projections. An example is provided by the work of Yoder and Chinner (1960) in the system CaO–MgO–Al_2O_3–SiO_2–H_2O. They studied the composition join grossularite ($Ca_3Al_2Si_3O_{12}$)–pyrope ($Mg_3Al_2Si_3O_{12}$), and they plotted on this join the phase fields intersected at a water pressure of 10 kb. The resulting diagram is complex, because of the large number of phases present, and the extensive solid solution which occurs in these phases. Nevertheless, Yoder and Chinner outline some applications which indicate the usefulness of the approach.

E. *Systems with Carbon Dioxide as a Volatile Component*

After water, carbon dioxide appears to be the most abundant volatile component in the earth's crust, and the spate of hydrothermal studies appearing after the development of simple high pressure, high temperature apparatus (Tuttle, 1948, 1949) was soon joined by studies of systems involving carbon dioxide as a volatile component. Details of work completed in such systems before 1949 can be found in several reviews (Roy and Tuttle, 1956; for accounts of earlier German work see especially Eitel, 1954).

1. *Solid-Solid*

The position of the solvus between calcite and dolomite has been measured experimentally by Graf and Goldsmith (1955), Harker and Tuttle (1955b), and Goldsmith and Heard (1961). Complete solid solubility exists above 1 075° C between calcite and a carbonate of dolomite composition, although there is a structural change between them involving order-disorder of Ca and Mg. This is discussed in some detail by Goldsmith and Heard. Their results are illustrated in Fig. 12, along with the solubility relationships between dolomite and magnesite. The curves illustrated are polybaric, the pressure ranging from 2 to 15 kb. Pressure does have a small but measurable effect on the position of the solvus.

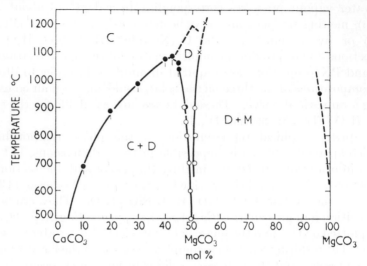

FIG. 12. The system $CaCO_3$–$MgCO_3$. (Reproduced with permission from Goldsmith and Heard, 1961.) C = calcitic phase, D = dolomitic phase, M = magnesite-rich phase.

Results have also been obtained in more complex systems. Goldsmith *et al.* (1960) and Rosenberg (1960) studied the extent of solid solution in the system $CaCO_3$–$MgCO_3$–$FeCO_3$. Goldsmith *et al.* worked with temperatures between 700° C and 800° C at a pressure of 15 kb with no vapour phase present. Rosenberg worked with temperatures between 400° C and 500° C at pressures between 2 and 3 kb using carbon dioxide, together with some carbon monoxide, as the pressure medium. Goldsmith and Graf (1960) have published the results of similar sub-solidus studies in the system $CaCO_3$–$MgCO_3$–$MnCO_3$ between 500° C and 800° C at 10 kb pressure.

2. *Solid-Vapour*

The dissociation of calcite, dolomite, and magnesite has been studied by several investigators, using a variety of experimental techniques (Fig. 13).

Smyth and Adams (1923) studied the dissociation of calcite using thermal analysis in an internally-heated pressure vessel, with carbon dioxide as the pressure medium, and Baker (1961) repeated the work in a similar type of apparatus using differential thermal analysis. Harker and Tuttle (1955a) measured a portion of the dissociation curve using carbon dioxide as a pressure medium in cold-seal pressure vessels, while Goldsmith and Heard (1961) used the sealed capsule method in an

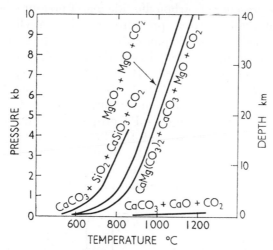

FIG. 13. Univariant decarbonation curves for magnesite, dolomite and calcite, and for calcite-quartz assemblages.

internally-heated hydrostatic pressure vessel. The thermal and DTA methods gave results in close agreement, but the " open tube " and the sealed capsule methods gave results which show significant differences between each other and from the thermal methods.

The dissociations of dolomite and magnesite were studied by Harker and Tuttle (1955a) and Graf and Goldsmith (1955), using open tubes in cold-seal pressure vessels, with carbon dioxide as the pressure medium. Goldsmith and Heard (1961) extended these measurements to pressures between 3 and 10 kb using the sealed capsule method in an internally-heated hydrostatic pressure vessel, and again they found significant differences between the different methods. They concluded that: " It is apparent that additional experimentation is needed to account for the rather large differences in the three sets of data. "

Many decarbonation reactions in metamorphism involve both carbonates and silicates. A PT curve for the univariant reaction:

$$CaCO_3 + SiO_2 \rightleftharpoons CaSiO_3 + CO_2$$
calcite   quartz   wollastonite

has been measured by Harker and Tuttle (1956), using the open tube technique in cold-seal pressure vessels. Several other geologically important reactions of this type have been investigated (L. S. Walter, 1963 in press).

3. *Solid-Liquid-Vapour*

Of the common carbonate minerals found in rocks, calcite, dolomite, magnesite, and siderite, only calcite has been melted experimentally. Smyth and Adams (1923) and Baker (1961) obtained data on the fusion of calcite in the presence of carbon dioxide under pressure, using thermal analysis in internally heated pressure vessels. Wyllie and Tuttle (1960a) determined an isobaric phase diagram for the system CaO–CO_2 at 1 kb pressure, using the sealed capsule quenching technique in an internally-heated pressure vessel. At this pressure, Smyth and Adams found that calcite melted at 1 339° C, Baker estimated 1 325° C, and Wyllie and Tuttle obtained a temperature of 1 310° C. Wyllie and Tuttle (1960a) presented a tentative PT projection showing the arrangement of univariant curves around the low pressure invariant point where the four phases CaO, $CaCO_3$, liquid, and vapour co-exist in equilibrium (Fig. 19). Baker's data leads to the revised diagram illustrated in Fig. 14, with the invariant point at 39·5 bars and 1 242° C.

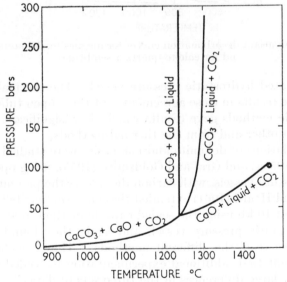

FIG. 14. PT projection for the system CaO–CO_2.

There are very few data on the effect of carbon dioxide on the melting temperatures of silicates. Wyllie and Tuttle (1959) studied the systems $NaAlSi_3O_8$–CO_2 and granite–CO_2 in cold-seal pressure vessels using dry carbon dioxide as the pressure medium. No melting was detected within the experimental range of the equipment, and very little crystallization of glasses occurred in sub-solidus regions in runs lasting for three days. Carbon dioxide appears to behave as an inert medium imparting pressure to the crystalline or glassy starting materials. Certainly, it cannot compare with water as a flux in silicate melts, so it seems unlikely that it is effective in breaking Si–O–Si bridges (Buerger, 1948). Silicate melts with a high proportion of alkali ions may be capable of dissolving carbon dioxide (Morey and Fleischer, 1940).

F. *Systems with Sulphur as a Volatile Component*

A great deal of work has been completed in systems containing sulphur, together with one or more metallic components, such as Cu, Fe, Zn, and Ni. In most studies, the runs were performed using evacuated silica tubes inside of which the vapour pressure of the system developed during each run. The actual pressures are unknown, but they may range as high as 200 bars (Barnes and Kullerud, 1961). The location of solvus boundaries between co-existing sulphides has found wide applications in geothermometery (Kullerud, 1959). Only few studies have been completed at high pressures, and in these the samples were sealed within gold capsules and placed inside cold-seal pressure vessels.

1. *Solid-Solid*

Clark (1960) studied the effect of pressure on the solvus curves bounding the arsenopyrite field of solid solution in the system Fe–As–S at pressures up to 2 kb. Pressure was found to shift the position of the solvus curves sufficiently to limit the usefulness of arsenopyrite in geothermometry. However, this leads to the possibility of estimating the confining pressure of arsenopyrite deposition, if the deposition temperature can be independently estimated.

Kullerud and Yund (1962) measured the upper stability limits of the mineral polydymite in the system Ni–S, up to 2 kb pressure. The univariant curve where polydymite (Ni_3S_4) breaks down to the minerals millerite ($Ni_{1-x}S$) and vaesite (NiS_2) has a slope of 6° C/kb.

2. *Solid-Vapour*

Measured reactions of this kind appear to be confined to rather low pressures. Some examples from the system Fe–S are illustrated in Fig. 15.

3. *Solid-Liquid-Vapour*

Solid-liquid-vapour equilibria in systems containing sulphur appear to be restricted to rather low pressure, as indicated by the schematic PT projection for the system Fe–S in Fig. 15. This diagram was

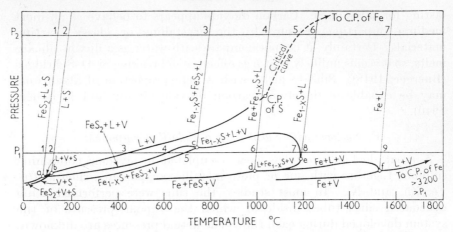

FIG. 15. Schematic PT projection for the system Fe–S. (Reproduced with permission from Kullerud and Yoder, 1959.) Pressure p_1 is approximately 1 bar; p_2 several kilobars.

deduced by Kullerud and Yoder (1959) from previously published work, and from their own determination of the stability field of pyrite. The solid-liquid (or solid-gas) reaction:

$$FeS_2 \rightleftharpoons Fe_{1-x}S \quad + \quad liquid$$
$$\text{pyrite} \quad \text{pyrrhotite}$$

was followed up to 5 kb pressure; its slope is about 14° C/kb.

G. *Systems with more than One Volatile Component*

When a vapour phase is present during geological processes, it contains more than one component. It is therefore desirable to evaluate the effects of volatile components additional to H_2O and CO_2 on reactions occurring in silicate and carbonate systems. Considerable data are now available on reactions involving H_2O or CO_2, but much less is known of the effect of other volatile materials, and of the effect of mixtures of volatile materials.

1. *Solid-Vapour*

Yoder (1954b) was the first to attempt quantitative studies of this type, in the system $NaAlSi_2O_6$–H_2O–Ar, but he encountered problems due probably to incomplete mixing of the water and argon in the vapour phase. Experimental difficulties were successfully resolved by Harker (1958), who studied the dissociation of magnesite in the presence of vapours containing known proportions of carbon dioxide and argon. Greenwood (1961) investigated the dissociation of analcite in the system $NaAlSi_2O_6$–H_2O–Ar, and by obtaining PV data for the system H_2O–Ar, at 500° C,he was able to compare his experimental results with thermodynamic predictions; he found good agreement between them. Walter *et al.* (1962), in a study of the system MgO–CO_2–H_2O, examined the effect of carbon dioxide on the dissociation of brucite and the effect of water on the dissociation of magnesite. A schematic isobaric TX prism, based on their data, is reproduced in Fig. 16. This illustrates the pattern of the reactions for pressures up to at least 4 kb.

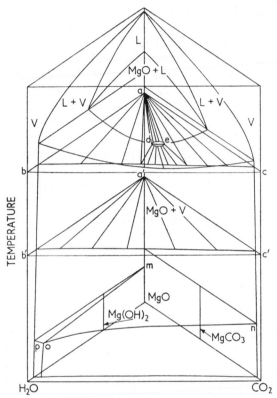

Fig. 16. Schematic isobaric TX prism for the system MgO–CO_2–H_2O at pressures up to 4 kb, at least. (Reproduced with permission from Walter *et al.*, 1962.) Curves *no* and *op* give the compositions of vapours in equilibrium with MgO and $MgCO_3$ on the one hand, and MgO and $Mg(OH)_2$ on the other hand. Line *mo* represents the isobaric invariant temperature at which MgO, $Mg(OH)_2$, $MgCO_3$, and V_0 co-exist.

Orville (1960) has investigated the partitioning of alkalis between alkali feldspars and dilute alkali chloride solutions at various temperatures, with a confining pressure of 2 kb. Under these conditions, the solution becomes a homogeneous vapour phase. The temperature-dependence of the exchange reaction provides an experimental basis for a mechanism of alkali metasomatism. This is discussed further in Section VI.

2. *Solid-Liquid-Vapour*

The dramatic effect of water vapour under pressure on the melting temperatures of silicates has been indicated in Section IV, D, 3. Addition of other volatile components to the water, at constant total pressure, may cause the melting temperature to increase or to decrease compared to its value in the presence of water alone.

Wyllie and Tuttle (1960b) described and illustrated some of the phase relationships which might be expected in ternary systems containing a silicate and two volatile components. This provided a framework for presentation of the experimental data obtained in a series of systems containing albite, water, and one of the additional volatile components: CO_2, HF, HCl, NH_3, SO_3, or P_2O_5 (Wyllie and Tuttle, 1957, 1959, 1961a, 1963).   Addition of HF, HCl, SO_3 and P_2O_5 to water at constant total pressure lowers the temperature of beginning of melting of albite. Addition of CO_2 and NH_3, on the other hand, raises the temperature of beginning of melting.

In most of these systems, reaction occurs between the second volatile and the silicate, and a common result is that quartz becomes a primary phase. This is illustrated in Fig. 17, which shows the phase fields intersected at 2 750 bars pressure by a join containing 50 weight %

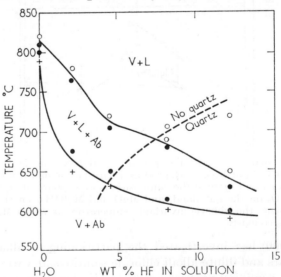

FIG. 17. Perspective TX projection for the system $NaAlSi_3O_8$–H_2O–HF at 2·75 kb pressure, determined for a 1: 1 weight ratio of silicate to total volatiles. (Reproduced with permission from Wyllie and Tuttle, 1961a.)

albite, and 50 weight % solution of HF with varying concentrations. At this pressure, albite melts dry at about 1 155° C; in the presence of water vapour, it melts at 810° C; in the presence of an aqueous vapour phase containing 4 weight % HF initially, it begins to melt at 640° C, and melting is completed at 720° C.

Experimental data from systems involving carbonates, liquids, and polycomponent vapour phases have applications to the genesis of carbonatites and to the metamorphism of limestones. Solid-liquid-vapour equilibria in the system CaO–CO_2–H_2O have been studied through a wide pressure range by Wyllie and Tuttle (1960a). Vapours with compositions ranging between H_2O and CO_2 co-exist with calcite and portlandite ($Ca(OH)_2$), together with liquids with compositions close to the join $CaCO_3$–$Ca(OH)_2$. The phase relationships are summarized in Figs. 18 and 19. Figure 18 is a schematic isobaric TX prism for the system, based on the experimental data at 1 kb, and Fig. 19 is a

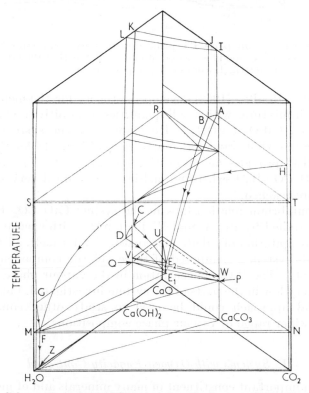

FIG. 18. Schematic isobaric TX prism for the system CaO–CO_2–H_2O at 1 kb pressure. (Reproduced with permission from Wyllie and Tuttle, 1960a.) Liquidus field boundaries are AE_1, BE_2, CE_2, DE_1, and E_1E_2. Vaporus field boundaries are HF, GF, and FZ. Liquid occupies the space $IJKLCDE_1E_2AB$.

PT projection of the univariant equilibria. The invariant point for the ternary system lies at a pressure less than 10 bars (Wyllie and Raynor,

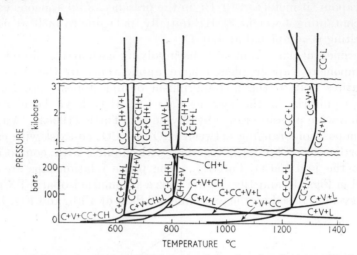

Fig. 19. Schematic (in part) PT projection of univariant equilibria in the system CaO–CO_2–H_2O (modified after Wyllie and Tuttle, 1960a). $C = CaO$, $CC = CaCO_3$, $CH = Ca(OH)_2$, $L = $ liquid, $V = $ vapour or gas.

unpublished). Bradley (1962) developed a theory for the melting-point curves of salt mixtures with small quantities of additives, and applied it to the join $CaCO_3$–$Ca(OH)_2$. He found that the system behaved ideally over the whole range of composition. Figure 18 for the system CaO–CO_2–H_2O provides an interesting contrast with Fig. 16 for the system MgO–CO_2–H_2O, where no melting occurs until very high temperatures are reached.

Phase equilibrium relationships in the system CaO–CO_2–H_2O-P_2O_5 have been studied by Biggar and Wyllie (1962), with special reference to the co-precipitation of calcite and apatite from a melt. The vapour phase in this system is composed of three volatile components: H_2O, CO_2 and P_2O_5. The P_2O_5 concentration in the vapour phase appeared to remain very low in the parts of the system investigated, but the same experimental approach could be used to study other compositions covering a wider range of vapour phase compositions.

H. *Systems with Oxygen Fugacity Controlled*

Iron is an important constituent of many minerals and of most rocks, and phase equilibrium data on iron-bearing systems are therefore required for the development of petrogenetic hypotheses. However, because iron exists in two valence states, the study of such systems requires that the fugacity of oxygen be known, as well as the bulk composition, temperature, and pressure. Eugster's (1957a) technique of buffers, which permit the control of oxygen fugacity in a system subjected to high pressures of water vapour (see Section III, D) has opened up a whole new field of experimentation in iron-bearing systems. This brings us one step closer to natural conditions, which is what the experimental petrologist strives for constantly.

1. *Solid-Vapour*

Eugster and Wones (1962; see also Eugster, 1957b) have recently published a detailed study of the stability of annite, which is the ferrous end-member of the biotite family, and data for biotites on the join phlogopite $(KMgAlSi_3O_{10}(OH)_2)$–annite $(KFe_3AlSi_3O_{10}(OH)_2)$ have been reported by Wones and Eugster (1959). The stability of iron-chlorites was determined by Turnock (1960). Ernst (1960) studied the stability of the amphibole magnesioriebeckite. It is of interest to note that the

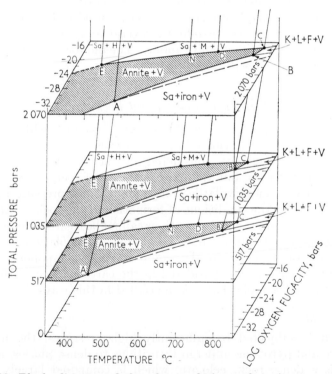

FIG. 20. Block diagram of the phase relations of annite (+vapour) bulk composition. (Reproduced with permission from Eugster and Wones, 1962.) Light lines through A, B, C, E are oxygen buffer curves. Sa =sanidine; H = hematite; M =magnetite; K =kalsitite; L =leucite; F =fayalite; V =vapour.

significant phase relationships in these multicomponent systems can often be presented quite successfully in a three-dimensional model, with total pressure, oxygen fugacity, and temperature as the three axes (Fig. 20).

Turnock (1959) used a hydrothermal technique to study the sub-solidus phase relationships for the spinel solid solution series magnetite (Fe_3O_4)–hercynite $(FeAl_2O_4)$, in the temperature range $500°$ C to $900°$ C, at pressures up to 4 kb. The buffer method was employed to control the oxygen fugacity. Solid solution between the end-members is limited by a solvus whose position was found to be insensitive to total pressure. Changes in the oxygen fugacity, however, may cause radical changes in the mineral assemblage co-existing with the vapour phase.

2. *Solid-Liquid-Vapour*

In his study of the stability relations of magnesioriebeckite $(Na_2Mg_3Fe_2Si_8O_{22}(OH)_2)$ at water-vapour pressures between 500 bars and 2 kb, Ernst (1960) found that the mineral was stable until it melted, within the range of oxygen fugacities used in the experiments $(10^{-5}$ to 10^{-20} bars). Above $900°$ C, several anhydrous iron-bearing minerals co-exist with liquid and vapour. The number and composition of these minerals vary with the oxygen fugacity.

I. *Systems Involving Natural Rock Samples*

Experimental studies on simple silicate systems, which can be treated theoretically in terms of the phase rule, establish patterns of behaviour which must be considered in the development of any petrological hypothesis, but the study of natural rock samples in the presence of one or more volatile components under pressure approximates more closely the conditions of formation of the rocks. Although the results of such empirical observations cannot be treated theoretically, they serve as useful intermediate checks on extrapolations from the simple synthetic systems to the complex, multicomponent natural systems which have to be considered in the earth sciences. In recent years, many rock samples have been studied in this way.

1. *Solid-Solid*

If basalt is subjected to sufficiently high pressures, the minerals plagioclase and pyroxene undergo transitions to dense phases, and the product is a dense rock, eclogite, which is composed largely of the pyroxene omphacite (jadeite-rich), and garnet (pyrope-rich). Preliminary measurements for this complex transition in the pressure range 10 to 15 kb at $500°$ C have been reported by Kennedy (1959). The results are illustrated in Fig. 21. Reaction curves for some of the minerals involved in the transition are shown in Fig. 8.

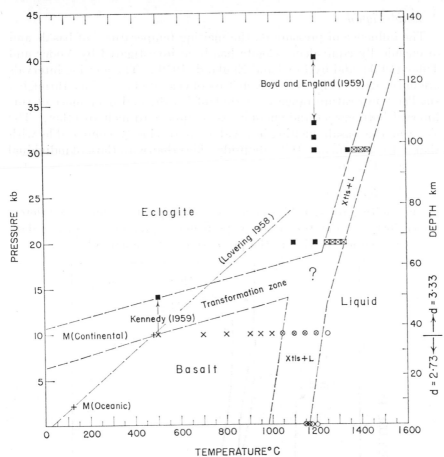

FIG. 21. The basalt–eclogite transition and the melting intervals of basalt and eclogite. (Reproduced with permission from Yoder and Tilley, 1961.) Compare Fig. 24 for the system basalt–water.

2. Solid-Vapour

Winkler and Platen have published a series of papers on the experimental metamorphism of shales and clays in the presence of water vapour and salt solutions at 2 kb pressure (Winkler, 1957; Winkler and Platen, 1958, 1960, 1961a, 1961b). The assemblages of minerals developed at various temperatures compare quite closely with natural metamorphic assemblages, and the results therefore help to provide temperature limits for metamorphic facies. Wyart and Sabatier (1959) have performed similar experiments. At higher temperatures, the samples are partially melted, and the melting relationships are considered in Section 4.

3. *Solid-Liquid*

The influence of pressure on the melting temperatures of basalt and of chemically equivalent eclogite has been investigated by Yoder and Tilley (1961), and by Boyd and England (1959). The melting intervals are illustrated in Fig. 21. The melting of eclogite takes place through a smaller temperature range than that of basalt, and over most of this interval both garnet and clinopyroxene appear to melt together. The slope of the basalt melting-interval is more closely comparable with that in the system anorthite–diopside–silica than with those of individual minerals (Fig. 9).

4. *Solid-Liquid-Vapour*

The melting relationships of many rock types have now been determined in the presence of water vapour under pressure, and some data are available for melting in the presence of additional volatiles.

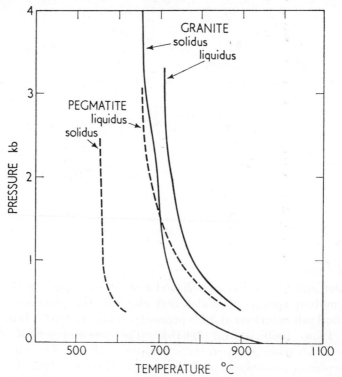

FIG. 22. Liquidus and solidus curves for granite and pegmatite samples in the presence of excess water.

(a) *Granite.* Goranson (1931, 1932) was the first to complete quantitative studies on solid-liquid-vapour equilibria using granite in the presence of water vapour under pressure. Experiments on the beginning of melting of granites were continued by Tuttle and Bowen, and the results are included in their memoir on the origin of granite (Tuttle and Bowen, 1958). Kranck and Oja (1960), using cylinders of granite instead of powders, obtained almost identical results for the beginning of melting of granites. Jahns and Burnham (1958) measured the temperatures of beginning of crystallization of granitic liquids in the presence of water vapour under pressure. Some of these results are summarized in Fig. 22.

Wyllie and Tuttle (1957, 1959, 1960c, 1961a, 1963) have measured the effect on the melting temperatures of the volatile components CO_2, HF, HCl, P_2O_5, SO_3, and Li_2O, when present in addition to H_2O. The effects are similar to those described when the same volatiles are added to the system albite–water (Section G, 2), only less marked. The effect of HF in addition to water vapour on the temperature of beginning of melting of granite, at a total pressure of 2 750 bars, is illustrated in Fig. 23. Addition of 4·3 weight % HF to the aqueous vapour phase at this pressure is sufficient to lower the melting temperature by a further 65° C.

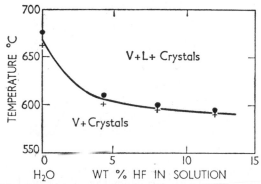

FIG. 23. TX projection for the system granite–H_2O–HF at 2·75 kb pressure. (Reproduced with permission from Wyllie and Tuttle, 1961a.) The diagram shows the effect of HF in addition to H_2O, at constant total pressure, on the temperature of beginning of melting of granite, compared to the effect of H_2O alone.

(b) *Pegmatite.* Jahns and Burnham (1958) have measured liquidus and solidus temperatures for natural pegmatites in the presence of water vapour under pressure. The liquidus temperatures are 25° C to 55° C lower than those for granites, depending upon the pressure, and the solidus temperatures are 175° C to 140° C below the temperature of beginning of melting of granites (cf. Fig. 22). Pegmatite compositions are very similar to granite compositions, but the pegmatites have higher contents of " volatile " components, and the lowering of melting temperatures compared to those of granites can be ascribed to the effect of these additional volatiles. Jahns and Burnham have also obtained results leading to the formulation of a satisfactory hypothesis for the crystallization of granitic pegmatites (Jahns and Burnham, 1962), which will be outlined in Section VI.

(c) *Basalts*. Yoder and Tilley (1956, 1959) have reported experiments on the melting behaviour of natural basalts and eclogites in the presence of water vapour under pressure. Results obtained for a tholeiite basalt at pressures up to 10 kb are illustrated in Fig. 24. The

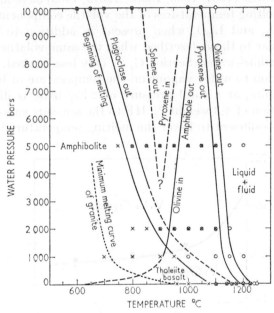

FIG. 24. PT projection of the tholeiite basalt–H_2O system based on reconnaissance runs. (Reproduced with permission from Yoder and Tilley, 1956.)

temperature of beginning of melting is lowered by nearly 500° C, whereas the liquidus temperature is lowered by only 150° C. One effect of increasing water-vapour pressure, therefore, is to increase the crystallization interval of a basaltic magma. With increasing pressure, the stability field of plagioclase is reduced, and the stability field of amphibole increases at the expense of pyroxene. Amphibole becomes stable in equilibrium with a liquid phase at a pressure of about 1·3 kb, and it appears that at pressures not much greater than 10 kb amphibole would become the primary phase on the liquidus. Although basalt is such a common rock, these results indicate that crystalline basalt (or gabbro) has only a limited stability field in the presence of water vapour under pressure. It is interesting to compare Fig. 24 with Fig. 21, which shows the effect of pressure alone on the melting interval for " dry " basalt. The oxygen fugacity in these experiments has not been reported.

Hamilton and Burnham (1962, and personal communication) used a buffer technique to study the effect of oxygen fugacity on the melting relationships of a Columbia River basalt in the presence of water vapour at pressures up to 4 kb. At a total pressure of 1 kb, pyroxene was the first silicate to crystallize from the liquid. With a high oxygen fugacity, magnetite was stable to higher temperatures than the silicates, but its stability field was much reduced as the oxygen fugacity decreased. With oxygen fugacities of 10^{-4} bars, 10^{-11} bars, and 10^{-13} bars, the " silicate liquidus " at a water-vapour pressure of 1 kb was $1080°$ C, $1035°$ C and $1015°$ C, respectively. Decreasing the oxygen fugacity thus lowers the liquidus temperature. Fudali *et al.* (1962) studied the melting relationships of several basaltic rocks at a pressure of 1 bar, with oxygen fugacity controlled, and the results suggest that the oxygen fugacities for the rocks studied were in the range 10^{-6} bars to 10^{-8} bars at the time of extrusion.

(d) *Sediments.* The melting relationships of several sediments in the presence of water vapour under pressure have been determined. In their studies of the experimental metamorphism of clays, calcite-bearing clays, and greywackes, Winkler and Platen (Winkler, 1957; Winkler and Platen, 1958, 1960, 1961a) found that melting occurred at 2 kb pressure at temperatures near $700°$ C, the precise temperature varying with the composition of the rock. Wyart and Sabatier (1959) also studied the melting relationships of several pelitic sediments, at 1 800 bars pressure of water vapour. Wyllie and Tuttle (1958, 1961b) determined the positions of PT curves for the beginning of melting of five " standard shale samples " from Pennsylvania, in the presence of water vapour, and found that the curves are $20°$ C to $30°$ C higher than the corresponding curve for granite (Fig. 35). Kranck and Oja (1960) reported some preliminary work with a solid sample of graywacke, and concluded that the temperature of beginning of melting was higher than that of granite.

All investigators found that the first liquid produced by partial melting was granitic in composition; with increasing temperature the liquid increased in amount and changed towards intermediate compositions. The applications of these studies to the formation of migmatites and granites is discussed in Section VI.

J. *Solubility Measurements*

1. *Critical End-points*

In most binary silicate–water systems, where the solubility of the silicate in aqueous solutions at normal pressures and temperatures is very low, the three-phase solubility curve (crystals + aqueous solution + vapour, or crystals + melt + vapour) will intersect a critical curve, producing first and second critical end-points. Between these end-points, crystalline phases co-exist with a single fluid phase, which may be transformed continuously into either liquid or vapour by suitable variations in pressure, temperature, and composition. The phase relationships described in detail by Wyllie and Tuttle (1960b) for the system $NaAlSi_3O_8$–H_2O serve as an example for this type of system.

Complete experimental data are available for only one system, SiO_2–H_2O (Kennedy, 1950; Tuttle and England, 1955; Stewart, 1957; Ostrovskii *et al.*, 1959; Kennedy *et al.*, 1961). PT, PX, and TX projections are shown in Fig. 25. The solubility curves described and

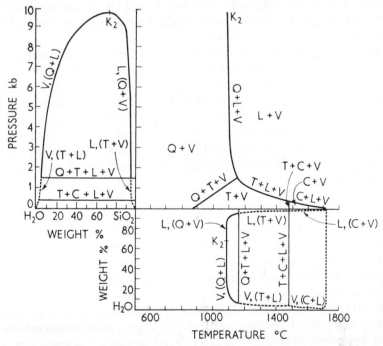

FIG. 25. PT, PX and TX projections for the system SiO_2–H_2O (modified after Kennedy *et al.*, 1961). C = cristobalite, T = tridymite, Q = quartz, L = liquid, V = vapour (or gas, or fluid), L, (Q + V) = liquid coexisting with quartz + vapour. K_2 is a critical end-point.

illustrated in the following sections are parts of curves similar to those illustrated in Fig. 25. At sufficiently high pressures, the liquids containing dissolved volatiles become continuous with the fluid phases containing dissolved solids.

2. *Solubility of Volatiles in Silicate Melts*

Results have been obtained for the solubility of water in melts of various compositions, and preliminary data are available for other volatiles. Goranson (1931, 1938) used a weight-loss method for his solubility measurements, and the same method was subsequently used by Tuttle and Bowen (1958), Yoder *et al.* (1957), Stewart (1957), and others. Kennedy *et al.* (1961) used a weight-gain method to measure the solubility of water in fused silica, and their results suggested that the weight-loss method gave results which were too high. Burnham and Jahns (1958) measured the solubility of water in granite and pegmatite liquids by melting known amounts of water and dry sample in sealed capsules, and by studying the quenched product. Crystallites were observed in undersaturated charges, and excess water formed bubbles in oversaturated charges. The solubility was given by the weight of water in charges estimated to be just saturated. Their results indicated that previous measurements for granitic melts, obtained by

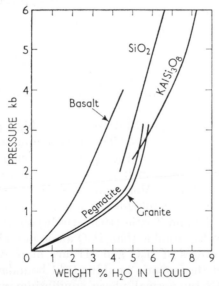

FIG. 26. PX projections showing the solubility of water in silicate liquids. The solubilities are dependent also on temperature (Fig. 27). $KAlSi_3O_8$ (Spengler and Burnham, 1962); SiO_2 (Kennedy *et al.*, 1961; compare Fig. 25); Granite and pegmatite (Burnham and Jahns, 1958); Basalt (Hamilton and Burnham, 1962, and personal communication).

the weight-loss method, were too high by a factor of two. The same method was used successfully by Spengler and Burnham (1962) in the system $KAlSi_3O_8-H_2O$, and by Hamilton and Burnham (1962) for the solubility of water in a natural basalt melt. Some results are illustrated in Figs. 26 and 27.

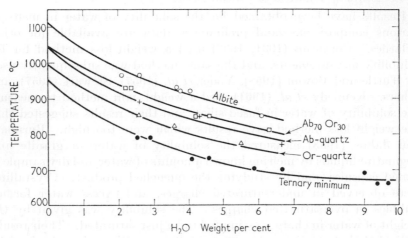

FIG. 27. TX projections showing the solubility of water in melts in the system $NaAlSi_3O_8$ (albite, Ab)–$KAlSi_3O_8$ (Or)–SiO_2 (quartz). (Reproduced with permission from Tuttle and Bowen, 1958.)

Theoretical discussions on the solubility of water and the lowering of melting temperatures in silicate systems, using available experimental data, have been presented by Goranson (1938), Wasserberg (1957), and Shaw (1962). Wasserberg showed that these are grossly governed by a perfect solid solution law.

There appear to be no quantitative data at high pressures on the solubility of CO_2 in silicate melts. The results obtained by Wyllie and Tuttle (1959) with feldspar and granite melts suggest that CO_2 is practically insoluble in these melts. It may be more soluble in melts which are rich in alkali ions (Morey and Fleischer, 1940).

Qualitative data are available for the solubility of mixed volatiles in silicate melts. Wyllie and Tuttle (1959, 1961a) showed that mixtures of H_2O and CO_2 are less soluble than H_2O alone in feldspar and granite melts, whereas mixtures of H_2O and HF are more soluble than H_2O alone. Location of the isobaric liquidus field boundary in the system $NaAlSi_3O_8-H_2O-HF$ by normal phase equilibrium methods provides complete data on the freezing-point depression, on the dissolved volatiles, and both the composition of the dissolved material, and the total percentage dissolved (Wyllie and Tuttle, unpublished). The solubility of the volatile components in melts in the system CaO–CO_2–H_2O as well as the partition of CO_2 and H_2O between the liquid and vapour phase can be obtained directly from the geometry of the phase relationships measured at a pressure of 1 kb (Wyllie and Tuttle, 1960a). Morey and Fleischer (1940) measured the solubility of H_2O and CO_2 mixtures in melts in the system K_2O–SiO_2–H_2O–CO_2 at pressures up to 412 bars.

3. *Solubility of Non-volatile Components in Dense Vapours or Gases*

Most available data are for the solubility of non-volatile components in water at high pressures and temperatures. The most direct method is to analyse a sample of the fluid separated from the melt or crystals (Morey and Fleischer, 1940), but experimental difficulties limit its general applicability. Morey and Hesselgesser (1951) used a continuous streaming method to measure the solubility of many minerals at pressures up to 2 kb and temperatures up to 600° C.

Kennedy (1950) published solubility data in the system SiO_2–H_2O up to 560° C and 1 kb, which included critical phenomena. The method involved measuring the weight loss of quartz plates enclosed in pressure vessels containing known amounts of water vapour. His results provide a fairly complete picture of the phase surfaces and phase volumes in this part of the system. The data agree well with those of Morey and Hesselgesser (1951). Mosebach (1955, quoted by Morey, 1957) made an extended examination of Kennedy's results, which indicated that silica was dissolved as $Si(OH)_4$, and he derived the equation:

$$\log L = 2 \log D - 2071/T + 3\cdot68,$$

where L is the solubility expressed as grammes SiO_2 per kilogram H_2O, D is the density of H_2O at the given temperature and pressure, and T is the absolute temperature. For measurements at higher pressures and temperatures more elaborate equipment is required. Kennedy *et al.* (1961) extended study of the system to 10 kb and 1400° C, using an internally-heated pressure vessel, and they located for the first time the position of a second critical end-point in a silicate-volatile system (Fig. 25). The solubility of solids in gases increases very rapidly with increasing pressure towards the second critical end-point.

In more complex systems, as shown by Morey and Hesselgesser (1951), the composition of the dissolved materials may depart appreciably from the composition of the co-existing crystal or liquid. Burnham and Tuttle (1960) designed internally-heated pressure vessels which could accommodate samples large enough (30 cm³ or more) to permit the solid content of the condensed gaseous phase to be weighed and analysed.

They measured the compositions of H_2O-rich vapours co-existing with
silicate melts of various compositions in the range 2 to 9 kb and 550° C
to 1 000° C. The composition of the aqueous fluid phase co-existing
with liquids approaching granites in composition has higher Na_2O/K_2O
and lower $Al_2O_3/(Na_2O + K_2O + SiO_2)$ ratios than co-existing liquids.
Burnham and Jahns (1962) extended these studies to natural pegmatite
samples, and found that the solubility ranges from 1 weight % at 2 kb,
550° C, to 12·8 weight % at 10 kb, 700° C. The partition of various
non-volatile components between liquid and vapour was also measured.

There appear to be no data on the solubility of non-volatile components in CO_2 at high pressures and temperatures, although it has been
suggested that its solvent properties may be significant in geological
processes (Garrels and Richter, 1955; Garson and Campbell Smith,
1958).

Some information on solubilities in mixed volatiles is available.
Wyllie and Tuttle (1961a) reported preliminary measurements on the
amount of dissolved material in the vapour phase at 2·75 kb pressure
and 820° C in the system $NaAlSi_3O_8$–H_2O–HF. Solubility measurements
of MgO in the vapour phase in the system MgO–CO_2–H_2O were made by
Walter *et al.* (1962). Less than 1·5 weight % of MgO dissolved in the
H_2O–CO_2 mixtures at 1 kb pressure and temperatures up to 1 200° C.
In a review on the solubility of solids in gases, Morey (1957) described
some preliminary results obtained with H_2O containing about 7 weight
% CO_2 at 500° C and 1 kb. Compared to their solubilities in H_2O alone,
the solubility of calcite went up from 120 mg/kg to 940 mg/kg, and that
of quartz went down from 26 000 mg/kg to 19 000 mg/kg.

V. Seismic and Density Discontinuities

The major and minor discontinuities within the earth have been
described in Section II. Most of these occur at pressures and temperatures beyond the experimental limits of available equipment. Conditions at M, the base of the crust, can be reproduced experimentally,
and the 400 km second order discontinuity in the mantle is not beyond
the range of reasonable extrapolation. The low-velocity layer in the
upper mantle (Gutenberg, 1959) lies between these discontinuities.
Experimental data providing information about the nature of these
three features are described below.

A. *The Second Order Discontinuities in the Mantle*

When evidence for the upper second order discontinuity was first
presented (Jeffreys, 1936), Bernal suggested, in the ensuing discussion,

that since Mg_2GeO_4 was known to exist in two forms, one isomorphous with olivine and the other cubic, it was possible that under the influence of very high pressures the orthorhombic mineral olivine might undergo a transition to a denser, cubic form which could account for the discontinuity. It has since been claimed several times that the spinel polymorph of Mg_2GeO_4 could not be synthesized. Dachille and Roy (1960c) have outlined the history of experiments and opinions on the olivine–spinel transition for the composition Mg_2GeO_4. With the aid of high water-pressures, Roy and Roy (1954) were able to prepare the phase reproducibly. The problem of locating a corresponding transition in Mg_2SiO_4 was approached in 1955 by studying the solid solution and transition in the system Mg_2GeO_4–Mg_2SiO_4 (Dachille and Roy, 1956, 1958, 1960c). The effect of Fe_2SiO_4 in this system was reported verbally in 1956. Attempts by Wentorf (1959) to synthesize a spinel form of Mg_2SiO_4 at 550° C and pressures reported to be near 100 kb were unsuccessful. The reported pressures may be at least 30% too high (Kennedy and LaMori, 1961), in which case the appropriate PT conditions were not attained (Fig. 30). Ringwood (1958d, 1959a) and Boyd and England (1960b) have obtained direct experimental data for the olivine–spinel transition in fayalite, Fe_2SiO_4.

There are many publications dealing with the thermodynamics of the olivine–spinel transition for various compositions. Ringwood has discussed the constitution of the mantle (1958a, 1958b, 1958c, 1959b) with particular reference to the olivine-spinel transition, using as a basis experimental results obtained in several systems which exhibit similar transitions. From experimental data on solid solution relationships, Ringwood developed a method for calculating the pressure required to cause Mg_2SiO_4 to invert from the olivine to the spinel form.

1. *The System* Mg_2GeO_4–Mg_2SiO_4

Dachille and Roy (1956, 1958, 1960c) studied this system at temperatures up to 950° C, and pressures up to 65 kb. The approach adopted illustrates how phase equilibrium data obtained in a restricted range of pressures and temperatures may be extrapolated to provide useful information about reactions occurring beyond the limits of available equipment.

The low-temperature spinel form of Mg_2GeO_4 is converted to the olivine structure at 810° C and 1 bar pressure. The PT curve for the transition, measured in the presence of water vapour under pressure, was followed up to 5·7 kb and 940° C. The slope of the curve is 246° C/kb. The effect of adding Mg_2SiO_4 as a component was established in isobaric and isothermal sections through the PTX model required to represent the binary system completely. An isobar for a pressure of 3·8 kb is illustrated in Fig. 28. This suggests that there is a simple solid solution loop in the system, descendent in temperature from Mg_2GeO_4 to Mg_2SiO_4.

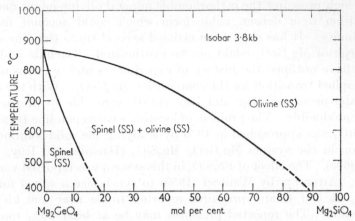

FIG. 28. 3·8 kb isobar in the system Mg_2GeO_4–Mg_2SiO_4. (Reproduced with permission from Dachille and Roy, 1960c.)

With increasing pressure, the germanate transition moves to higher temperatures, the extent of the spinel field increases, and that of the olivine field decreases. An isotherm at 542° C was obtained up to 65 kb pressure (Fig. 29). Extrapolation of the measured solid solution

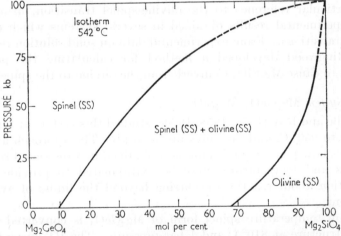

FIG. 29. 542° C isotherm in the system Mg_2GeO_4–Mg_2SiO_4. (Reproduced with permission from Dachille and Roy, 1960c.)

boundaries to a closure point for the composition Mg_2SiO_4 provides an estimate of 100 kb for the olivine–spinel transition in forsterite at this temperature. This corresponds to a point on the univariant curve for the transition. Dachille and Roy (1960c) estimated that the slope of the PT curve passing through this point would be between 13° C/kb and 25° C/kb (Fig. 30).

Ringwood (1958b) obtained data on the extent of solid solution in this system at 660° C and 30 kb, and this information was used to calculate a transition pressure for Mg_2SiO_4 at 660° C. The most probable pressure was 88 kb, the maximum 116 kb, and the minimum 72 kb (Fig. 30).

2. The System Mg_2SiO_4–Fe_2SiO_4

Olivine in the earth's mantle probably contains fayalite in solid solution. Dachille and Roy (1960c; verbal report in 1956) completed a number of runs in the system Mg_2GeO_4–Mg_2SiO_4 with iron replacing the magnesium. The data showed clearly that in any isobaric section the spinel solution area is appreciably larger than for the composition Mg_2SiO_4.

On the basis of thermodynamic calculations, Ringwood (1958b) predicted that a spinel polymorph of fayalite should become stable around 50 kb as 700° C. Subsequent experimental measurements (1958d, 1959a) placed the transition at 600° C near 38 kb, and at 500° C in the range 30 to 35 kb. The fayalite–spinel transition was located at higher temperatures by Boyd and England (1960b), who reported a preliminary point on the curve at 60 kb and 1 500° C.

Figure 30 is a PT projection showing available data for the olivine–

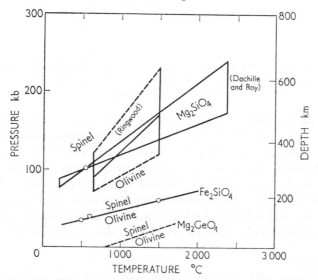

FIG. 30. PT curves for the olivine–spinel transition in Mg_2GeO_4, Fe_2SiO_4, and estimates for Mg_2SiO_4, with probable limits of error.

spinel transition in Mg_2SiO_4, Fe_2SiO_4, and Mg_2GeO_4. Two PT curves for the transition in Mg_2SiO_4 representing the limits of uncertainty were presented by Dachille and Roy (1960c); these pass through the point obtained by extrapolation from the system Mg_2GeO_4–Mg_2SiO_4. Ringwood's (1958b) calculated curve for the Mg_2SiO_4 transition, with the ranges of possible error due to experimental uncertainty, lies close to these two curves. The line for the transition in Fe_2SiO_4 is drawn through the points determined experimentally by Ringwood (1958d, 1959a) and Boyd and England (1960b).

These PT curves provide limits for the schematic PTX model illustrated in Fig. 31. A mean value has been taken from the various

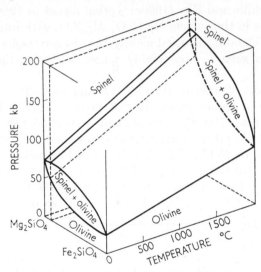

FIG. 31. Schematic PTX model for the system $Mg_2SiO_4(Fo)$–$Fe_2SiO_4(Fa)$ based on Fig. 30. A constant composition plane for the composition $Fo_{90}Fa_{10}$ intersects the two-phase space olivine + spinel in a band (see Fig. 32).

estimates for Mg_2SiO_4. A two-phase space for co-existing olivine and spinel separates the one-phase spaces for olivine and spinel solid solutions. The same pattern was illustrated in the PTX model for the system Mg_2GeO_4–Mg_2SiO_4 constructed by Dachille and Roy (1960c, Fig. 9) from the measured isobaric and isothermal sections. Figure 31 shows that forsteritic olivine containing fayalite in solid solution passes through a transition interval while being converted into the spinel form. The first spinel developed is richer in iron than the original olivine.

3. Conclusion

For an olivine with the composition 90% forsterite, 10% fayalite, the transition interval in which olivine and spinel co-exist is given by the intersection of a constant composition plane in Fig. 31 with the two-phase space. Figure 32 is a PT projection showing this transition band

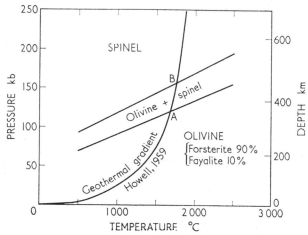

FIG. 32. PT projection showing the olivine–spinel transition for the composition $Fo_{90}Fa_{10}$ (Fig. 30), with an estimate of the geothermal gradient.

(the boundaries are not known precisely), which lies between the univariant curves for forsterite and fayalite. An estimate of the geothermal gradient is also plotted. If the mantle were composed only of olivine containing 10% fayalite in solid solution, this would be progressively converted to a denser spinel phase between A and B, in the depth range of 360 to 450 km. Uncertainties regarding the geothermal gradient have been mentioned previously, and the position of the transition interval in Fig. 32 is only tentative. However, as Dachille and Roy (1960c) concluded, the seismic discontinuity at a depth of 400 km can be reconciled " reasonably " with this transition. On the basis of Fig. 32, it appears that some other factor must be responsible for the 1 000 km discontinuity.

The olivine–spinel transition within the mantle could occupy a much wider depth range, perhaps extending as far as the 1 000 km discontinuity, if (i) the transition band illustrated in Fig. 32 had a much steeper slope, and (ii) there were a marked increase in the earth's temperature gradient between the two discontinuities. This was the model first adopted by Ringwood (1958c, Fig. 2), but in a subsequent revision (Ringwood, 1959b) he presented reasons for reducing the slope of the transition band to conform approximately with that illustrated in Fig. 32. If the interval between the two discontinuities in the mantle corresponds to the beginning and end of a transition of mantle materials from less dense to more dense phases, then the explanation of the wide

transition zone in the mantle, compared to the relatively narrow band
illustrated in Fig. 32 may possibly be attributed to solid solution effects.

The composition of mantle material may correspond to that of a garnet
peridotite. Ringwood (1959b) discussed a series of transitions and
reactions which could lead to a progressive increase in density of the
material between the two discontinuities. The transition would begin
with the formation of a spinel phase from the olivine forming the bulk
of this rock. This would occur in the interval AB (Fig. 32).

At somewhat higher pressures (Ringwood, 1958b), orthopyroxene
may break down to form spinel and coesite. At still higher pressures,
garnet and coesite could dissolve in the spinel phase to form disordered
defect spinel structures. The effect of solid solution between diopside
and enstatite might extend the transition range for the mantle material
to even higher pressures. The heterogeneous mantle material existing
above the 400 km discontinuity would thus pass through a wide
transition interval until by the time it reached the 1 000 km discontinuity,
it would be converted into a homogeneous rock composed only of
spinel. No experimental data are yet available for these proposed
reactions, so they will not be discussed further.

B. *The M Discontinuity and the Low-Velocity Layer in the Upper Mantle*

1. *The M Discontinuity*

The conventional view that the M discontinuity at the base of the
crust is caused by a chemical change from basaltic rock to peridotite has
been expounded recently by Hess (1955), Wager (1958), and Harris and
Rowell (1960). There is a wealth of geological data which can be
satisfactorily explained on the basis of this model, but the model also
presents some severe physical problems which have been discussed by
Birch (1958). Kennedy (1959) outlined other major problems facing
this model.

An alternative hypothesis originated with Fermor (1914), who suggested that the mantle was composed of eclogite, the high pressure
equivalent of basalt. M is then due to a high pressure mineralogical
phase change rather than to a chemical change. Following recent
theoretical and experimental studies, this hypothesis has been revived
by Lovering (1958) and Kennedy (1959), discussed by MacDonald and
Ness (1960), Wetherill (1961), Noble (1961), and Howell and Woodtli
(1961), and refuted by Harris and Rowell (1960), and Ringwood (1962).
The great attraction of the hypothesis lies in the fact that vertical
movements of geo-isotherms will cause M to migrate up or down,
producing changes in crustal thickness, with consequent changes in

surface elevation occurring to maintain isostatic equilibrium. This process has far-reaching implications for orogenetic theories. Hess (1955) had discussed similar effects caused by serpentinization of dehydration of the upper mantle material if this were composed of peridotite, with specific reference to suboceanic topography.

(a) *Experimental data*. The phase change from basalt to eclogite involves a change from the mineral assemblage pyroxene + plagioclase (+ olivine) to jadeitic pyroxene + pyrope-rich garnet (+ olivine). Experimentally measured curves for transitions involving these minerals are shown in Fig. 8. Boyd and England (1959) concluded that, together, the pyrope and jadeite stability curves can be taken as an approximation to the basalt–eclogite transition. Uncertainties in this approximation include: (i) solid solution effects which would tend to lower the pressure required for the formation of eclogite, and to spread out the transition interval, and (ii) the degree of silica saturation of the basalt; the presence of quartz rather than nepheline increases the pressure required to form jadeite.

A preliminary diagram for the transition between natural basalt and eclogite, and for the melting relations of both rocks, based on experiments with natural rock samples, has been published by Yoder and Tilley (1961). This diagram (Fig. 21) incorporates results obtained by Boyd and England (1959) and Kennedy (1959), and shows the position of the transition as predicted by Lovering (1958). The experimental data are meagre, but the few runs completed with natural samples provide limits for the gradient of the phase transition between basalt and eclogite, and show reasonable agreement with extrapolations from studies of the mineral components.

(b) *Conclusion*. Kennedy (1959) presented a phase boundary for the basalt–eclogite transition, based on the work of Robertson *et al.* (1957) on jadeite stability, and on his own work with natural basalt glass. The position of M within the earth is determined by the point of intersection of the crustal geothermal gradient with the PT curve (or zone) for the transition (Fig. 33). Kennedy suggested that if the slope of the phase change were approximately the same as the geothermal gradient, then a small change in the temperature gradient would produce a large change in the depth at which the phase transition occurred. He concluded that the M discontinuity, occurring at different depths beneath the oceans, the continental platforms, and the mountain ranges, can be explained by means of a single phase transition if the geothermal gradients increase slightly in this sequence, as illustrated in Fig. 33. The combined data obtained for natural rock samples, however, suggest a different pattern (Figs. 21 and 33). Although the phase change may be a reasonable explanation for the continental M, it appears to occur at depths too great to account for M under the oceans.

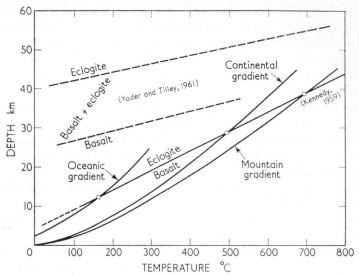

FIG. 33. The points of intersection of geothermal gradients for three environments, with an estimated curve for the basalt–eclogite transition, give the positions of M in these environments, assuming that M is due to a phase change. (Reproduced with permission from Kennedy, 1959.) The dashed lines illustrate preliminary experimental data for the basalt–eclogite transition (from Fig. 21).

If the M discontinuity beneath the oceanic crust is not due to the basalt–eclogite phase change, then it is reasonable to conclude that the upper mantle is composed of ultrabasic material not only beneath the oceanic crust, but also beneath the continents. If the upper mantle material is feldspathic peridotite, then the basaltic portion of the rock would undergo a phase transition to eclogite at the appropriate pressure and temperature range yielding a garnet peridotite. Such a phase change would not be detected readily by seismic techniques because both rocks have similar seismic wave velocities. These velocities would also be similar to those of eclogite.

Since the available experimental data indicate that the basalt–eclogite phase change occurs at about the same depth as the M discontinuity beneath the continents, there is a possibility that intersections occur between a zone of chemical discontinuity, and a phase transition zone. Under some parts of the continents the M discontinuity could be represented by a chemical discontinuity from basalt to feldspathic peridotite, and under other parts it could be represented by a phase transition from basalt to eclogite, with a chemical discontinuity from eclogite to garnet peridotite occurring at greater depths than M.

It may be expected that the depth of the chemical discontinuity will vary between continental shield areas and orogenic regions. Similarly, as indicated in Fig. 33, the depth of the phase change will vary according to the geothermal gradient. These variations produce great flexibility in possible models. It appears to be quite possible for the M discontinuity to be represented by the chemical discontinuity in the continental shields, and by the phase transition in orogenic regions.

Vertical movements of geo-isotherms in any region would cause the phase transition zone to migrate upwards or downwards, as mentioned previously. When the transition zone lies within the ultrabasic material, only a small density change would be involved, and changes in surface level required to maintain isostatic equilibrium would also be small. However, when the transition zone lies within basic material above the chemical discontinuity, the density change involved may be sufficient to cause significant changes in surface level. The orogenetic possibilities arising from this model will be considered elsewhere (Wyllie, unpublished).

2. The Low-velocity Layer in the Upper Mantle

On the basis of seismic studies, Gutenberg for many years maintained that a low-velocity layer existed within the mantle, with a velocity minimum for wave propagation at a depth of about 150 km (see Gutenberg, 1960, for a summary of his earlier work). He suggested that this occurs because the decrease in wave velocity caused by increasing temperature may preponderate, in this region, over the increase caused by increasing pressure. The low-velocity layer is now regarded as a decoupling zone between the material above it and that below it.

Ringwood (1962) concluded that probable temperature gradients in a homogeneous mantle would be too low to account for the low-velocity layer. He adopted a tentative model in which the mantle material immediately below M consisted of a mixture of dunite and peridotite, passing down into more primitive mantle material with composition corresponding to 1 part basalt and 4 parts peridotite (pyrolite). He suggested that the low-velocity zone is caused by the downward transition from feldspar-deficient material beneath M into the primitive feldspathic peridotite (plagioclase pyrolite). The velocity then increases with depth as this is transformed into garnet peridotite (garnet pyrolite). Relationships between oceanic, precambrian shield, and active orogenic regions were discussed in terms of this model.

On the basis of petrological considerations and available experimental data, Ringwood placed the transition between plagioclase and garnet pyrolite in a broad zone, with a gradient almost parallel to the geothermal gradient in the depth range 50–150 km. More recent experimental data (Yoder and Tilley, 1961) suggest that this estimate is too deep, and the gradient too steep (Fig. 21). However, the consequences of the model put forward by Ringwood are interesting, and some may perhaps be fitted to experimental data as they accrue.

On the basis of their work on crystalline phases in the system $CaMgSi_2O_6$–$CaAl_2SiO_6$–SiO_2 at 20 kb pressure, Clark and Neufville (1962) suggested that the low-velocity zone might be caused by reactions involving aluminous pyroxenes, but the data have not been published in detail.

VI. Granites and Related Rocks

Bowen (1928) demonstrated convincingly, on the basis of experimental studies of silicate systems, that fractional crystallization of basaltic magma *could* lead to the development of most naturally-occurring igneous rocks. Residual liquids approach compositions in the low-temperature region of " Petrogeny's Residua System " (Bowen, 1937), $NaAlSiO_4$(Ne)–$KAlSiO_4$(Kp)–SiO_2(Q), Fig. 34. Crystallization of these liquids would produce granites, or syenites, or nepheline syenites. Granites can be represented conveniently within the portion $NaAlSi_3O_8$(Ab)–$KAlSi_3O_8$(Or)–SiO_2(Q). Bowen (1947) also pointed out that the first liquid produced by partial melting of many rocks would have compositions lying near the low-temperature region of the Residua System. In view of the abundance of granitic rocks, a knowledge of the phase relationships in this system is of vital importance for the comprehension of geological processes occurring within the earth's crust.

A. *Petrogeny's Residua System*

Liquids in this system are extremely viscous, and even after years of patient work many of the phase relationships remain uncertain (Schairer, 1950). However, the development of hydrothermal equipment permitted definition of the significant phase relationships in the system Ab–Or–Q–H_2O (the " Granite System ") at pressures up to 4 kb (Bowen and Tuttle, 1950; Tuttle and Bowen, 1958). Tuttle and Luth (personal communication, 1962) have recently extended study of the melting relationships to 10 kb. Crystallization of liquids in this system leads to the co-precipitation of quartz and an alkali feldspar (Figs. 34 and 36). At pressures greater than about 3·5 kb, the solidus passes below the alkali feldspar solvus (Section IV, D), and quartz crystallizes alongside two feldspars, one sodic, and the other potassic.

If natural granites are plotted on this diagram in terms of their normative or modal quartz and feldspar content, they show a remarkable concentration near the temperature minima on the isobaric quartz–

feldspar field boundaries. Thus, the crystallization of liquids in the Granite System does lead to the formation of mineral assemblages

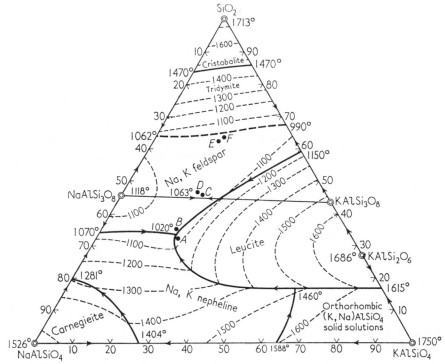

FIG. 34. Petrogeny's Residua System. (Reproduced with permission from Bowen, 1937; Schairer, 1950.)

which correspond to natural granites. The partial fusion of crystalline assemblages in the system similarly yields first a liquid on the quartz–feldspar field boundary which corresponds closely in composition to a granitic magma.

Tuttle and Bowen (1958) also measured the PT curve for the minimum liquidus temperature in the Granite System, and found it to be identical, within the limits of experimental error, with the curve for the beginning of melting of natural granites in the presence of water vapour under pressure (Fig. 22). The system Ab–Or–Q–H_2O thus appears to be a satisfactory model for the complex natural systems including granites.

The relevance of the system Ne–Kp–Q to the genesis of alkaline rocks, many of which are composed largely of feldspars and feldspathoids, is clearly indicated by Tilley's (1958) review of the problem. The difficulties of interpretation inherent in " dry " studies of this system have been partially overcome by the completion of several hydrothermal studies in the system Ne–Kp–Q–H_2O at high pressures (Tuttle and Smith, 1958; Hamilton and Mackenzie, 1960; Fudali, 1960, 1962; Hamilton, 1961).

B. *Granites*

The term granite is used loosely to define an entire family of massive, coarse-grained rocks composed largely of feldspar and quartz. The origin of granite has been hotly debated for more than 150 years, and it would be impossible to do justice to the controversy here. Readers are referred to petrological texts such as Barth (1952), and Turner and Verhoogen (1960) for detailed discussions. A clear statement of the problem is contained in a recent review by Walton (1960), which outlines succinctly the developments in theory since Hutton (1794) recognized a major class of rocks, the plutonic rocks, which had crystallized at great depths from a molten state. It seems unlikely that a satisfactory solution to the granite problem can ever be reached on the basis of field studies alone, but experimental data are helping to decide which of the various hypotheses are more nearly correct.

According to classic igneous theory, granitic magmas developed by a process of differentiation from a parent basaltic magma. This theory presents several major difficulties for the interpretation of the most abundant granites, those masses which form the cores of mountain ranges, and the granitic portions of migmatites in the " basement " rocks of the continental shields. Attempts to explain these difficulties led to various theories of granitization, which state that pre-existing rocks were transformed into granites through metasomatic processes, involving the migration of emanations or pore fluids from greater depths, or the migration of ionic and molecular particles by intergranular diffusion in the solid state. These processes may culminate in fusion of the granitized rocks with the formation of granitic magmas, but transformists claim that these magmas, if formed at all, are but local incidents at an advanced stage of granitization. A delightful account of the viewpoints of magmatists (" pontiffs ") and granitizers (" soaks ") has been published by Bowen (1947). Experimental data are now available to support the conclusions of field geologists that granites may be magmatic or metasomatic in origin, and the influence of volatile components is most important in both processes.

Walton (1960) concluded his account with an outline of the " anatectic model ". This is based on recent experimental studies on silicate systems and rock samples in the presence of water vapour under pressure, which open up " exciting possibilities . . . for reconciling many anomalies in the geology of granite and migmatite with growing experimental knowledge of the chemistry of silicates." The model bears resemblances to some granitization theories, but " the difference is that modern experimental research is beginning to explore rather than hypothesize physical-chemical processes which can ultimately reconcile the many puzzles presented by the geology of granite."

1. *Magmatic Granites*

Tuttle and Bowen (1958) discussed in detail the melting behaviour of granitic rocks in the earth's crust on the basis of their experimental work in the Granite System, and with natural granites in the presence of water under pressure. The stability field for granitic liquids extends well into the range of pressures and temperatures believed to be attained during high grade regional metamorphism. If even a trace of water is present during metamorphism, therefore, the conclusion is inescapable that many rocks must become partially melted. The experimental data thus confirm the hypothesis involving an anatectic model, which Bowen (1947) had outlined before the experimental data were available. The anatectic model was discussed further by Wyllie and Tuttle (1960c), incorporating additional experimental data on the melting of sediments and on the effect of other volatile components on the melting temperatures of granite (Section IV, I). The formation of granitic magmas by anatexis has also been discussed by Wyart and Sabatier (1959) and by Winkler and Platen (1961b), using as a basis their experimental data on the melting of sediments.

Melting in the earth's crust is controlled by the temperature, the pressure, and the bulk composition of the rocks. An important proportion of the rocks in geosynclines can be represented in terms of the compositions of granitic rocks, arkoses, and shales. Using a conservative estimate of 30° C/km (linear) for the geothermal gradient in geosynclines, this accounting for the variables pressure and temperature, the experimental data show that rocks of many compositions will begin to melt in the depth range 20–25 km (Fig. 35).

The liquid will be granitic or granodioritic in composition, and the amount developed will depend upon the availability of water and other volatiles. Melting will proceed, with the volatile components saturating the liquid, either until all the available volatiles are dissolved, or until all the " granitic components " of the rock have been melted. One weight % of water may be sufficient to melt 10 to 15% of the rock under these conditions. The amount of liquid would increase with depth as the temperature increases (assuming no decrease in the amount of volatiles available), giving rise to a zone of melting within the earth's crust.

Formation of granitic magmas *in situ* in this fashion could explain the occurrence of migmatites, and mobilization of the liquid-crystal

c*

mush could lead to the intrusion of migmatite domes. Settling out of the "nongranitic" crystalline fraction would yield a substantial

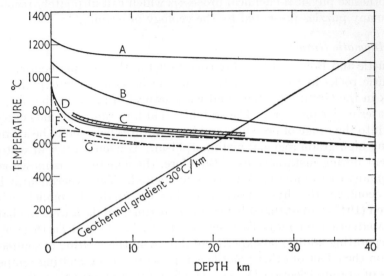

FIG. 35. Depth-temperature curves for melting, assuming that sufficient volatiles are present. (Reproduced with permission from Wyllie and Tuttle 1960c.) A, B, liquidus and solidus of basalt (see Fig. 24). C solidus region for natural shales. D solidus for granite (Fig. 22). F solidus for granite in the presence of 4 weight % HF solution (Fig. 23). E solidus in the system $CaO-CO_2-H_2O$ (Fig. 19). F solidus in the system $CaO-MgO-CO_2-H_2O$.

amount of granitic magma which could, in some circumstances, be displaced upwards as a separate granite intrusion, with discordant contacts against the country rock. Processes of this kind are discussed by Tuttle and Bowen (1958, p. 123–126).

2. *Metasomatic Granites*

Crystallization of a saturated granitic magma, be it a separate intrusion or a portion of a migmatite, leads to expulsion of the dissolved volatile components. Experimental data on the compositions of aqueous fluids in equilibrium with silicate melts are meagre (Section IV; Burnham and Tuttle, 1960; Burnham and Jahns, 1962), but solubility measurements indicate that the dense aqueous phase, or pore fluid, so produced may contain significant amounts of dissolved materials; alkalis are important constituents of the fluids.

The transfer of materials through an aqueous vapour phase was demonstrated by the leaching experiments of Tuttle and Bowen (1958, p. 89). When a charge of powdered granite was exposed to the circulating vapour in a pressure vessel, at high pressures and temperatures, the charge lost silica, alumina, and alkalis, with potassium being extracted at a greater rate than sodium. Appreciable changes in composition and mineralogy were obtained in experiments lasting a week. Mackenzie (1960) performed experiments of a similar type and stressed the significance of such studies to natural processes.

Recent work by Orville (1960) on alkali ion-exchange reactions at high pressures, between an alkali chloride vapour phase and alkali feldspars, provides additional data on the possible effects of the fluid expelled from a crystallizing granitic magma. The experimental data show that in the presence of a thermal gradient, a potential is developed for reciprocal alkali transfer within the vapour phase. There is a tendency for potassic feldspar to be replaced by sodic feldspar in the higher temperature rocks, and for sodic feldspar to be replaced by potassic feldspar in the lower temperature rocks. This provides an explanation for the potash metasomatism which occurs near the margins of granitic intrusions, and the process could lead to granitization of rocks with suitable compositions. Granitization is here a secondary effect of magmatic crystallization.

The pore fluid during metamorphism, as indicated by fluid inclusions trapped in metamorphic minerals, contains water, carbon dioxide, and alkali salts, with chlorides generally predominating. The solutions may be as concentrated as 2 to 4 normal. Ion-exchange reactions take place rapidly and reversibly in the laboratory, and similar reactions probably take place during metamorphism between alkali feldspars and the water-rich pore fluid. Orville (1960) found a surprising similarity between the equilibrium of alkali feldspar and alkali chloride solutions, and that of alkali feldspar and its water-saturated melt. He concluded that the continued solution of alkali feldspar from one volume of rock and reprecipitation in another volume of rock through the medium of the pore fluid, caused by the alkali concentration gradients which accompany thermal gradients, could lead to the same differentiation with respect to alkalis as that produced by partial melting of the rock at the same temperature. Conceivably, therefore, rocks with suitable compositions would be converted to granites, or granitized.

It should be noted that it takes more than the appropriate feldspar composition to make a granite; the quartz content must lie within certain limits, and the alkali feldspar and quartz must together exceed 80% of the rock. However, here for the first time is direct experimental evidence that some rocks, at least, may be converted to granitic rocks *before* partial melting occurs. Orville's projected ion-exchange experiments in lime-bearing systems should yield important data on the feasibility, the mechanism, and the extent of granitization during regional metamorphism.

C. *Alkaline Rocks*

It is important to check back and forth from field to laboratory frequently if maximum advantage is to be gained from the increasing amount of controlled experimental data now becoming available, and systematic efforts to solve petrological problems using the combined data of geological and experimental approaches have proved most rewarding. Good examples of the interdependence of the two approaches are afforded by recent work on pantellerites and related synthetic systems (Carmichael, 1962; Carmichael and Mackenzie, 1963), and by studies related to alkaline rocks containing pseudoleucite (Fudali, 1960, 1962).

1. *Pantellerites*

The extrusive equivalents of granite include rhyolites and obsidians. Analyses of these rocks, plotted in the Granite System in terms of their normative orthoclase, albite, and quartz, lie close to the experimentally-determined minima on the isobaric quartz–feldspar field boundaries, as expected in view of their origin by crystallization of a melt. Rare sodic rhyolites and obsidians (peralkaline), the pantellerites and comendites, contain a molecular excess of soda over alumina, and this requires the formation of the mineral molecule sodium metasilicate (*ns*) in the norm. Part of the excess alkali is contained in sodic pyroxene. Carmichael (1962) demonstrated that as the normative *ns* increased, there was a slight, progressive shift in the projected positions of these rocks towards the Or–Q side of the system. This suggests that addition of sodium silicate to the Granite System might cause a corresponding shift in the position of the minimum liquidus composition.

A more striking indication of this is given by the positions of tie-lines between feldspar phenocrysts and the residual glasses in rhyolites. An important result of the Granite System study (Tuttle and Bowen, 1958), which has not been mentioned previously, was the location of the tie-lines connecting co-existing feldspars and liquids. Some of these are illustrated in Fig. 36. The chemical compositions of glasses in rhyolitic rocks correspond to the compositions of the residual liquids developed by crystallization of the original melt. The tie-lines between these glasses and the feldspar phenocrysts of normal rhyolites have the same general trend as the experimental tie-lines in the Granite System. For pantellerites, on the other hand, the positions of tie-lines between phenocrysts (anorthoclase, Ab_{61}–Ab_{67}) and the residual glasses intersect the Granite System tie-lines. For some liquids of similar salic compositions, the liquid–feldspar tie-lines for pantellerites contrast markedly with those in the Granite System. This can be explained if the position of the liquidus minimum in the " Pantellerite System ", when projected onto the Granite System, is shifted towards Or–Q compared to the

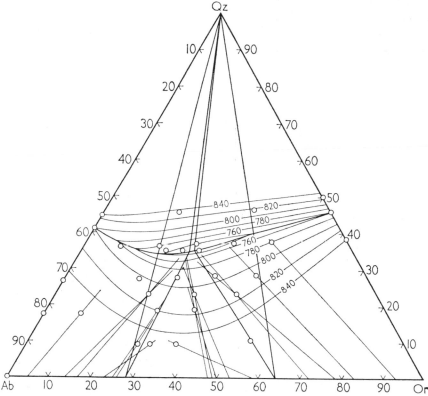

FIG. 36. Isobaric projection for 1 kb onto the anhydrous base of the system NaAlSi$_3$O$_8$ (Ab)–KAlSi$_3$O$_8$ (Or)–SiO$_2$ (Qz)–H$_2$O, showing the liquidus surface, three-phase triangles locating the minimum on the quartz–feldspar boundary, and some feldspar–liquid tie-lines: compare Fig. 34. (Modified slightly after Tuttle and Bowen, 1958).

minimum in the Granite System. This prompted Carmichael and Mackenzie (1963) to study the phase relationships in parts of the system formed by adding sodium silicate (*ns*) and aegirine (*ac*) to the Granite System. The compositions used correspond closely to pantellerites, and to peralkaline nepheline syenites of the agpaitic series (Carmichael, 1962).

In order to illustrate the phase relationships in this complex system, the components H$_2$O + *ns* + *ac* were plotted together at the apex of a tetrahedron with Ab–Or–Q as the base. This approach is satisfactory as long as quartz and feldspar are the only crystalline phases appearing in the system, and as long as no compositions too close to the sides of the

tetrahedron are considered. The feldspar and quartz fields of the
Granite System extend upwards into the tetrahedron as spaces, the
quartz–feldspar field boundary extends upwards as a surface, and from
the liquidus minimum in the Granite System there extends a line which
is the locus of minimum liquidus temperatures on composition planes
parallel to the base of the tetrahedron. Liquidus temperatures at a
pressure of 1 kb were measured on parts of two planes: the planes
containing $4 \cdot 5\%$ *ns* $+ 4 \cdot 5\%$ *ac*, and $8 \cdot 3\%$ *ns* $+ 8 \cdot 3\%$ *ac*. Tie-lines were
located between alkali feldspars, and liquids on these planes. For each
composition plane, the measured liquidus surface, the line of intersection
of the quartz–feldspar boundary surface, the minimum liquidus
temperature, and the feldspar–liquid tie-lines, were projected onto the
base of the tetrahedron. The results obtained for the $8 \cdot 3\%$ *ns* $+ 8 \cdot 3\%$ *ac*
plane are illustrated in Fig. 37. It can be seen that the position of the

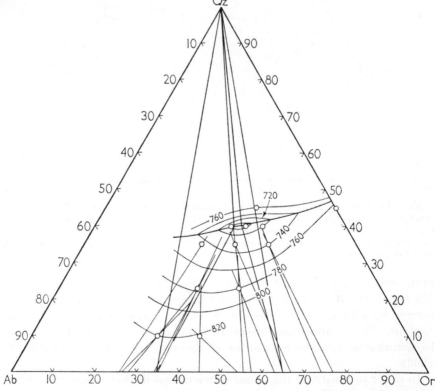

FIG. 37. Isobaric projection for 1 kb from the apex X of the liquidus surface
of the $8 \cdot 3\%$ *ac* $+ 8 \cdot 3\%$ *ns* plane in the system $NaAlSi_3O_8$ (Ab)–$KAlSi_3O_8$ (Or)–
SiO_2 (Qz)–X, where X represents $(H_2O + Na_2SiO_3 + NaFeSi_2O_6)$. (Reproduced with
permission from Carmichael and Mackenzie, 1963.) Compare the three-phase
triangles and feldspar–liquid tie-lines with those in Fig. 36.

liquidus minimum has been shifted towards the Or–Q join quite appreciably, in projection, as had been indicated by Carmichael's (1962) petrological study on pantellerites. The explanation proposed by Carmichael (1962, Fig. 3) to account for the apparently anomalous liquid–feldspar tie-lines in pantellerites is confirmed by the new experimental data.

Although the liquidus minimum is shifted in the direction of increasing Or/Ab ratio, this does not imply that the residual liquid is enriched in the ratio K_2O/Na_2O. Simultaneously, the liquid at the minimum is being enriched in $ns + ac$, components rich in Na_2O, and, in fact, little change occurs in the K_2O/Na_2O ratio.

2. *Pseudoleucites*

A thorough knowledge of the relationships between nepheline, alkali feldspar, and leucite is essential for an understanding of alkaline rocks. The condensed phase diagram for the Residua System, which contains these minerals, is illustrated in Fig. 34. The bulk compositions of many rocks plot within the leucite field of this system (Tilley, 1958), which suggests that leucite should have crystallized at an early stage in the cooling history of many alkaline magmas. However, plutonic rocks are characterized by alkali feldspar–nepheline assemblages, and leucite occurs only in extrusive rocks or minor intrusions. Some information about the phase relationships between these minerals in natural systems can be obtained from their study in rocks. Tilley (1958) has summarized what can be done in this way with alkali feldspar–nepheline parageneses. Information about the behaviour of leucite may be obtained from the rather rare rocks which contain phenocrysts of pseudoleucite.

Pseudoleucite phenocrysts contain mixtures of nepheline and alkali feldspar, apparently as pseudomorphs of leucite. They are usually considerably altered to zeolites. Knight (1906) suggested that they were formed by unmixing of a soda-rich leucite on cooling, but Bowen (1928) pointed out that if this were the origin, one would expect to find examples of soda-rich leucites in rapidly cooled volcanic lavas. Bowen (1928, pp. 240–245) predicted the presence of a reaction point, where leucite reacts with the remaining magma to form nepheline and sanidine, and the existence of such a reaction point was later verified experimentally in the Residua System (Fig. 34). The reaction point and the minimum on the liquidus field boundary between nepheline and alkali feldspar are very close together in temperature and in composition. Larsen and Buie (1938) were unable to reconcile their studies of pseudoleucites with an origin by crystal–liquid reaction, and they suggested that some pseudoleucites may have formed by unmixing of a potash-rich analcite.

Fudali (1960, 1962) studied the phase relationships in selected parts of the Residua System, in the presence of water vapour under pressure, in an attempt to resolve the problem related to the origin of pseudo-leucites and the crystallization of alkaline magmas. His equilibrium diagram for the system at a pressure of 1 kb is shown in Fig. 38. This

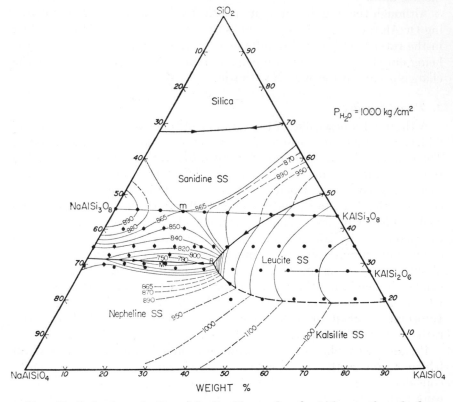

FIG. 38. Isobaric projection of the liquidus surface for 1 kb onto the anhydrous base of the system $NaAlSiO_4$–$KAlSiO_4$–SiO_2–H_2O. (Reproduced with permission from Fudali, 1960, 1962, incorporating data of Tuttle and Bowen, 1958, and Hamilton, 1961.)

diagram incorporates some liquidus data obtained by Hamilton (1961), as well as the results of Tuttle and Bowen (1958). All liquids in the system contain dissolved water, and all phases co-exist with a vapour phase.

The influence of water-pressure causes several changes compared to results in the dry system (Figs. 34 and 38). Liquidus temperatures are substantially lower (by 200° C to 400° C), and the primary field of leucite is considerably diminished. The reaction point therefore moves towards the leucite composition, with the result that the minimum on the alkali feldspar–nepheline field boundary can be clearly distinguished from it. Fudali reported that leucite can dissolve 28 weight % of $NaAlSi_2O_6$ at 1 kb; the amount of solid solution increases as the H_2O pressure decreases, reaching a maximum of about 40 weight % in the dry system. Below the solidus, soda-rich leucite becomes unstable, and breaks down to a mixture of nepheline and sanidine. This process was deduced from the equilibrium phase diagrams and it was also confirmed experimentally. The conversion occurs very rapidly, and the outlines of the original leucite crystals become indistinguishable from the groundmass crystals. Fudali also converted a sample of natural pseudoleucite to a homogeneous leucite solid solution by heating at 1 000° C at atmospheric pressure.

These results confirm that pseudoleucites can be formed by the breakdown of a soda-rich leucite which crystallized at higher temperatures. The unmixing occurs with ease, and in plutonic rocks which crystallized slowly, all traces of the former leucite would be erased. Fudali also discussed the possibility that the same effect could be obtained by breakdown of a potash-rich analcite, but definitive experimental data are not yet available. The existence of a reaction point at high water-pressures confirms that some pseudoleucites could be formed by reaction between leucite and magma, but Fudali (1962) presents reasons for favouring an origin by unmixing. These experiments confirm a fact well-known to petrologists, namely, that apparently identical end-products (rocks) can be produced by several different processes.

D. *Pegmatites*

Associated with many intrusive igneous masses, especially those of granitic composition, are smaller bodies of pegmatite, which are believed to represent the final products of crystallization and differentiation of the parent magma. They are compositionally almost equivalent, but volumetrically insignificant as compared with the intrusions from which they were derived. However, they have attracted a great deal of attention because they are very coarse grained and many contain elements and minerals, in economic concentrations, that are rare in the parent rocks. These elements presumably remained in the liquid phase during crystallization of the magma, and only in the final stages did their concentrations become high enough for their precipitation in minerals.

Characteristic features of pegmatites are their great range in grain size and the presence of individual crystals that may be measured in metres rather than millimetres (Jahns, 1953). The large size of some crystals suggests that the pegmatite magmas were rich in volatile components. Water is believed to have been dominant among these, but fluorine, lithium, boron, phosphorus, and carbon dioxide also may have been important in many occurrences. Numerous varieties of pegmatite are known; some bodies, for example, are simple and of fairly uniform composition throughout, whereas others are internally zoned into systematically disposed layers, lenses, and pods of contrasting composition, mineralogy, and texture. Details of pegmatite bodies, and of the various hypotheses which have been proposed for their origin, can be found in a comprehensive review by Jahns (1955).

Many pegmatites evidently have been developed by metamorphic or metasomatic processes, but this section is concerned only with the formation and crystallization of magmatic pegmatites. Most petrologists are agreed that the magmatic pegmatites have crystallized from a melt derived from the associated plutonic intrusions. On the other hand, controversy has centred about such topics as the amount and nature of the volatile components in the pegmatite melt; the behaviour of these volatile components; the extent of replacement undergone by the pegmatites through pneumatolytic or hydrothermal processes; the source of the solutions causing alteration; and the causes of zoning and giant crystals.

Jahns and Burnham (1958) embarked on an experimental programme, using natural pegmatite samples in the presence of water under pressure, aimed at answering some of the controversial questions related to the origin and crystallization of pegmatites. This programme, which soon achieved spectacular success, is a fine example of how natural rock samples may yield useful experimental data despite the fact that the system is too complex to be treated theoretically in terms of the phase rule.

The first step was to measure the liquidus and solidus temperatures of natural pegmatites in the presence of H_2O under pressure (Section IV, I; Jahns and Burnham, 1958), and the results confirmed that liquids persisted in pegmatite systems to lower temperatures than in granites (Fig. 22), as would be expected if pegmatite magmas were volatile-charged derivatives of granitic magmas. With these data known, the next step was to reproduce conditions for pegmatite formation.

Crushed samples of the pegmatite were sealed within large gold capsules together with water. The amount of water was somewhat less than that required to saturate the melt at the liquidus. The temperature of each capsule was raised to a level above the liquidus, at a selected pressure, and held there long enough to ensure that the capsule contained only one phase—a silicate liquid undersaturated with water. In successive experiments, the liquid was cooled to various temperatures within the melting interval, and the partially crystallized charge was then quenched. The textures produced at various stages of crystallization were studied microscopically in thin sections made from the charges. A photomicrograph showing most of the significant features is reproduced in Fig. 39, which illustrates many of the textural features occurring in natural pegmatites.

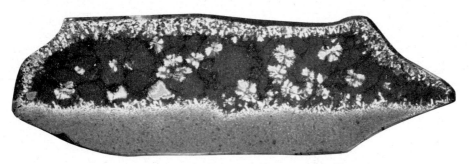

FIG. 39. Photomicrograph (crossed nicols) of synthetic pegmatite (by courtesy of R. H. Jahns and W. C. Burnham). The section measures one half inch from top to bottom. Fine-grained crystalline border encloses glass (isotropic) studded with radial groups of large crystals (compare Fig. 40). The development of a wide border facies at the bottom of the sample is due to a vertical temperature gradient.

On cooling, the silicate liquid begins to crystallize first around the walls of the container. The product is a border of fine-grained sanidine and quartz enclosing liquid. Crystallization continues in this way until the remaining silicate liquid becomes saturated with water, at which stage an aqueous vapour phase appears. This phenomenon of " resurgent boiling " occurs at a " second boiling point ", whose temperature depends upon the proportion of water in the charge, the amount of water fixed in minerals, and the total pressure on the system. Crystallization continues with decreasing temperature, and more water is displaced from the liquid to the vapour phase.

As soon as a free vapour phase makes its appearance in the system (recognized by the preservation of bubble cavities in glass, the quenched liquid) there is a marked change in texture of the solid phases produced (well illustrated in Fig. 39). Very much larger crystals grow inwards from the fine-grained border zone, and groups of large crystals also occur farther toward the centre of the charge. Transfer of alkalis is indicated by an increase in the sanidine/quartz ratio for the aggregates of large crystals outward from the centre of the charge, and selective vertical transfer of major alkalis is indicated by higher K_2O/Na_2O ratios of the sanidine in the upper part of the charge as compared with the sanidine in the lower part. The radial groups of large crystals in the " experimental pegmatite " are analogous to radial groups of large crystals occurring in natural pegmatites (Fig. 40). Fringes of giant

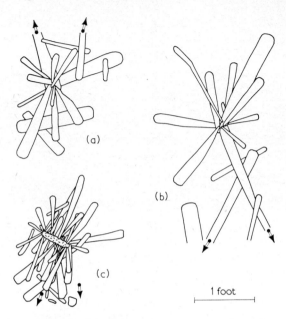

FIG. 40. Radial distribution of large spodumene prisms in coarse grained pegmatite in Arizona. (Reproduced with permission from Jahns, 1953.)

crystals, rather like those near the bottom of the charge in Fig. 39, are also found in natural pegmatites (Jahns, 1953, Fig. 1).

The large crystals appear to grow principally from the aqueous fluid phase, commonly along interfaces with the silicate melt. Solubility measurements (Section IV, I; Burnham and Jahns, 1962) show that the amount of material dissolved in the aqueous fluid ranges from 1 weight % at 2 kb and 550° C, to 12·8% at 10 kb and 700° C. Rapid and selective transfer of this material by diffusion through the vapour phase appears to be necessary for the growth of giant crystals, and Orville's (1960) work on alkali ion-exchange reactions between crystals and vapour confirms the efficiency of such processes. When the reactions involve a liquid phase as well as crystals and vapour, gravitational rising of the vapour phase through the melt may contribute to the formation of pods and zones of unusual composition in pegmatites.

When crystallization of a natural pegmatite is completed, it may be expected that the vapour phase will continue to react with the crystalline phases, as the temperature decreases, and this could account for much of the hydrothermal alteration which occurs in pegmatites. Under suitable conditions, some of this aqueous fluid phase may escape into the country rocks surrounding the pegmatites.

Jahns and Burnham (1962) have published an outline of a model for the crystallization of granitic pegmatites, based on the experimental studies described above, but complete details are not yet available.

VII. METAMORPHIC ROCKS

Preceding sections (II and IV) have dealt with the range of composition and the mineralogical constitution of metamorphic rocks, with the processes which may be involved in their formation, and with the types of experimental data which can be applied to metamorphic problems. Experimental data are usually obtained under clearly defined conditions, and they are strictly applicable only to processes occurring under similar conditions. Their direct application to metamorphic reactions is therefore limited, but comparison of the results of experimental studies with metamorphic parageneses may shed light on the processes involved, and once the processes have been inferred, then the experimental data may be used to obtain realistic estimates of temperatures and pressures attained during metamorphism.

A. *Presentation of Experimental Data*

1. *Experimental Grids*

Experimental results can be represented conveniently on a PT projection, and the univariant reaction curves measured in the presence of a one-component vapour phase constitute Bowen's (1940) petrogenetic grid which is discussed in the next section. Univariant reaction curves and divariant reaction bands measured in the presence of mixed volatiles are displaced to lower temperatures (Harker, 1958; Greenwood, 1961; Wyllie, 1962a) and these should be distinguished from the curves of the petrogenetic grid. Each set of reaction curves and bands corresponding to a specific set of experimental conditions may be called an experimental grid. This is an unambiguous term with no petrogenetic significance.

Most available experimental data involve a vapour phase consisting of essentially one volatile component, with the pressure on the vapour phase (p_f) equal to the pressure on the crystalline phases (p_s). Dehydration reactions have been studied in the presence of water, and decarbonation reactions in the presence of carbon dioxide. A few systems have been studied recently with vapour phases consisting of two components, e.g. $H_2O + Ar$, $CO_2 + Ar$, or $H_2O + CO_2$ (Section IV, G);

although these experiments were performed in closed pressure vessels, the nature of some reactions under open conditions can be estimated from the phase relationships. This was discussed by Wyllie (1962a). Greenwood (1960) has reported preliminary experiments with $p_f < p_s$. With the increasing range of experimental techniques now being developed, we may expect that many experimental grids will be measured.

2. *Petrogenetic grid and petrogenetic model*

Progressive metamorphism results in a series of dehydration and decarbonation reactions, and other reactions involving no release of volatile components (solid–solid reactions). Bowen's (1940) petrogenetic grid is a PT projection containing univariant curves for these reactions occurring in the presence of " pure " vapour phases (water for dehydration reactions, and carbon dioxide for decarbonation reactions) with the vapour phase pressure equal to the total pressure ($p_f = p_s$). It is a projection onto a pT plane of parts of two experimental grids, one for a vapour phase with the composition of water and the other for a vapour phase with the composition of carbon dioxide. Examples of the three types of reaction are illustrated in Fig. 41.

Bowen made it quite clear that the reaction curves represent upper temperature limits for the stability of particular minerals or mineral

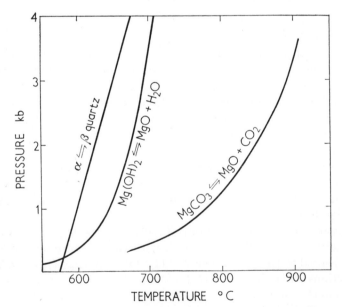

FIG. 41. A portion of the petrogenetic grid: solid–solid, dehydration, and decarbonation reactions. (Reproduced with permission from Wyllie, 1962c.)

assemblages, and that under appropriate metamorphic conditions the reactions could proceed at lower temperatures. The petrogenetic grid has been widely used, but the term is useful only as long as it is retained for the limiting conditions defined by Bowen. Otherwise, it will become a receptacle for all kinds of experimental and petrological data and inferences, with the result that it will cease to have any petrogenetic significance.

Two metamorphic conditions can cause dissociation reactions to proceed at temperatures lower than those indicated on the petrogenetic grid. The first occurs if the pore fluid contains more than one component, with $p_f = p_s$, and the second arises if the pressure on the pore fluid is less than the lithostatic pressure on the crystalline phases, $p_f < p_s$; the pore fluid may be " pure " or " impure ". Both of these conditions reduce the chemical potential of the reacting volatile component involved in a dissociation reaction, compared to its maximum value on the petrogenetic grid, and this in turn lowers the reaction temperature. The reaction is then represented by a divariant surface extending to lower temperatures from the univariant curve on the petrogenetic grid.

Three-dimensional diagrams, with two of the axes being p_s and T, are required to illustrate the divariant surfaces graphically. The third axis must be some function of the chemical potential of the volatile component involved in the reaction. Thompson (1955) suggested using the chemical potential of the component (a mobile component), or the pressure on the pure fluid phase in osmotic equilibrium with the system, p_F. Greenwood (1961) used the quantity p_E, the equilibrium pressure, which is similar to Thompson's parameter p_F. With these approaches, separate diagrams are required for illustration of decarbonation and dehydration teactions, the third axis in one case being a function of the chemical potential of CO_2, and in the other case being a function of the chemical potential of H_2O. Furthermore, a system may reach a particular position within these diagrams by at least two processes: the pore fluid may be impure, while the pore fluid pressure (p_f) remains equal to the pressure on the crystalline phases ($p_f = p_s$), or the pore fluid pressure may be reduced compared to the load pressure ($p_f < p_s$). Wyllie (1962b, c) suggested using, as the third axis, the chemical composition of the vapour phase, or pore fluid, expressed in molecular or weight % between water and carbon dioxide. These volatiles are believed to be the dominant components in pore fluids. For the divariant decarbonation surfaces, the critical value is the carbon dioxide content of the vapour phase, and for dehydration surfaces the critical value is the water content of the vapour phase. Therefore, other non-reacting volatile components can be taken into consideration on this CO_2–H_2O composition axis, with little loss in accuracy on the temperature scale (Wyllie, 1962a).

A three-dimensional model, with mutually perpendicular axes representing the variables p $(p_f = p_s)$, T, and vapour phase (or pore fluid) composition varying between H_2O and CO_2 is the petrogenetic model (Wyllie, 1962b, c). One face of the model is a PT plane for reactions occurring in the presence of pure H_2O, and the opposite face is a PT plane for reactions occurring in the presence of CO_2. Superposition of these two faces gives the petrogenetic grid. Figure 42 is a

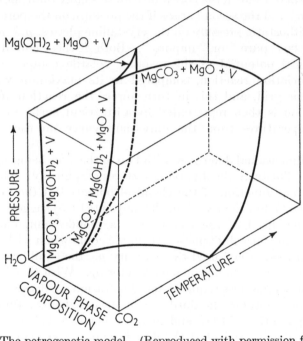

Fig. 42. The petrogenetic model. (Reproduced with permission from Wyllie, 1962c.) Divariant surfaces extend from the univariant dissociation curves of Fig. 41.

petrogenetic model illustrating the reactions which occur in the system MgO–CO_2–H_2O. The univariant curves plotted on the PT faces correspond to the dissociation of brucite and of magnesite on the petrogenetic grid (Fig. 41), and these same reactions are represented within the model by divariant surfaces extending to lower temperatures as the proportion of non-reacting volatile increases. They meet along a curved univariant line, quite close to the water vapour composition, which represents the co-existence of four phases, $MgCO_3 + Mg(OH)_2 + MgO + vapour$. Extending from this line to lower temperatures is a third surface representing the co-existence of the three phases $MgCO_3 + Mg(OH)_2 + vapour$.

This surface has a different shape because it does not represent a dissociation reaction.

Any dehydration or decarbonation reaction can be plotted in the petrogenetic model in a similar fashion, and the shapes of the dissociation surfaces can be measured experimentally or calculated thermodynamically. Solid–solid reactions are independent of the pore fluid composition, and on both PT faces of the petrogenetic model they appear as univariant lines corresponding to those of the petrogenetic grid (Fig. 41). Within the model, they are represented by surfaces parallel to the vapour composition axis and perpendicular to the PT planes. These surfaces divide the model into smaller spaces, or pigeonholes, each containing a particular mineral assemblage.

An advantage of the petrogenetic model is that the divariant surfaces for both dehydration and decarbonation reactions are represented in the same diagram, and the reactions which may occur among carbonates, hydrates, and pore fluids are also represented. Isobaric sections through the model may be used to illustrate different metamorphic processes. Wyllie (1962c) described reactions occurring at constant pressure with (1) pore fluid composition remaining constant during the reaction, (2) pore fluid changing composition as the reaction proceeds with increasing temperature, and (3) pore fluid changing composition at constant temperature.

An assemblage of phases of known composition at fixed pressure $(p_f = p_s)$ and temperature gives a unique solution for the chemical potential or fugacity of the reacting volatile component. When sufficient experimental and theoretical data are available, it will be possible to contour the divariant surfaces in the petrogenetic model with lines of equal chemical potential or fugacity of carbon dioxide for decarbonation reactions, and with lines of equal chemical potential or fugacity of water for dehydration reactions. Similarly, for reactions involving iron-bearing compounds, it should be possible to contour lines of equal oxygen fugacity. Alternatively, lines of equal equilibrium pressure may be plotted on the surfaces, in accordance with the approach used by Greenwood (1961).

The petrogenetic model refers to the condition $p_f = p_s$. However, when the divariant surfaces are contoured with lines of equal fugacities, it will also provide, for the condition $p_f < p_s$, essentially the same information as the diagrams using chemical potentials, osmotic pressure, or equilibrium pressure as the third axis. The petrogenetic model combines in one diagram all of this information, as well as the vapour phase composition. It provides a simple framework to accommodate a great number of experimental data in such a way that the relationships among the experimentally-measured reactions are easily seen, and in such a way that the effects of various metamorphic processes on the sequences of mineral assemblages can also be seen. Given the necessary experimental data for various bulk compositions (approximating rock compositions as closely as possible), the sequences of mineral parageneses developed by these different processes can be ascertained from the arrangement of pigeonholes within the model.

B. *The Elucidation of Metamorphic Processes*

1. *Metamorphic Grids*

One aim of petrologists is to locate on PT diagrams the relative positions of natural metamorphic reactions (Fyfe *et al.*, 1958, p. 20). The mineral parageneses stable in fields between the lines for selected reactions represent metamorphic facies and sub-facies. There has been a tendency to describe any PT diagram of this type as a petrogenetic grid (e.g. Francis, 1956). However, as previously mentioned in connection with the presentation of experimental data, the indiscriminate use of the term petrogenetic grid must lead to confusion. In order to avoid this, a PT grid representing reactions as they are presumed to occur during metamorphism, without reference to the variables pore fluid

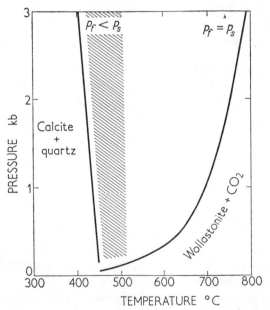

FIG. 43. PT projection for the reaction $CaCO_3 + SiO_2 = CaSiO_3 + CO_2$. If $p_f = p_s$, the reaction is represented by the right hand curve, but if CO_2 escapes so that $p_f < p_s$, it is represented by the left hand curve. According to Barth (1952) the shaded area represents the reaction in most rocks (compare Fig. 13).

pressure, composition, mobility, etc., may be called a metamorphic grid. In many respects, the term petrogenetic grid is more appropriate, but this has already been clearly defined as a limiting condition.

A metamorphic grid, if $p_f = p_s$, would have the same general pattern as the petrogenetic grid, but dissociation reactions would be somewhat lowered in temperature according to the pore fluid composition (Figs. 41 to 44). A metamorphic grid if $p_f < p_s$ would present quite a different pattern because the dissociation reactions would occur at much lower temperatures (Figs. 43 and 44b). This is illustrated in a useful paper by Francis (1956), who constructed a metamorphic grid for the regionally metamorphosed rocks of the Scottish Highlands, *assuming* that $p_f < p_s$.

2. *Comparison of Metamorphic Grids with Experimental Grids*

In their " Introduction to the Petrogenic Grid ", Fyfe *et al.* (1958, p. 20) write: " In the depth-zone classification of Grubenmann and in the facies classification of Eskola, mineral assemblages are arranged in a network of pigeonholes as functions of chemical composition and of grade of metamorphism (as indicated in the first place by field relations) . . . Bowen stresses the need for building up a " petrogenic grid " in which experimentally determined curves for metamorphic reactions ultimately will be plotted on co-ordinates of pressure and temperature. The two networks will be developed and refined on the basis of independently determined data—geological-petrographic observations and physicochemical experimental data. *The aim of all students of metamorphic petrology is to superpose the two grids one on the other.*" (italics mine).

The first grid is a metamorphic grid, and the second grid is the petrogenetic grid. These two grids can only be usefully superposed if it is known that pore fluids are " pure ", and that $p_f = p_s$ during metamorphism. However, there is an impressive body of opinion supporting the view that $p_f < p_s$ during metamorphism. In order to distinguish between these two conditions, it is necessary to compare metamorphic grids not only with the petrogenetic grid, but also with all available experimental grids. In this way, we should eventually be able to infer which variables are the most important in natural systems. The pressures and temperatures, and perhaps even the pore fluid composition, in various parts of a metamorphic grid could then be read directly from the appropriate experimental grids.

The significance of the pore fluid pressure during metamorphism has been mentioned. Of critical importance in deciding whether $p_f = p_s$ or $p_f < p_s$ are the relative positions of dissociation and solid–solid reactions in experimental and metamorphic grids. Solid–solid reactions are relatively independent of the pore fluid, whereas dissociation reactions may be shifted in position through more than 200° C between these two limiting conditions (Fig. 43). If metamorphic conditions should correspond to $p_f < p_s$, the relative positions of dissociation reactions and solid–solid reactions could therefore be interchanged on a metamorphic grid compared to their positions on the petrogenetic grid. This is illustrated in Fig. 44, which shows the positions of the quartz inversion

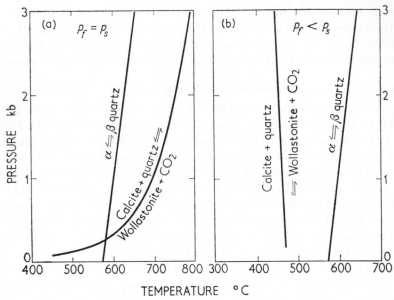

Fig. 44. Portions of metamorphic grids for the limiting conditions (a). $p_f = p_s$, and (b). $p_f < p_s$. The relative positions of the decarbonation and the solid–solid reactions are interchanged between these conditions. (Reproduced with permission from Wyllie, 1962c.)

(solid–solid) and the wollastonite reaction (dissociation) for the conditions $p_f = p_s$ and $p_f < p_s$.

Precise experimental data are available for only few solid–solid reactions of significance in metamorphism. The kyanite⇌sillimanite equilibrium is one example (Clark *et al.* 1957; Clark, 1961). As shown in Fig. 8, kyanite is stable at temperatures above 500° C at pressures in excess of 10 kb. This suggests that rocks containing kyanite were formed at depths greater than 35 km. Experimental data on jadeite, pyrope, and alumina-bearing enstatite (Section IV, C) similarly suggest that many metamorphic rocks now exposed at the surface were formed at pressures of the same order of magnitude. This implies either that vertical displacements of many rock masses have approximated the total thickness of the earth's crust, or that pressures attained during metamorphism were systematically higher than the estimated litho-static pressure. Clark (1961) calculated that " tectonic overpressures " of 1 kb or more (corresponding to about 4 km overburden in the crust) could be developed and sustained by the strength of buried rocks. Sobolev (1960) and Semenenko (1960) suggested that the pressure in the earth's crust fluctuates through a wide range as a result of tectonic stress. In particular, regions of superpressure greatly in excess of lithostatic pressure may be developed in metamorphic belts.

There is no known way of estimating depth independently of pressure, so that if tectonic overpressures are developed during metamorphism, the experimental location of solid–solid reactions on PT projections is still insufficient to provide definitive fixed boundaries on metamorphic grids (Figs. 5 and 44). However, these reactions remain much more reliable PT indicators than the dissociation reactions (Fig. 44).

C. *Conclusions*

The temperatures of many metamorphic reactions depend upon the process of metamorphism. For this reason, not until the processes are more clearly defined will refinement of experimental measurements provide better estimates of the temperatures prevailing during meta-morphism. Different interpretations of the behaviour of the pore fluid may be resolvable by comparing metamorphic grids with experimental grids. Once the relative pressure and the function of the pore fluid on a regional scale have been estimated, details of its behaviour on a local scale may be obtained by comparing specific reactions in rocks with similar reactions within an experimental framework such as the petrogenetic model. Given a reasonable approximation to the processes involved in mineral formation, experimental grids will provide temperature and pressure estimates.

VIII. Concluding Remarks

There is little to add here to what has already been covered in the preceding pages, but it may be apposite to summarize some of the remarks scattered through the chapter, and to venture a few predictions about future developments.

A. *Retrospect*

Much of the impetus for high pressure-high temperature studies has come from attempts to reproduce geological processes in the laboratory. In the dozen years since the design of simple equipment suitable for such studies, more data have been gathered than in all of the preceding years. The stability fields of many minerals have been measured, and much useful information has been obtained by subjecting natural rock samples to various conditions. Some reaction curves have been revised repeatedly as techniques have become more refined, and as research workers have become more acutely aware of equilibrium problems involved in these investigations. An extreme example of multiple revision is provided by the simple reaction: $Mg(OH)_2 \rightleftharpoons MgO + H_2O$ (Fyfe, 1960). It may be noted that despite the ever-increasing range of experimental equipment and techniques, the extent of the experimental probe within the earth is still very limited (cf. Fig. 6). Conditions through the earth's crust can now be reproduced readily, but conditions in the mantle, where most of the igneous and metamorphic phenomena have their ultimate origins, are inadequately covered.

A great deal of the experimental work so far completed is in the nature of a reconnaissance—a reconnaissance of possible processes that could lead to the formation of a particular assemblage of minerals with specific textural relationships (i.e. a particular rock). Even a cursory examination of the geological literature shows that it is practically impossible to reach a definite conclusion about the origin of many rocks on the basis of field and petrographic studies alone. By comparing these studies with experimental results, however, it may be possible to decide which of several geological hypotheses can be discounted as improbable, and which may be considered as the most likely. The two approaches, geological and experimental, are interdependent, and the results from each approach stimulate research in the other.

Experimental studies have also provided data yielding estimates of temperatures and, more rarely, of pressures attained during the formation of various rocks. However, most of these estimates must be regarded as preliminary because: (i) in most cases the processes involved in the formation of the rocks must be known before experimental data can provide realistic estimates, and (ii) many published reaction curves used to provide the estimates may not represent the stable equilibrium curves.

B. *Prospect*

Possibilities for future research are too numerous for detailed consideration. According to Fyfe (1960), the period of reconnaissance in experimental petrology must now be followed by a period in which more precise data are sought. This involves evaluation of the limitations of laboratory procedures, and attempts to establish true, stable equilibrium in the experiments. Equilibrium reaction curves should be tested through consideration of available thermodynamic data and by thermodynamic arguments, and more thermodynamic data must be gathered.

Nevertheless, a great deal of reconnaissance work remains to be completed.

New or modified equipment to permit routine work in the higher pressure-temperature ranges will undoubtedly be developed. The construction of large capacity pressure vessels for detailed studies of liquid and vapour compositions has opened a new field of study. Investigations of the deformation of minerals and rocks have advanced so rapidly in the past few years that major developments can be expected in the near future.

Experiments on mineral stability are expanding in several directions. Iron-bearing minerals can now be studied with adequate controls. The effect of solid solution on the stability of minerals must be determined. Natural dissociation reactions usually involve several minerals, and multi-mineral reactions must be investigated in the laboratory. Among these are reactions involving more than one volatile component. Reactions between carbonates and hydrated minerals, and reactions involving sulphides, carbonates, hydrates, and silicates can now be studied with proven techniques.

Experimental work on natural rock samples is likely to increase, and some of this will be concerned with the effects of oxygen fugacity. Most studies so far completed have been concerned with individual rocks. Investigation of the melting relationships of series of rocks from various igneous associations should yield useful data.

Another field opening up is the investigation of dynamic effects—the transfer of material through a liquid or vapour phase in response to temperature and concentration gradients. Akin to these studies is the possibility of reproducing a geological process within a pressure vessel, forming in miniature the characteristic features of a large rock body. So far, this has been attempted only for pegmatites, but other model studies are feasible.

Finally, it is worthwhile to emphasize once again that problems in the earth sciences require a combined attack involving experimental studies and field studies (geological, geophysical, and geochemical). Individually, the laboratory and field studies cannot be definitive, but together they complement each other extremely well. Prospects for major advances in the earth sciences are most favorable. If only the effects of geological time could be reproduced in the laboratory, it could be said that they were excellent.

ACKNOWLEDGMENTS

I wish to acknowledge gratefully the time, attention, and assistance provided by many colleagues in the College of Mineral Industries, The

Pennsylvania State University, and elsewhere, in connection with various parts of this chapter. Specific thanks are due to: H. S. Yoder for providing Fig. 21 before its publication; D. L. Hamilton for providing unpublished data used in Section IV, J; F. Dachille for providing diagrams and critical comments for Section V, A; O. F. Tuttle and W. C. Luth for providing unpublished data used in Section VI, B; I. S. E. Carmichael and W. S. Mackenzie for providing the unpublished manuscript discussed in Section VI, C; R. F. Fudali for providing the unpublished manuscript discussed in Section VI, C; R. H. Jahns for providing Fig. 39, previously unpublished, and for critical comments on Section VI, D.

REFERENCES

Baker, E. H. (1961). *J. chem. Soc.* **87**, 464.
Barnes, H. L., and Ernst, W. G. (1960). In *Carnegie Inst. Washington Year Book* **59**, 63.
Barnes, H. L., and Kullerud, G. (1961). *Econ. Geol.* **56**, 648.
Barth, T. F. W. (1952). "Theoretical Petrology," John Wiley, New York.
Bernal, J. D. (1936). *Observatory* **59**, 267.
Biggar, G. M., and Wyllie, P. J. (1962). *J. geophys. Res.* **67**, 3542.
Birch, F. (1958). *Bull. geol. Soc. Amer.* **69**, 483.
Birch, F. (1960). *J. geophys. Res.* **65**, 1083.
Birch, F. (1961). *J. geophys. Res.* **66**, 2199.
Birch, F., and LeComte, P. (1960). *Amer. J. Sci.* **258**, 209.
Birch, F., Schairer, J. F., and Spicer, H. C. (1942). "Handbook of Physical Constants ", *Spec. Pap. Geol. Soc. Amer.* 36.
Bowen, N. L. (1928). "The Evolution of the Igneous Rocks," Princeton University Press. Reprinted by Dover Publications, Inc. (1956).
Bowen, N. L. (1937). *Amer. J. Sci.* **33**, 1.
Bowen, N. L. (1940). *J. Geol.* **48**, 225.
Bowen, N. L. (1947). *Bull. geol. Soc. Amer.* **58**, 263.
Bowen, N. L., and Tuttle, O. F. (1949). *Bull. geol. Soc. Amer.* **60**, 439.
Bowen, N. L., and Tuttle, O. F. (1950). *J. Geol.* **58**, 489.
Boyd, F. R., and England, J. L. (1959). In *Carnegie Inst. Washington Year Book* **58**, 83.
Boyd, F. R., and England, J. L. (1960a). *J. geophys. Res.* **65**, 741.
Boyd, F. R., and England, J. L. (1960b). In *Carnegie Inst. Washington Year Book* **59**, 48.
Boyd, F. R., and England, J. L. (1961). In *Carnegie Inst. Washington Year Book* **60**, 113.
Bradley, R. S. (1962). *Amer. J. Sci.* **260**, 374.
Buerger, M. J. (1948). *Amer. Min.* **33**, 744.
Bullen, K. E. (1936). *Mon. Not. R. astr. Soc. geophys. Suppl.* **3**, 395.
Burnham, C. W., and Jahns, R. H. (1958). *Bull. geol. Soc. Amer.* **69**, 1544.
Burnham, C. W., and Jahns, R. H. (1962). *Spec. Pap. geol. Soc. Amer.* **68**, 143.
Burnham, C. W., and Tuttle, O. F. (1960). *Bull. geol. Soc. Amer.* **71**, 1837.
Carmichael, I. S. E. (1962). *Miner. Mag.* **33**, 86.

Carmichael, I. S. E., and Mackenzie, W. S. (1963). *Amer. J. Sci.* **261**. 382.

Christensen, C. J., and Roedder, E. (1952). *Ann. Rev. phys. Chem.* **3**, 171.

Clark, L. A. (1960). *Econ. Geol.* **55**, 1345; 1631.

Clark, S. P. (1961). *Amer. J. Sci.* **259**, 641.

Clark, S. P., and Neufville, J. de (1962). *J. geophys. Res.* **67**. 3550.

Clark, S. P., Robertson, E. C., and Birch, F. (1957). *Amer. J. Sci.* **255**, 628.

Clayton, R. N. (1959). *J. chem. Phys.* **30**, 1246.

Coes, L. (1953). *Science* **118**, 131.

Dachille, F., and Roy, R. (1956). *Bull. geol. Soc. Amer.* **67**, 1682.

Dachille, F., and Roy, R. (1958). *Bull. geol. Soc. Amer.* **69**, 1550.

Dachille, F., and Roy, R. (1960a). *In* " Encyclopedia of Science and Technology ", 441–446, McGraw-Hill, New York.

Dachille, F., and Roy, R. (1960b). *In* " Reactivity of Solids " (J. H. de Boer, ed.), 502–511, Elsevier, Amsterdam.

Dachille, F., and Roy, R. (1960c). *Amer. J. Sci.* **258**, 225.

Dachille, F., and Roy, R. (1962). *In* " Modern Very High Pressure Techniques " (R. H. Wentorf, ed.), 163–180, Butterworths Scientific Publications, London.

Donnay, G., Wyart, J., and Sabatier, G. (1959). *Z. Kristallogr.* **112**, 161.

Eitel, W. (1954). " The Physical Chemistry of the Silicates ", Chicago University Press, Chicago.

Ellis, A. J., and Fyfe, W. S. (1957). *Revs. Pure Appl. Chem. Australia* **7**, 261.

Epstein, S., Buchsbaum, R., and Lowenstam, H. A., and Urey, H. C. (1953). *Bull. geol. Soc. Amer.* **64**, 1315.

Ernst, W. G. (1960). *Geochim. et cosmoch. Acta* **19**, 10.

Eugster, H. P. (1957a). *J. chem. Phys.* **26**, 1760.

Eugster, H. P. (1957b). In *Carnegie Inst. Washington Year Book* **56**, 161.

Eugster, H. P., and Wones, D. R. (1962). *J. Petrology* **3**, 82.

Fermor, L. L. (1914). *Geol. Mag.* **51**, 65.

Francis, G. H. (1956). *Geol. Mag.* **93**, 353.

Fudali, R. F. (1960). " Experimental Studies bearing on the Origin of Pseudoleucite and Associated Problems of Alkaline Rock Systems," Ph.D. Dissertation, The Pennsylvania State University.

Fudali, R. F. (1962). Unpublished manuscript, kindly made available.

Fudali, R. F., Maun, A., and Osborn, E. F. (1962). *Spec. Pap. geol. Soc. Amer.* **68**, 179.

Fyfe, W. S. (1960). *J. Geol.* **68**, 553.

Fyfe, W. S. (1962). *Amer. J. Sci.* **260**, 460.

Fyfe, W. S., Turner, F. J., and Verhoogen, J. (1958). " Metamorphic Reactions and Metamorphic Facies," *Mem. geol. Soc. Amer.* **73**.

Garrels, R. M., and Richter, D. H. (1955). *Econ. Geol.* **50**, 447.

Garson, M. S., and Campbell Smith, W. (1958). " Chilwa Island," *Geol. Surv. Nyasaland Mem.* **1**.

Goldsmith, J. R. (1953). *J. Geol.* **61**, 439.

Goldsmith, J. R., and Graf, D. L. (1960). *J. Geol.* **68**, 324.

Goldsmith, J. R., and Heard, H. C. (1961). *J. Geol.* **69**, 45.

Goldsmith, J. R., Graf, D. L., and Witters, J. (1960). *Bull. geol. Soc. Amer.* **71**, 1871.

Goranson, R. W. (1931). *Amer. J. Sci.* **22**, 481.

Goranson, R. W. (1932). *Amer. J. Sci.* **23**, 227.

Goranson, R. W. (1938). *Amer. J. Sci.* **35***A*, 71.

Graf, D. L., and Goldsmith, J. R. (1955). *Geochim. et cosmoch. Acta* **7**, 109.

Greenwood, H. J. (1960). In *Carnegie Inst. Washington Year Book* **59**, 58.

Greenwood, H. J. (1961). *J. geophys. Res.* **66**, 3923.

Griggs, D. T. (1940). *Bull. geol. Soc. Amer.* **51**, 1001.

Griggs, D. T., and Handin, J. (1960). " Rock Deformation, a Symposium", *Mem. geol. Soc. Amer.* 79.

Griggs, D. T., and Kennedy, G. C. (1956). *Amer. J. Sci.* **254**, 722.

Gutenberg, B. (1959). " Physics of the Earth's Interior ", Academic Press, New York.

Gutenberg, B. (1960). *Science*, **131**, 959.

Hamilton, D. L. (1961). *J. Geol.* **69**, 321.

Hamilton, D. L., and Burnham, C. W. (1962). *Spec. Pap. geol. Soc. Amer.* **68**, 190.

Hamilton, D. L., and Mackenzie, W. S. (1960). *J. Petrology* **1**, 56.

Handin, J. (1960). *Trans. Amer. geophys. Un.* **41**, 162.

Harker, R. I. (1958). *Amer. J. Sci.* **256**, 128.

Harker, R. I., and Tuttle, O. F. (1955a). *Amer. J. Sci.* **253**, 209.

Harker, R. I., and Tuttle, O. F. (1955b). *Amer. J. Sci.* **253**, 274.

Harker, R. I., and Tuttle, O. F. (1956). *Amer. J. Sci.* **254**, 239.

Harris, P. G., and Rowell, J. A. (1960). *J. geophys. Res.* **65**, 2443.

Hess, H. H. (1955). In " Crust of the Earth," *Spec. Pap. Geol. Soc. Amer.* **62**, 391.

Hess, H. H. (1960). *Amer. Scient.* **48**, 254.

Howell, B. F. (1959). " Introduction to Geophysics", McGraw-Hill, New York.

Howell, B. F., and Woodtli, R. A. (1961). *J. geophys. Res.* **66**, 2601.

Hutton, J. (1794). *Trans. roy. Soc. Edinb.* **3**, 77 (quoted by Walton, 1960).

Jacobs, J. A., Russell, R. D., and Wilson, J. T. (1959). " Physics and Geology ", McGraw-Hill, New York.

Jahns, R. H. (1953). *Amer. Min.* **38**, 563.

Jahns, R. H. (1955). *Econ. Geol.*, 50th Anniv. Vol., 1025.

Jahns, R. H., and Burnham, C. W. (1958). *Bull. geol. Soc. Amer.* **69**, 1592.

Jahns, R. H., and Burnham, C. W. (1962). *Spec. Pap. Geol. Soc. Amer.* **68**, 206.

Jeffreys, H. (1936). *Mon. Not. R. Astr. Soc. geophys. Suppl.* **3**, 401.

Kennedy, G. C. (1950). *Econ. Geol.* **45**, 629.

Kennedy, G. C. (1959). *Amer. Scient.* **47**, 491.

Kennedy, G. C. (1960). *Trans. Amer. geophys. Un.* **41**, 283.

Kennedy, G. C., and LaMori, P. N. (1961). In " Progress in Very High Pressure Research " (F. P. Bundy, W. R. Hibbard, and H. M. Strong, eds.) p. 304, Wiley, New York.

Kennedy, G. C., Wasserberg, G. J., Heard, H. C., and Newton, R. C. (1961). In " Progress in Very High Pressure Research " (F. P. Bundy, W. R. Hibbard, and H. M. Strong, eds.), p. 28, Wiley, New York.

Knight, C. W. (1906). *Amer. J. Sci.* **21**, 286.

Kranck, E. H., and Oja, R. V. (1960). *Proc. 21st Session Int. Geol. Congress* **14**, 16.

Kullerud, G. (1959). In " Researches in Geochemistry " (P. H. Abelson, ed.) p. 301, Wiley, New York.

Kullerud, G., and Yoder, H. S. (1959). *Econ. Geol.* **54**, 533.

Kullerud, G., and Yund, R. A. (1962). *J. Petrology* **3**, 126.

Larsen, E. S., and Buie, B. F. (1938). *Amer. Min.* **23**, 837.

Loewinson-Lessing, F. Y. (1954). " A Historical Survey of Petrology " (S. I. Tomkeieff, trans.), Oliver and Boyd, London.

Lovering, J. F. (1958). *Trans. Amer. geophys. Un.* **39**, 947.

MacDonald, G. J. F. (1955). *J. Geol.* **63**, 244.
MacDonald, G. J. F. (1959). *In* " Researches in Geochemistry " (P. H. Abelson, ed.), p. 476, Wiley, New York.
MacDonald, G. J. F., and Ness, N. F. (1960). *J. geophys. Res.* **65**, 2173.
Mackenzie, W. S. (1957). *Amer. J. Sci.* **255**, 481.
Mackenzie, W. S. (1960). *Liverpool and Manchester Geol. Jour.* **2**, 369.
Mason, B. (1958). " Principles of Geochemistry ", 2nd Edition, Wiley, New York.
Morey, G. W. (1953). *J. Amer. ceram. Soc.* **36**, 279.
Morey, G. W. (1957). *Econ. Geol.* **52**, 225.
Morey, G. W., and Fleischer, M. (1940). *Bull. geol. Soc. Amer.* **51**, 1035.
Morey, G. W., and Hesselgesser, J. R. (1951). *Econ. Geol.* **46**, 821.
Morey, G. W., and Ingerson, E. (1937). *Econ. Geol.* **32**, 607.
Morey, G. W., and Niggli, P. (1913). *J. Amer. chem. Soc.* **35**, 1086.
Mosebach, R. (1955). *Neues Jb. Miner.*, *Mh.* **87**, 351 (quoted by Morey, 1957).
Neufville, J. de, Clark, S. P., and Schairer, J. F. (1962). *J. geophys. Res.* **67**, 3583.
Noble, D. C. (1961). *Bull. geol. Soc. Amer.* **72**, 287–291.
O'Neil, J. R., and Clayton, R. N. (1962). *Spec. Pap. geol. Soc. Amer.* **68**, 241.
Orville, P. M. (1960). In *Carnegie Inst. Washington Year Book* **59**, 104.
Ostrovskii, I. A., Mishina, G. P., and Povilaitis, V. M. (1959). *C. R. Acad. Sci. U.R.S.S.* **126**, 645.
Poldervaart, A. (1955). Editor of " Crust of the Earth (A symposium) ", *Spec. Pap. geol. Soc. Amer.* **62**,
Ramberg, H. (1952). " The Origin of Metamorphic and Metasomatic Rocks " University of Chicago Press, Chicago.
Ringwood, A. E. (1958a). *Geochim. et cosmoch. Acta* **13**, 303.
Ringwood, A. E. (1958b). *Geochim. et cosmoch. Acta* **15**, 18.
Ringwood, A. E. (1958c). *Geochim. et cosmoch. Acta* **15**, 195.
Ringwood, A. E. (1958d). *Bull. geol. Soc. Amer.* **69**, 129.
Ringwood, A. E. (1959a). *Amer. Min.* **44**, 659.
Ringwood, A. E. (1959b). *Geochim. et cosmoch. Acta* **16**, 192.
Ringwood, A. E. (1962). *J. geophys. Res.* **67**, 857.
Robertson, E. C., Birch, F., and MacDonald, G. J. F. (1957). *Amer. J. Sci.* **255**, 115–137.
Roedder, E. (1959). *In* " Physics and Chemistry of the Earth " (L. H. Ahrens, F. Press, K. Rankama, S. K. Runcorn, eds.) Vol. III, p. 224, Pergamon Press, London.
Rosenberg, P. E. (1960). *Bull. geol. Soc. Amer.* **71**, 1959.
Roy, D. M., and Roy, R. (1954). *Amer. Min.* **39**, 957.
Roy, D. M., and Roy, R. (1955). *Amer. Min.* **40**, 147.
Roy, D. M., and Roy, R. (1957). *Amer. J. Sci.* **255**, 573.
Roy, R. (1956). *J. Amer. ceram. Soc.* **39**, 145.
Roy, R., and Tuttle, O. F. (1956). *In* " Physics and Chemistry of the Earth " (L. H. Ahrens, K. Rankama, and S. K. Runcorn, eds.) Vol. I, 138–180, Pergamon Press, London.
Schairer, J. F. (1950). *J. Geol.* **58**, 512.
Schairer, J. F. (1959). *In* " Physicochemical Measurements at High Temperatures " (J. O. Bockris, J. D. Mackenzie, J. L. White, eds.) p. 117, Butterworths Scientific Publications, London.
Semenenko, N. P. (1960). *Proc. 21st Int. Geol. Congress,* **14**, 62.
Shaw, H. R. (1962). *J. geophys. Res.* **67**, 3598.

Smyth, F. H., and Adams, L. H. (1923). *J. Amer. chem. Soc.* **45**, 1167.

Sobolev, V. S. (1960). *Proc. 21st Int. Geol. Congress*, **14**, 72.

Spengler, C. J., and Burnham, C. W. (1962). *Spec. Pap. Geol. Soc. Amer.* **68**, 277.

Stewart, D. B. (1957). In *Carnegie Inst. Washington Year Book* **56**, 214.

Thompson, J. B. (1955). *Amer. J. Sci.* **253**, 65.

Tilley, C. E. (1958). *Quart. J. geol. Soc. Lond.* **113**, 323.

Turner, F. J., and Verhoogen, J. (1960). " Igneous and Metamorphic Petrology ", Second Edition, McGraw-Hill, New York.

Turnock, A. C. (1959). In *Carnegie Inst. Washington Year Book* **58**, 134.

Turnock, A. C. (1960). In *Carnegie Inst. Washington Year Book* **59**, 98.

Tuttle, O. F. (1948). *Amer. J. Sci.* **246**, 628.

Tuttle, O. F. (1949). *Bull. geol. Soc. Amer.* **60**, 1727.

Tuttle, O. F., and Bowen, N. L. (1958). " Origin of Granite in the Light of Experimental Studies in the System $NaAlSi_3O_8$–$KAlSi_3O_8$–SiO_2–H_2O", *Mem. Geol. Soc. Amer.* **74**, 123.

Tuttle, O. F., and England, J. L. (1955). *Bull. geol. Soc. Amer.* **66**, 149.

Tuttle, O. F., and Smith, J. V. (1958). *Amer. J. Sci.* **256**, 571.

Wager, L. R. (1958). *Advanc. Sci., Lond.* **15**, 31.

Walter, L. S. (1963). *Amer. J. Sci.*, in press.

Walter, L. S., Wyllie, P. J., and Tuttle, O. F. (1962). *J. Petrology*, **3**, 49.

Walton, M. (1960). *Science*, **131**, 635.

Wasserberg, G. J. (1957). *J. Geol.* **65**, 15.

Wentorf, R. H. (1959). *Nature, Lond.* **183**, 1617.

Wetherill, G. W. (1961). *J. geophys. Res.* **66**, 2983.

Winkler, H. G. F. (1957). *Geochim. et cosmoch. Acta* **13**, 42.

Winkler, H. G. F., and Platen, H. von (1958). *Geochim. et cosmoch. Acta* **15**, 91.

Winkler, H. G. F., and Platen, H. von (1960). *Geochim. et cosmoch. Acta* **18**, 294.

Winkler, H. G. F., and Platen, H. von (1961a). *Geochim. et cosmoch. Acta* **24**, 48.

Winkler, H. G. F., and Platen, H. von (1961b). *Geochim. et cosmoch. Acta* **24**, 250.

Wones, D. R., and Eugster, H. P. (1959). In *Carnegie Inst. Washington Year Book* **58**, 127.

Wyart, J., and Sabatier, G. (1959). *Bull. Soc. franc. Miner. et Crist.* **82**, 201.

Wyllie, P. J. (1962a). *Miner. Mag.* **33**, 9.

Wyllie, P. J. (1962b). *Spec. Pap. geol. Soc. Amer.* **68**, 303.

Wyllie, P. J. (1962c). *Geol. Mag.* **99**, 558.

Wyllie, P. J., and Tuttle, O. F. (1957). *Trans. Amer. geophys. Un.* **38**, 413.

Wyllie, P. J., and Tuttle, O. F. (1958). *Trans. Amer. geophys. Un.* **39**, 537.

Wyllie, P. J., and Tuttle, O. F. (1959). *Amer. J. Sci.* **257**, 648.

Wyllie, P. J., and Tuttle, O. F. (1960a). *J. Petrology* **1**, 1.

Wyllie, P. J., and Tuttle, O. F. (1960b). *Amer. J. Sci.* **258**, 498.

Wyllie, P. J., and Tuttle, O. F. (1960c). *Proc. 21st Int. Geol. Congress* **18**, 227.

Wyllie, P. J., and Tuttle, O. F. (1961a). *Amer. J. Sci.* **259**, 128.

Wyllie, P. J., and Tuttle, O. F. (1961b). *Geol. Mag.* **98**, 56.

Wyllie, P. J., and Tuttle, O. F. (1963). *Spec. Pap. Geol. Soc. Amer.* in press.

Yoder, H. S. (1950a). *Trans. Amer. geophys. Un.* **31**, 827.

Yoder, H. S. (1950b). *Amer. J. Sci.* **248**, 225; 312.

Yoder, H. S. (1952a). *J. Geol.* **60**, 364.

Yoder, H. S. (1952b). *Amer. J. Sci., Bowen Vol.* 569.

Yoder, H. S. (1954a). In *Carnegie Inst. Washington Year Book* **53**, 106.

Yoder, H. S. (1954b) In *Carnegie Inst. Washington Year Book* **53**, 121.

Yoder, H. S. (1958). In *Carnegie Inst. Washington Year Book* **57**, 189.

Yoder, H. S., and Chinner, G. A. (1960). In *Carnegie Inst. Washington Year Book* **59**, 78.

Yoder, H. S., and Eugster, H. P. (1954). *Geochim. et cosmoch. Acta* **6**, 157.

Yoder, H. S., and Tilley, C. E. (1956). In *Carnegie Inst. Washington Year Book* **55**, 169.

Yoder, H. S., and Tilley, C. E. (1959). In *Carnegie Inst. Washington Year Book* **58**, 89.

Yoder, H. S., and Tilley, C. E. (1961). In *Carnegie Inst. Washington Year Book* **60**, 106.

Yoder, H. S., Stewart, D. B., and Smith, J. R. (1957). In *Carnegie Inst. Washington Year Book* **56**, 206.

Chapter 7.i

CHEMICAL EQUILIBRIA IN GASES

BARNETT F. DODGE

Chemical Engineering Department, Yale University,
New Haven, Conn., U.S.A.

I. INTRODUCTION

IN this chapter equilibria in gas reactions with particular emphasis on the effect of pressure will be treated mainly from an engineering, or application, point of view. In other words the objective of the treatment is to provide a basis for the calculation of the degree of conversion at equilibrium, of a reactant either in a single reaction or in a set of simultaneous reactions, as it is influenced by pressure, with various values of other parameters such as temperature and ratio of reactants. This is of practical importance in various ways. It enables one to predict whether or not a proposed new reaction is possible and under what conditions favourable yields could be expected. It is useful in guiding research and development on reactions of actual or potential industrial importance to arrive at optimum conditions. It is necessary in the analysis and correlation of kinetic data on reactions.

The first important industrial use of pressure as a tool to influence the equilibrium in a reaction was for the synthesis of ammonia from the elements. Since then, many other reactions have been carried out under elevated pressure on a large scale; for example, the synthesis of methanol and higher alcohols from CO and H_2, urea from CO_2 and NH_3, the hydration of ethylene to ethanol, polymerization of ethylene and the OXO reaction between H_2, CO and an olefin to produce aldehydes and alcohols with one more carbon atom than in the olefin. This is, of course, only a few of the many reactions of industrial importance which are now in operation or which have a potential importance.

II. Qualitative Considerations

From the general principle underlying any equilibrium, one would predict that a reaction such as the ammonia-synthesis reaction for which there is a decrease in the number of moles, would be favoured in the forward direction by pressure. More strictly, a reaction is favoured by pressure in the direction in which a decrease in volume occurs. It is probably obvious, but perhaps should be stated, that the converse is also true, namely that a reaction proceeding in the direction of a volume increase is favoured by lowering the pressure. For example, the water-gas shift reaction

$$CO + H_2O = H_2 + CO_2 \tag{I}$$

involves no change in number of moles but the departure from the ideal-gas state of the four components is such that an increase in volume results when the reaction proceeds from left to right and hence it is favoured by low pressure. In such a case, of course, the effect of pressure is small because if the gases were ideal there would be no effect at all.

The two main factors that govern the course of any chemical reaction, namely equilibrium and rate, are in one sense entirely separate but in another are closely related as will be illustrated presently. Equilibrium is the state approached when the rates in the two directions approach equality and in theory an infinite time is required to reach an equilibrium. In practice an equilibrium in a gas reaction may be very closely approached in a very short time or, on the contrary, may not be even closely approached in a long period of time, all depending on the reaction rates under a given set of conditions. This can be nicely illustrated by considering the ammonia-synthesis reaction

$$\tfrac{1}{2}N_2 + \tfrac{3}{2}H_2 = NH_3 \qquad\qquad \text{(II)}$$

At 25° C and 1 atm., the reactant mixture is thermodynamically unstable and one can readily calculate that about 97% of the nitrogen would be converted to ammonia and the gas mixture would contain about 94 mole per cent NH_3, if chemical equilibrium were achieved. We know from observation that this is not so; no appreciable formation of ammonia can be detected even after years of waiting. In this situation it is the kinetics or rate considerations and not equilibrium which control. The usual method of increasing the rate is to increase the temperature or employ a catalyst or both. No reasonable amount of pressure increase will do any good, short of pressures high enough to affect the kinetic energy of the valence electrons. Now suppose one increases the temperature to 450° C keeping the pressure at 1 atm, and uses a catalyst known to promote this reaction, one observes that very little reaction will take place, just as before. The reaction is now equilibrium-controlled and one can readily calculate that the reacting system will reach a concentration of about 0·2% NH_3, just about enough to detect easily by analysis and certainly not enough to form the basis of a useful process for production of ammonia. Next, the factor of pressure can be brought into action and the concentration of NH_3 increases rapidly as pressure increases. Some equilibrium concentrations as a function of pressure and temperature with an initial gas mixture in the stoichiometric proportions are shown in Fig. 1.

It seems worth emphasizing that what is actually observed in any

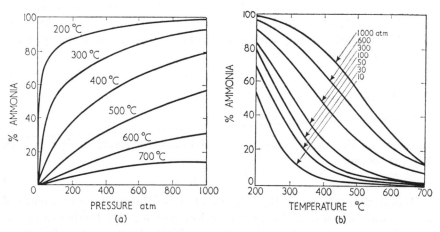

FIG. 1. Per cent ammonia at equilibrium from an initial mixture in stoichiometric proportions
(a) % *vs* p at constant *t*.
(b) % *vs* t at constant *p*.
(Reproduced with permission from Comings, 1956.)

chemical reaction is a result of the interplay of the two factors of rate and equilibrium and, in order to interpret observed results correctly, one must know where the equilibrium point is. Fortunately this can be rigorously calculated with the aid of thermodynamics and does not involve doubtful assumptions except as they may be made because of the lack of the necessary thermal and compressibility data. The remainder of this chapter will be largely concerned with the quantitative treatment of equilibrium in gas-phase reactions.

III. Thermodynamic Basis for Calculation of Chemical Equilibrium†

A. *General Relations*

The basic differential equation for a homogeneous equilibrium, derived from the first and second laws of thermodynamics is

$$d\underline{G} = V\,dp - \underline{S}\,dT + \sum_i \mu_i\,dn_i \tag{1}$$

for an n-component system. From the criterion of equilibrium expressed by

$$dG_{p,T} = 0 \tag{2}$$

Eq. (1) becomes

$$\sum_i \mu_i\,dn_i = 0. \tag{3}$$

Although we are concerned primarily with homogeneous equilibrium in the gas phase in this chapter, it is to be noted that the treatment of chemical equilibrium in heterogeneous systems merely requires the additional conditions imposed by the following set of equations applying to phase equilibria:

$$\mu_i = \mu_i'' = \ldots = \mu_i^z. \tag{4}$$

Consider the generalized reaction

$$aA + bB + \ldots = lL + mM + \ldots . \tag{A}$$

In view of the mass-balance or stoichiometric relationships in (A), Eq. (3) becomes

$$\sum \nu_i \mu_i = 0. \tag{5}$$

This equation tells us all that the two laws of thermodynamics can tell about equilibrium in a chemical-reaction system. Its further development into more useful forms is a matter of introducing certain functions such as fugacity, activity and the equilibrium constant, and relating these to the variables of state.

† A list of symbols used is given at the end of the section.

B. *Fugacity, Activity and Equilibrium Constants*

Equations defining fugacity and activity are

$$d\mu_i = RT \, d \ln \hat{f}_i \qquad (6)$$

$$\mu_i - \mu_i^\circ = RT \ln (\hat{f}_i/f_i^\circ). \qquad (7)$$

$$\mu_i - \mu_i^\circ = RT \ln a_i. \qquad (8)$$

Equation (6) only partially defines the fugacity of a component in a solution; the definition will be completed later. Equation (7) is merely an integral form of Eq. (6) and Eq. (8) defines the activity. Combining Eq. (5) and Eq. (8), one has

$$\sum_i \nu_i(RT \ln a_i + \mu_i^\circ) = 0 \qquad (9)$$

and this may be rearranged to

$$\sum_i \nu_i\mu_i^\circ = RT\sum_i \nu_i \ln a_i. \qquad (10)$$

Since the standard state, in the case of gases, is always taken as that of the pure component, $\mu_i = G_i$ and since $\sum \nu_i G_i^\circ$, or ΔG° as it is usually written, is a constant at a given temperature, $\sum \nu_i \ln a_i$ must also be a constant which is usually written as K_a and designated as an equilibrium constant. Thus we may write Eq. (10) in the form

$$\Delta G^\circ = - RT \ln K_a. \qquad (11)$$

The ΔG in a reaction at constant p and T is a measure of the work if the reaction were carried out reversibly. Since most reactions are carried out in a very irreversible manner, ΔG has little practical interest. It must not be confused with ΔG°, the *standard free-energy change* which is directly related to the equilibrium constant. From Eq. (10) and the nature of μ_i° it should be clear that K_a is independent of pressure and concentration and a function of temperature only.

It is to be noted, however, that the numerical value of K_a depends on the choice of standard state, the pressure unit and the stoichiometric numbers used to write the reaction.

From Eqs. (10) and (11) one can write

$$K_a = \frac{(a_L)^l \cdot (a_M)^m \cdot \ldots}{(a_A)^a \cdot (a_B)^b \cdot \ldots} \qquad (12)$$

In the case of pure solids or liquids, the activity can be taken as unity at any p or T but at quite high pressure it may be desirable to take account of the effect of p.

Since the standard state for a gas is commonly taken to be one of an ideal gas at unit fugacity, Eq. (12) can also be written

$$K_a = K_f = \frac{(\bar{f}_L)^l \cdot (\bar{f}_M)^m \cdots}{(\bar{f}_A)^a \cdot (\bar{f}_B)^b \cdots} \qquad (13)$$

Although K_f is a function of temperature only, each fugacity is a function of p, T and the composition of the system. Consequently the calculation of the equilibrium conversion of a reactant or of the equilibrium composition reduces to the problem of calculating the fugacity of a component in a solution.

The free energy of a solution of n components is related to the pressure and composition at constant temperature by the relation

$$\underline{G} = \int_{p^\circ}^{p} V \, \mathrm{d}p + \sum n_i G_i^\circ + RT \sum \left(n_i \ln \frac{n_i}{N} \right). \qquad (14)$$

Differentiation of Eq. (14) with respect to n_i gives

$$\mu_i = \int_{p^\circ}^{p} \left(\frac{\partial V}{\partial n_i} \right)_{p,t,n_j} \mathrm{d}p + RT \ln y_i + G_i^\circ. \qquad (15)$$

Substituting this Eq. into Eq. (7) gives

$$RT \ln \bar{f}_i - RT \ln f_i^\circ = \int_{p^\circ}^{p} \bar{v}_i \, \mathrm{d}p + RT \ln y_i + G_i^\circ - \mu_i^\circ. \qquad (16)$$

The pressure, p°, is some arbitrarily chosen low pressure. It cannot be made to approach the limit of $p = 0$ with the equation in this form because V becomes infinite as $p \to 0$. To avoid this difficulty one may proceed as follows:

Add $RT \ln (p/p^\circ)$ to both sides of Eq. (16) giving

$$RT \ln \frac{\bar{f}_i}{f_i^\circ} = \int_{p^\circ}^{p} \left(\bar{v}_i - \frac{RT}{p} \right) \mathrm{d}p + RT \ln \frac{p}{p^\circ} + RT \ln y_i + G_i^\circ - \mu_i^\circ. \qquad (17)$$

Both from experimental data and from an equation of state, the quantity $(\bar{v}_i - RT/p)$ can be shown to approach a finite value as $p^\circ \to 0$. Complete the definition of fugacity by making $f_i^\circ = p^\circ$ and note that $G_i^\circ = \mu_i^\circ$ since gases are ideal at this limit and each gas in the mixture behaves as a pure component. Consequently by taking p° to the limit of $p = 0$, (17) becomes

$$\ln \frac{\bar{f}_i}{p y_i} = \ln \phi_i = \frac{1}{RT} \int_{0}^{p} \left(\bar{v}_i - \frac{RT}{p} \right) \mathrm{d}p. \qquad (18)$$

By a similar procedure one can derive

$$\ln \frac{\bar{f}_i}{f_i y_i} = \frac{1}{RT} \int_{0}^{p} (\bar{v}_i - v_i) \, \mathrm{d}p. \qquad (19)$$

The quantity $(\bar{v}_i - v_i)$ may also be shown to approach a finite value as $p \to 0$.

Both of these equations are in terms of p, T as the independent variables but since most equations of state which would be used for the calculation of fugacity are explicit in p, it is sometimes more convenient to use the following form of the fugacity equation.

$$\ln \frac{\bar{f}_i}{y_i} = \ln \rho \, RT + \frac{1}{RT} \int_0^p \left[\left(\frac{\partial p V}{\partial n_i} \right)_{V, T, n_j} - RT \right] d \ln \rho. \tag{20}$$

Any one of these three equations may be used for the calculation of the fugacity of a component of a gaseous solution. For a mixture of ideal gases, the right-hand side of Eq. (18) equals zero and

$$\bar{f}_i = p y_i, \tag{21}$$

or the fugacity of a gas in a mixture is equal to its partial pressure.

Let us define an ideal solution by the equation

$$v_m = \sum y_i v_i, \tag{22}$$

where v_i is the molal volume of each component when in the pure state at the p and T of the solution. (Note that a gaseous solution may be very far from behaving as an ideal gas and yet may follow Eq. (22) quite closely.) Since $v_m = \sum y_i \bar{v}_i$, it is clear from Eq. (22) that $\bar{v}_i = v_i$ and therefore, for an ideal solution, Eq. (19) reduces to

$$\bar{f}_i = y_i f_i, \tag{23}$$

which is often given as the definition of an ideal solution. For a pure component, Eq. (18) reduces to

$$\ln \frac{f}{p} = \frac{1}{RT} \int_0^p \left(v - \frac{RT}{p} \right) dp, \tag{24}$$

or as sometimes expressed

$$\ln \gamma \text{ (fugacity coefficient)} = -\frac{1}{RT} \int_0^p \alpha \, dp, \tag{25}$$

where α is a residual volume which is known to approach a finite value at $p = 0$. Another common form of Eq. (24) is the following

$$\ln \gamma = \int_0^p \frac{Z - 1}{p} \, dp \tag{26}$$

and $(Z - 1)/p$ also has a finite value at $p = 0$. The equation analogous to Eq. (26) for a component of a solution is

$$\ln \phi_i = \int_0^p \frac{z_i - 1}{p} \, dp, \tag{27}$$

where

$$z_i = \left(\frac{\partial Z}{\partial n_i}\right)_{p, T, n_j}.$$

In the case of solids and liquids, assumed to be incompressible, one readily obtains the equation

$$\ln a_i = \frac{v_i(p - p^\circ)}{RT}. \tag{27a}$$

An equilibrium constant may be defined by the expression

$$K_p = \frac{(y_L p)^l (y_M p)^m \cdots}{(y_A p)^a (y_B p) \cdots} = \prod (y_i p)^{\nu_i}. \tag{28}$$

From Eqs. (13) and (21) it is readily seen that Eq. (28) is the special form of Eq. (13) for the limiting case where $p \to 0$, i.e. for the case of ideal gases. It may be, and often is, used for finite pressures but it should be recognized as only an approximation used for convenience. Naturally, the higher the pressure, the greater will be the deviation from the ideal-gas state and the poorer the approximation. At the limit where $p = 0$, we can write

$$K_p = K_{p*} = K_a = K_f$$

K_{p*}, K_a and K_f are all functions of T only, but K_p is a function of p, T and y. The relation between K_p and K_{p*} is readily obtained from Eqs. (28) and (13) and is

$$\ln \frac{K_p}{K_{p*}} = -\Sigma \left[\nu_i \ln \left(\frac{\bar{f}_i}{p y_i}\right)\right], \tag{29}$$

or, introducing Eq. (18), one gets

$$\ln \frac{K_p}{K_{p*}} = -\frac{1}{RT}\left\{\Sigma \left[\nu_i \int_0^p \left(\bar{v}_i - \frac{RT}{p}\right) dp\right]\right\}. \tag{30}$$

It is convenient to define the function

$$K_\phi = \frac{(\phi_L)^l \cdot (\phi_M)^m \cdot \cdots}{(\phi_A)^a \cdot (\phi_B)^b \cdot \cdots}, \tag{31}$$

so that Eq. (29) can be abbreviated to

$$K_p = \frac{K_{p*}}{K_\phi}. \tag{32}$$

Equation (30) might be described as the basic equation for the calculation of the effect of pressure on chemical equilibrium in a system of reacting gases. It would probably be well to make its meaning somewhat clearer by expanding it for the case of the reaction

$$aA + bB = cC + dD \tag{B}$$

as follows:

$$-RT \ln \frac{K_p}{K_{p*}} = c \int_0^p \left(\bar{v}_C - \frac{RT}{p} \right) dp + d \int_0^p \left(\bar{v}_D - \frac{RT}{p} \right) dp$$

$$- a \int_0^p \left(\bar{v}_A - \frac{RT}{p} \right) dp - b \int_0^p \left(\bar{v}_B - \frac{RT}{p} \right) dp. \qquad (33)$$

The partial molal volumes are obtainable from a relation between the total volume of the solution and the number of moles of each component, since by definition

$$\bar{v}_i = \left(\frac{\partial V}{\partial n_i} \right)_{p, t, n_j}. \qquad (34)$$

This relation can also be developed in terms of the molal volume of the solution and the mole fractions of the various components, and becomes

$$\bar{v}_i = v + \left(\frac{\partial v}{\partial y_i} \right)_{p, T, y_j} - y_A \left(\frac{\partial v}{\partial y_A} \right)_{p, T, y_j} - y_B \left(\frac{\partial v}{\partial y_B} \right)_{p, T, y_j} - \dots$$

$$- y_{n-1} \left(\frac{\partial v}{\partial y_{n-1}} \right)_{p, T, y_j}. \qquad (35)$$

This equation applies to all but the nth component whose composition was eliminated by

$$\sum y_i = 1. \qquad (36)$$

$\bar{v}_n$ is given by Eq. (35) with omission of $\left(\frac{\partial v}{\partial y_i} \right)_{p, T, y_j}$.

It seems worthwhile at this point to note that Eq. (35) is a general one for any partial molal quantity. In other words it can also be written for U, H, S, G etc as well as for z and even f.

We may summarize the foregoing treatment by stating that it is possible in principle to calculate rigorously the effect of pressure on chemical equilibrium if one has compressibility data for the system in question over a range of pressure, temperature and composition. If one is interested in just one temperature, only isothermal data for volume as a function of pressure and composition are required but note that the pressure range must extend all the way from $p = 0$ to the reaction pressure in order to be able to evaluate the integrals of Eq. (33).

Let us admit that the rigorous calculation of the effect of pressure is rather impractical at the present time, primarily for two reasons (1) the necessary p, v, T, y data are not available for any system and (2) the calculation would be an exceedingly tedious one assuming the data were available. [The modern high-speed digital computers have already, or soon will, make (2) no longer a valid reason.]

IV. Approximations for Calculation of the Effect of Pressure

A. *Fugacity from an Equation of State*

We will now consider various approximations that might be made in the absence of actual experimental equilibrium data for the system in question or in the absence of experimental compressibility data, from which the effect of pressure can be calculated given the value of the equilibrium constant at low pressure.

The fugacity of any gas in a solution may be calculated from an equation of state. This would be a rigorous method if the equation of state accurately reproduced the experimental PVT data over the full range in question. This is a very difficult condition to impose on an equation of state and few can meet it. Those which approach it are usually so complex as to discourage their use. One of the most successful equations and one that has been widely used for the calculation of various thermodynamic properties including fugacity is the one proposed by Benedict *et al.*, (BWR) (1951), and applied by them and others particularly to hydrocarbon systems both single and multicomponent. This equation written in virial form is

$$p = \frac{RT}{v} + \frac{B_0 RT - A_0 - C_0/T^2}{v^2} + \frac{bRT - a}{v^3} + \frac{a\alpha}{v^6}$$

$$+ \frac{c}{v^3 T^2}\left[1 + \frac{\gamma}{v^2}\right]\exp(-\gamma/v^2). \tag{37}$$

It contains 8 empirical constants which must be evaluated from experimental data. Even with 8 constants the fit is not as good as desired in some regions, for example at high densities well above the critical density. Bloomer and Rao (1952) found it desirable to introduce 2 additional constants for calculation of the thermodynamic properties of nitrogen at densities up to 1·8 times the critical.

The determination of the best numerical values for the constants is a formidable task in itself, and they are now available for only 17 substances: CH_4, C_2H_6, C_2H_4, C_3H_6, C_3H_8, i-C_4H_{10}, i-C_4H_8, n-C_4H_{10}, i-C_5H_{12}, n-C_5H_{12}, n-C_6H_{14}, n-C_7H_{16}, n-C_9H_{20}, n-$C_{10}H_{22}$, C_6H_6, SO_2, and NO, and for some of these the range of conditions is rather limited.

Another equation that has been widely employed for representation of PVT data is the following one with five empirical constants due to Beattie and Bridegman:

$$p = \frac{RT(1-\epsilon)}{v_2}(v+B) - \frac{A}{v^2}, \tag{38}$$

where $\epsilon = c/(vT^3)$, $B = B_0(1 - b/v)$, $A = A_0(1 - a/v)$.

The constants have been evaluated for helium, neon, argon, hydrogen, nitrogen, oxygen, air, iodine, carbon dioxide, ammonia, methane, ethylene, ethane, propane, butene-1, iso-butene, n-butane, iso-butane, n-pentane, neo-pentane, n-heptane, methanol, and ethyl ether, and are given by Beattie (1949).

This is a good place to emphasize the fact that all equations of state so far developed are essentially empirical, and they may not be extrapolated into regions other than those for which the constants were determined without running the risk of introducing serious errors.

The data on mixtures are very scarce, and the usual procedure is to combine the constants for the pure components by certain empirical rules which have been tested to a limited extent on mixture data. The combining rules recommended by Benedict *et al.* (1951) are:

$$B_0 = \sum_i y_i B_{0i}, \tag{39}$$

$$A_0 = [\sum_i y_i A_{0i}^{\frac{1}{2}}]^2 \quad \text{(also for } C_0 \text{ and } \gamma), \tag{40}$$

$$b = [\sum_i y_i b_i^{\frac{1}{3}}]^3 \quad \text{(also for } a, \alpha, \text{ and } c). \tag{41}$$

Using equation of state (37) with these combining rules to perform the integration in Eq. (20) leads to the following equation for calculation of fugacity of component i in a solution:

$$
\begin{aligned}
RT \ln \frac{\bar{f}_i}{y_i} &= RT \ln \frac{RT}{v} + \left[(B_0 + B_{0i})RT - 2(A_0 A_{0i})^{\frac{1}{2}} - \frac{2(C_0 C_{0i})^{\frac{1}{2}}}{T^2} \right] \frac{1}{v} \\
&+ \frac{3}{2} \left[RT(b^2 b_i)^{\frac{1}{3}} - (a^2 a_i)^{\frac{1}{3}} \right] \frac{1}{v^2} + \frac{3}{5} \left[a(\alpha^2 \alpha_i)^{\frac{1}{3}} + \alpha(a^2 a_i)^{\frac{1}{3}} \right] \frac{1}{v^5} \\
&+ \frac{3(c^2 c_i)^{\frac{1}{3}}}{v^2 T^2} \left[\frac{1 - \exp(-\gamma/v^2)}{\gamma/v^2} - \frac{\exp(-\gamma/v^2)}{2} \right] \\
&- \frac{2c}{v^2 T^2} \left(\frac{\gamma_i}{\gamma} \right)^{\frac{1}{2}} \left[\frac{1 - \exp(-\gamma/v^2)}{\gamma/v^2} - \exp(-\gamma/v^2) - \frac{\exp(-\gamma/v^2)}{2v^2} \right]. \tag{42}
\end{aligned}
$$

The constants without subscripts are for the mixture as a whole. The application of this equation to the calculation of chemical equilibria is hopelessly complex unless programmed for machine computation. Not only that, but its application is very limited because the constants are available for so few substances.

Another approach, more approximate but much less complex, is to use a simpler equation of state and one whose constants can be more readily obtained. The simplest equation which still gives fair accuracy over wide ranges is probably the following one due to Redlich and Kwong (R-K) (1949):

$$p = \frac{RT}{v - b} - \frac{a}{T^{\frac{1}{2}} v(v + b)}. \tag{43}$$

The constants a and b can be evaluated from PVT data but even in the absence of such data they can still be evaluated if the critical constants are known. The equations for this purpose are

$$a = \frac{0 \cdot 4278 R^2 T_c^{2 \cdot 5}}{p_c} \tag{44}$$

and

$$b = \frac{0 \cdot 0867 R T_c}{p_c}. \tag{45}$$

For more convenient calculation of fugacity, Redlich and Kwong wrote the equation in the form

$$z = \frac{pv}{RT} = \frac{1}{1-h} - \frac{(A^2/B)h}{1+h}, \tag{46}$$

where

$$h = \frac{Bp}{z}, \quad A = \frac{a^{0 \cdot 5}}{RT^{1 \cdot 25}} \quad \text{and} \quad B = \frac{b}{RT}.$$

Using the R-K equation to perform the integration in Eq. (26) leads to:

$$\ln \gamma = (z-1) - \ln (z - Bp) - \frac{A^2}{B} \ln \left(1 + \frac{Bp}{z} \right), \tag{47}$$

from which the fugacity of a pure component may readily be calculated. A similar treatment for a solution leads to

$$\ln \phi_i = (z-1)\frac{B_i}{B} - \ln (z - Bp) - \frac{A^2}{B} \left[\frac{2A_i}{A} - \frac{B_i}{B} \right] \ln \left(1 + \frac{Bp}{z} \right). \tag{48}$$

A and B without subscript refer to the mixture and are related to the A and B for components by the equations

$$A = \sum_i y_i A_i \tag{49}$$
$$B = \sum_i y_i B_i. \tag{50}$$

At moderate pressures, the following simple equation of state involving only the second virial coefficient, B, is sometimes useful

$$z = 1 + \frac{Bp}{RT}. \tag{51}$$

This gives for a pure component

$$\ln \gamma = \frac{Bp}{RT}. \tag{52}$$

For a mixture, the second virial coefficient based on the R-K equation is

$$B = RT \left[\sum_i y_i B_i - \left(\sum y_i A_i \right)^2 \right] \tag{53}$$

and this used in Eq. (27) gives

$$\ln \phi_i = [B_i - A_i^2 + (A_i - A)^2]p. \tag{54}$$

The Beattie-Bridgeman equation reduced to the form of Eq. (51) by omission of coefficients higher than the second is very useful for approximations at moderate pressures. When it is used for the integration in Eq. (3) there results

$$\ln \frac{K_p}{K_{p*}} = - \left[\sum \nu_i B_{0_i} - \frac{\sum \nu_i A_{0_i}}{RT} - \frac{\sum \nu_i c_i}{T^3} \right] \frac{p}{RT}$$

$$+ \left\{ \frac{3}{4} [\sum \nu_i (B_{0_i}^{\frac{1}{2}} - \sum y_i B_{0_i}^{\frac{1}{2}})(B_{0_i}^{\frac{2}{3}} - \sum y_i B_{0_i}^{\frac{2}{3}})] \right.$$

$$\left. - \frac{1}{RT} [\sum \nu_i (A_{0_i}^{\frac{1}{2}} - \sum y_i A_{0_i}^{\frac{1}{2}})^2] - \frac{1}{T^3} [\sum \nu_i (c_i^{\frac{1}{3}} - \sum y_i c_i^{\frac{1}{3}})^2] \right\} \frac{p}{RT}. \tag{55}$$

The constants A_0, B_0 and c are the same as those in the complete Beattie-Bridgeman equation

Using the virial equation of state with second, third and fourth virial coefficients, namely

$$p = RT \left[\frac{1}{v} + \frac{B}{v^2} + \frac{C}{v^3} + \frac{D}{v^4} \right] \tag{56}$$

one can derive, for a pure component

$$\ln \frac{f}{p} = \ln \gamma = \frac{Bp}{RT} + \frac{(C - B^2)}{2R^2T^2} p^2 + \frac{(D - 3BC + 2B^3)}{3R^3T^3} p^3. \tag{57}$$

Another convenient approximation is the assumption of an ideal solution which is expressed by Eq. (22) or (23). Introducing Eq. (23) into Eq. (29) one gets

$$\ln \frac{K_p}{K_p{}^*} = - \sum_i \nu_i \ln \gamma_i, \tag{58}$$

and defining another equilibrium constant by the equation

$$K_\gamma = \frac{(\gamma_L)^l . (\gamma_M)^m . \cdots}{(\gamma_A)^a . (\gamma_B)^b . \cdots}, \tag{59}$$

Eq. (58) becomes

$$K_p = \frac{K_{p*}}{K_\gamma}. \tag{60}$$

Equation (60) combined with Eq. (28) offers a simple and convenient way to calculate the equilibrium composition of a reacting mixture at elevated pressures when the ideal-gas law is not a good enough approximation. K_γ is a function of p and T only and graphs may be prepared such as the one shown in Fig. 2 for quick evaluation.

K_{p*} is obtained by methods discussed later in this chapter and then having K_p at any specified p and T, one can solve Eq. (28) by trial for the equilibrium conversion or composition. All but one of the y's can be eliminated by Eq. (36) and by mass balances.

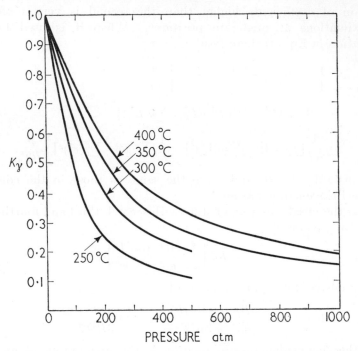

FIG. 2. K_γ for the methanol-synthesis reaction as a function of pressure and temperature. (Reproduced with permission from Newton and Dodge, 1935.)

It should be emphasized that the use of Eq. (60) depends on the validity of the law of ideal solutions or additive volumes. This law is only strictly obeyed for a solution of ideal gases but it appears to be a useful approximation for elevated pressures in that it gives better results than the assumption of ideal gas.

B. *Use of the Concept of Corresponding States*

The fugacity of pure components or components in solutions may also be approximated with the aid of the concept of corresponding states which might be expressed by the relation

$$z = \phi(p_r, T_r). \tag{61}$$

This relationship in graphical form is available from many sources. In recent years the agreement with experimental data has been improved by the introduction of a third parameter. One commonly used is z_c, the compressibility factor at the critical point. A tabulation giving z as a function of p_r and T_r for $z_c = 0 \cdot 27$ accompanied by a simple equation to correct z for other values of z_c is presented by Hougen *et al.* (1959).

Another commonly used third parameter is the acentric factor, ω, of Pitzer *et al.* (1955) defined by the relation

$$\omega = -\log\left(\frac{p}{p_c}\right)_{\text{sat}} - 1 \cdot 00, \tag{62}$$

where $(p/p_c)_{\text{sat.}}$ is the reduced vapour pressure at $T_r = 0 \cdot 70$. z is related to ω by the linear equation

$$z = \phi_0 + \phi_1 \omega \tag{63}$$

where ϕ_0 and ϕ_1 are universal functions of p_r and T_r. A similar relation is given for $\log (f/p)$ and the values of the two functions are tabulated by Curl and Pitzer (1958) for even values of p_r and T_r closely enough spaced to allow linear interpolation.

With either of these tabulations it is a fairly simple matter to calculate the fugacity for any pure component whose p_c and T_c are known. The extension to mixtures can be made in several empirical ways. One procedure is to reduce the mixture to a single hypothetical component by calculating a pseudocritical pressure and temperature of the mixture. Several equations have been proposed for this. The original ones proposed by Kay (1936) are the simplest and are as follows

$$p_{cm} = \sum_i y_i p_{ci}, \tag{64}$$
$$T_{cm} = \sum_i y_i T_{ci}. \tag{65}$$

Joffe (1947) recommends the following equations for use in the calculation of the fugacity of a mixture

$$\frac{T_{cm}}{p_{cm}^{\frac{1}{2}}} = \sum_i y_i \left(\frac{T_{ci}}{p_{ci}^{\frac{1}{2}}}\right), \tag{66}$$

$$\frac{T_{cm}}{p_{cm}} = \frac{1}{8} \sum_i \sum_j y_i y_j \left[\left(\frac{T_{ci}}{p_{ci}}\right)^{\frac{1}{3}} + \left(\frac{T_{cj}}{p_{cj}}\right)^{\frac{1}{3}} \right]^3 \tag{67}$$

The summation in Eq. (67) involves all binary pairs of all the components. Prausnitz and Gunn (1958) give still another set of equations for this purpose. In this way one gets a fugacity of a solution as a whole which is then related to the fugacities of the individual components in the solution through the use of Eq. (35) for the partial molal volume. Joffe (1948) developed the following equation for calculation of fugacity of any component i of a solution

$$\log \bar{f_i}/y_i = \log f_m + (T_c - T_i)(H^\circ - H)/2 \cdot 303RTT_c$$
$$+ (p_c - p_i)(z - 1)/2 \cdot 303p_c, \qquad (68)$$

in which f_m, T_c, H°, H, p_c and z refer to the mixture. Admittedly, f_m of a mixture has no real physical significance but it can be obtained from the pseudocritical p and T of the mixture and a generalized f/p chart, just as the fugacity for a single pure component. Likewise $H^\circ - H$ and z are obtained from the usual generalized correlations (this refers to any correlation of compressibility or thermodynamic properties in terms of reduced pressures and temperatures with or without the introduction of a third parameter).

Joffe applied Eq. (68) to the calculation of the equilibrium constant for the ammonia-synthesis reaction over the pressure range from 100 to 1 000 atm with excellent results.

C. *Application to the Ammonia-Synthesis Equilibrium*

Some of the preceding discussion will be illustrated with a few experimental results and calculations. Table I shows some results obtained by Winchester and Dodge (1957) in an experimental investigation of the ammonia-synthesis reaction at pressures from 1 000 to 3 500 atm.

TABLE I. Effect of Pressure on the Equilibrium Constant, K_p, for the Reaction $\frac{1}{2}N_2 + \frac{3}{2}H_2 = NH_3$

Temperature, °C	Pressure, atm	$K_p = \dfrac{(y_{NH_3})p^{-1}}{(y_{N_2})^{1/2}(y_{H_2})^{3/2}}$
450	1 000	0·02496
450	1 500	0·06962
450	1 650	0·09404
450	2 000	0·1337
450	3 500	1·0751
400	1 000	0·06136
400	1 500	0·1384
400	2 000	0·2977
400	2 500	0·7864
400	3 000	1·2543
400	3 500	1·6283

At 1 atm and 450° C the value of K_p calculated from the equation of Harrison and Kobe (1953) is 0·00675. For ideal gases, K_p is, of course, independent of pressure. As the table shows, its value has increased 159-fold in going from 1 atm to 3 500 atm.

In Table II there is a comparison of several methods of calculating the effect of pressure on the ammonia equilibrium. The effect is expressed in two ways: (1) by calculation of K_p, and (2) by calculation of the percent of NH_3 at equilibrium.

Table II. Comparison of Calculated and Experimental Values of the Equilibrium Constant, K_p, and the Percentage of Ammonia at Equilibrium at 450° C.

Method of calculation	K_p		% NH_3 at equilibrium	
	1 000 atm	3 000 atm	1 000 atm	3 000 atm
1	0·00675	0·00675	51·5	67·9
2	0·01537	0·03214	64·2	83·6
3	—	—	66·8	86·9
4	0·0239	0·600	70·0	96·0
5	—	—	70·6	91·1
Experimental value	0·02496	0·484	70·51	95·5

The methods of calculation are:

1. Ideal gases assumed and $K_p = K_{p*}$. %NH_3 from Eq. (28).
2. Ideal solution with fugacities estimated from the generalized chart of Newton (1935) and using the pseudocritical p and T for H_2 recommended by Newton. This involved the use of Eqs. (59), (60), and (28). It should be noted that at 3 000 atm the use of Newton's chart involved a very uncertain extrapolation.
3. Use of Redlich-Kwong equation (Eq. 43), the constants for the individual gases being calculated from Eqs. (44) and (45) and combined by Eqs. (49) and (50). For H_2 the Newton pseudocritical constants were used.
4. Use of the equation of Gillespie and Beattie (1930).
5. Use of Joffe's method, Eq. (68).

All the last 4 methods are a considerable improvement over the assumption of ideal gases and methods 4 and 5 gave surprisingly good agreement with the experimental data.

V. EFFECT OF TEMPERATURE ON THE EQUILIBRIUM CONSTANT

A. *General*

So far we have considered only the effect of pressure on chemical equilibrium but the starting point for dealing with this is a value for K_a which is a function of temperature only. K_a can always be obtained from an experiment in which equilibrium is established at some given p and T and the concentrations of all components determined. This leads to a value of K_p which can then be converted to $K_a(K_{p*})$ by Eq. (30). If p is about 1 atm or not far above it the correction will be small and one can use one of the approximations previously described or even assume that $K_p = K_a$.

If good thermal data for the reactants and products are available it is necessary to measure K_p at only one temperature. Exact thermo-dynamic relationships are available for relating K_a to the temperature. These will now be presented.

From the definition of the function G, we can write

$$\Delta G° = \Delta H° - T \,\Delta S°. \tag{69}$$

$\Delta G°$ is the standard molal free-energy change in the reaction, which is equal to the free energies of the products minus those of the reactants each in its standard state at the given temperature, or

$$\Delta G° = lG_L° + mG_M° + \ldots - aG_A° - bG_B° - \ldots \tag{70}$$

with similar expressions for $\Delta H°$ and $\Delta S°$. The standard is chosen as that of an ideal gas at low pressure, usually one atm. This is a hypo-thetical and not a real state because no gas is truly ideal except at $p = 0$. It is impractical to take $p = 0$ as a standard state for G because S approaches ∞ as $p \to 0$. Gases are so nearly ideal at 1 atm that this hypothetical state need not trouble us.

From the first law of thermodynamics we have

$$H - H_0 = \int C_p \, dt \tag{71}†$$

C_p has been obtained for many substances either by experiment or by calculation from statistical thermodynamics using spectroscopic data to establish energy levels within the molecule. C_p is usually related to temperature by an empirical equation of which the following power series is the commonest.

$$C_p = a + bt + ct^2 + \ldots . \tag{72}$$

or

$$C_p = A + BT + CT^2 + \ldots . \tag{73}$$

Using Eq. (73) to integrate Eq. (71) the result is

$$H = H_0 + AT + \tfrac{1}{2}BT^2 + \tfrac{1}{3}CT^3 + \ldots . \tag{74}$$

From the two laws of thermodynamics one has the relation

$$S - S_0 = \int C_p \, d \ln T \tag{75}$$

† In this equation and subsequent ones dealing with the effect of temperature, all of the thermal quantities will be considered in the standard state but the superscript ° has been omitted for simplicity.

or

$$S - S_0 = A \ln T + BT + \tfrac{1}{2} CT^2 + \ldots . \tag{76}$$

H_0 and S_0 are merely constants of integration.

Applying Eq. (74) and Eq. (76) to a reacting system, one has

$$\Delta H = \Delta H_0 + \Delta A \, T + \tfrac{1}{2}\Delta B \, T^2 + \tfrac{1}{3}\Delta C \, T^3 + \ldots \tag{77}$$

with an analogous expression for ΔS. Each Δ represents an expression of the same form as Eq. (70).

Substituting ΔH and ΔS in Eq. (69) results in

$$\Delta G = \Delta H_0 - \Delta A \, T \ln T - \tfrac{1}{2}\Delta B \, T^2 - \tfrac{1}{6}\Delta C \, T^3 - \ldots + (\Delta A - \Delta S_0) \, T \tag{78}$$

which is commonly written

$$\Delta G = \Delta H_0 - \Delta A \, T \ln T - \tfrac{1}{2}\Delta B \, T^2 - \tfrac{1}{6}\Delta C \, T^3 - \ldots + IT \tag{79}$$

ΔH_0 and I are constants of integration which can be evaluated in various ways.

B. *Evaluation of Constants of Integration*

ΔH_0 may be computed from Eq. (77) given the value of the heat of reaction, ΔH, at some one temperature and the heat capacities of all the components as a function of T over the range of interest. It should be emphasized that the constants ΔA, ΔB etc, are valid only over the range of temperatures for which the C_p's were determined and the empirical C_p equations should not be extrapolated. ΔH_0 may also be obtained from two values of $\Delta G°$ at two different temperatures.

The constant, I, can be determined in two different ways. One way is to establish equilibrium for the reaction in question (or for others from which the desired reaction can be obtained by addition) and obtain an experimental value of K_p from which K_{p*} (or K_a) may then be obtained as previously indicated. From Eq. (11) and Eq. (79)

$$\ln K_a = -\frac{\Delta H_0}{RT} + \frac{\Delta A}{R} \ln T + \frac{1}{2}\frac{\Delta B}{R} T + \frac{1}{6}\frac{\Delta C}{R} T^2 + \ldots + \frac{I}{R}, \tag{80}$$

and from this I may be obtained. The establishment of equilibrium at only one temperature is required.

If one rearranges Eq. (80) to

$$\frac{\Delta H_0}{T} + I = -R \ln K_a + \Delta A \ln T + \tfrac{1}{2} \Delta B \, T + \tfrac{1}{6} \Delta C \, T^2 \ldots \tag{81}$$

and determines K_a at more than one temperature, a plot of the right-hand side of Eq. (81) *vs* $1/T$ yields a straight line from which both ΔH_0 and I can be obtained.

Two special forms of Eq. (80) are very useful in some applications. If ΔH of reaction is assumed to be independent of temperature, this equation takes the simple forms

$$\log K_a = \frac{A}{T} + B \tag{82}$$

or

$$\log \frac{K_{a_2}}{K_{a_1}} = \frac{\Delta H}{2 \cdot 303 R} \left[\frac{1}{T_1} - \frac{1}{T_2} \right]. \tag{83}$$

The linear relation between $\log K_a$ and $1/T$ is a rather good approximation even over fairly wide temperature ranges and is very useful for interpolation and even some extrapolation.

C. *Use of the Third Law*

The other method of determining I is to make use of the Third Law of thermodynamics which fixes the entropy at $T = 0$, either as zero for a pure crystalline substance or greater than zero for an amorphous solid, a solid solution or a mixture of isotopes. As a consequence absolute values of entropy can be assigned to substances at a given p and t and $\Delta S°$ in Eq. (69) can be computed and from this $\Delta G°$ and eventually K_a. In other words, the Third Law makes it possible to predict an equilibrium constant purely from thermal measurements—i.e. from heat capacities, latent heats and heats of reaction and hence without the necessity of establishing a state of equilibrium in the reaction.

To show the relation between chemical equilibrium and the entropy change in the reaction at $T = 0$, consider the following treatment: From Eqs. (69) and (77) we can write

$$\Delta G = \Delta H_0 + \Delta A \, T + \tfrac{1}{2} \Delta B \, T^2 + \tfrac{1}{3} \Delta C \, T^3 + \ldots - T \, \Delta S. \tag{84}$$

We will now relate ΔS to the temperature taking over-all limits of T and $T = 0$ (absolute zero) by the relation

$$\Delta S = \Delta S_0° + \int_{T_B}^{T} \phi_1(T) \, \mathrm{d} \ln T + \frac{\Delta H_v}{T_B} + \int_{T_F}^{T_B} \phi_2(T) \, \mathrm{d} \ln T + \frac{\Delta H_F}{T_F}$$
$$+ \int_0^{T_F} \phi_3(T) \, \mathrm{d} \ln T, \tag{85}$$

where $\Delta S_0°$ is the change of entropy in the reaction at $T = 0$ (not to be confused with the ΔS_0 in Eq. (78) which is simply a constant of integration) T_B is the boiling-point temperature, T_F the freezing-point temperature both at the given pressure, ΔH_B and ΔH_F are the corresponding latent heats of phase change and $\phi(T)$ represents a heat-capacity function over the temperature range of the respective integral. If there should be one or more solid phase transitions between T_F and $T = 0$, there should, of course, be added the respective $\Delta H/T$ terms. Note that $\phi_3(T)$ is of the form

$$C_p = aT^3 \tag{86}$$

in the neighbourhood of $T = 0$ so that the final integral is determinate which would not be the case if the C_p relation were of the form of Eq. (73). Combining Eqs. (84) and (85) with Eq. (69) one has a relation for calculating ΔG° from thermal data alone provided these data are known to $T = 0$ or close to it and provided ΔS_0° can be evaluated. This is where the Third Law comes into use because according to it $\Delta S_0^\circ = 0$ and all the other quantities are determinable from thermal measurements carried close to absolute zero with a small extrapolation using Eq. (86). Note that the coefficients ΔA, ΔB, etc. in Eq. (84) do not have to be valid to $T = 0$ but only over the range of temperatures for which ΔG° is desired starting from the temperature, usually 25° C, at which ΔH is known.

It is worth noting that small errors in some of the thermal data are often greatly magnified when these data are used to calculate an equilibrium constant. This is a result of the fact that many heats of reaction are obtained as a small difference of much larger numbers (an extreme case is the heat of an isomerization of a hydrocarbon from heats of combustion) and also because of the log relationship between K_a and ΔG°. This is a point of considerable practical importance which is sometimes overlooked.

VI. NUMERICAL DATA ON THERMODYNAMIC FUNCTIONS AND EQUILIBRIUM CONSTANTS

The first law of thermodynamics allows us to write for any reaction

$$\Delta G_R^\circ = l\, \Delta G_{f_L}^\circ + m\, \Delta G_{f_M}^\circ + \ldots - a\, \Delta G_{f_A}^\circ - b\, \Delta G_{f_B}^\circ - \ldots, \tag{87}$$

or, stated in words, the standard free-energy change for a reaction can be easily calculated from the standard free energies of formation of the elements and compounds involved. For any element $\Delta G_f^\circ = 0$. From the standpoint of application, the ultimate goal is a tabulation of standard free energies of formation or of the values of ΔH_f° and ΔS_f° from which ΔG_f° may be calculated, of all compounds as a function of temperature. Some significant beginnings have been made in this direction. By way of example one may cite the tables published by the American Petroleum Institute (1945 to date) for hydrocarbons and a few related substances. Various properties are tabulated but ones most pertinent to this discussion are heat capacity, standard enthalpy of formation, absolute entropy, free energy of formation and logarithm of the equilibrium constant of formation. The temperature range is 0–$1\,500°$ K. From Eqs. (11) and (87) it is obvious that $\ln K_a$ for any reaction may be obtained by appropriate combination of the logarithms of the equilibrium constants of formation and this leads to the equation

$$K_{\text{reaction}} = \prod K_f^{\nu_i}. \tag{88}$$

Another comprehensive tabulation is that of the U.S. National Bureau of Standards (1952). This gives values of the standard heat of formation at $0°$ K and $25°$ C, the standard free energy of formation and logarithm of the equilibrium constant of the formation reaction, both at $25°$ C, for a wide variety of chemical species. Note that these values are not given for any temperature above $25°$ C and this limits their usefulness but, of course one can calculate the values at any other temperature if the heat capacities are available.

With the aid of statistical thermodynamics and with information on the energy levels in the molecule it is possible to calculate $E° - E_0°$, the energy in the ideal gas state above that at $T = 0$. The methods of doing this are beyond the scope of this chapter but the following references are suggested for details: The books by Aston and Fritz (1959), Dole (1954) and Pitzer (1953).

Knowing $E° - E_0°$ at any temperature the other common thermodynamic functions can be calculated at the same temperature by well-known thermodynamic relations.

The basic quantities for the construction of tables such as those of the U.S. National Bureau of Standards are $\Delta H_f°$ at $25°$ C, $(H° - H_0°)/T$ and $(G° - H_0°)/T$. From these the other properties tabulated are calculated from the following equations:

$$S° = \left(\frac{H° - H_0°}{T}\right) - \left(\frac{G° - H_0°}{T}\right) \tag{89}$$

$$\Delta H_f° = \Delta H_{f_0}° + \Delta(H° - H_0°), \tag{90}$$

where

$$\Delta(H° - H_0°) = (H° - H_0°)_{\text{compound}} - \sum \nu(H° - H_0°)_{\text{elements}}. \tag{91}$$

$\Delta H_{f_0}°$ is obtained from

$$\Delta H_{f_0}° = \Delta H_{f_{25}}° - \Delta(H_{25}° - H_0°), \tag{92}$$

where

$$\Delta(H_{25}° - H_0°) = (H_{25}° - H_0°)_{\text{compound}} - \sum \nu(H_{25}° - H_0°)_{\text{elements}}, \tag{93}$$

$$\Delta G_f° = \Delta H_{f_0}° + T \Delta \left(\frac{G° - H_0°}{T}\right), \tag{94}$$

where

$$\Delta\left(\frac{G^\circ - H_0^\circ}{T}\right) = \left(\frac{G^\circ - H_0^\circ}{T}\right)_{\text{compound}} - \sum \nu \left(\frac{G^\circ - H_0^\circ}{T}\right)_{\text{elements}}, \qquad (95)$$

$$\log_{10} K_f = -\frac{\Delta G_f^\circ}{4 \cdot 575 T}. \qquad (96)$$

Then for any reaction the K_a is obtained from Eq. (88).

Note that at $T = 0$, $E_0 = H_0 = G_0$.

Luft (1957) has given a nomograph from which one may quickly obtain K_a for 51 gas reactions for t from $0°$ C to $1\,000°$ C and ΔH of reaction at $25°$ C.

One frequently encounters the situation where no data, or insufficient data, on thermodynamic properties are available for the calculation of equilibrium in a particular reaction. In such a case it is very convenient to have a method for estimating the necessary properties from a minimum of data. Many attempts have been made to develop such a method and as a result there are now available several empirical correlations based on structural considerations which permit an approximate estimation of properties such as C_p, ΔH, ΔS and ΔG of formation of many organic compounds. In the absence of experimental data these are very useful for making at least an order-of-magnitude estimate of the probable extent of a reaction. It is beyond the scope of this chapter to describe any of these methods but the reader is referred to the book by Janz (1958) which reviews the whole subject.

VII. Feasibility of a Reaction

The remark is sometimes made that a given reaction is " thermodynamically impossible ". This is a loose statement that has no meaning in the absence of qualifying statements. For example, any reaction, starting with pure reactants uncontaminated by any of the products, will have a tendency to proceed to some extent, though this may be only infinitesimal. Thus the reaction

$$H_2O(gas) = H_2 + \tfrac{1}{2}O_2$$

proceeds to some extent at $25°$ C; we can even calculate with considerable assurance the percentage of water vapour that would be decomposed. From the accurately known value of ΔG° of this reaction at $25°$ C, the equilibrium constant is about 1×10^{-40} and the extent of decomposition is infinitesimally small but definite.

From the value of the standard free-energy change for any reaction, we can form an opinion about the feasibility of the reaction without further calculation. Thus if $\Delta G^\circ = 0$ at a given temperature, then

$K_a = 1$ and it is obvious that the reaction must proceed to a considerable extent before equilibrium is reached. The situation becomes less favourable as $\Delta G°$ increases in the positive direction, but there is no definite value that one can choose as clearly indicating that the reaction is not feasible from the standpoint of industrial operation. At 600° K, the $\Delta G°$ for the methanol-synthesis reaction is $+11\,000$ cal/mole, and yet the reaction is certainly feasible at this temperature. In this case the unfavourable free-energy change for the standard state is partly overcome by utilizing high pressure to displace the equilibrium. Other means can also be used for this purpose, such as changing the ratio of reactants on removing one of the reaction products.

For the purpose of ascertaining quickly and only approximately if any given reaction is promising at a given temperature, the following guide may be useful:

$\Delta G° < 0$. Reaction is promising.

$\Delta G° > 0$ but $< +10\,000$ cal/mole. Reaction is of doubtful promise but warrants further study.

$\Delta G° > +10\,000$ cal/mole. Very unfavourable. Would be feasible only under unusual circumstances.

It should be understood that these are only approximate criteria that are useful in preliminary exploratory work.

VIII. CALCULATION OF CONVERSION IN A REACTION

The fraction x, of A converted in the reaction

$$aA + bB = lL + mM \tag{C}$$

at equilibrium is given by

$$\frac{(n_L + r_L n_A x)^l (n_M + r_M n_A x)^m}{[n_A(1-x)]^a (n_B - r_B n_A x)^b} (N)^{-\Sigma \nu} = K_p p^{-\Sigma \nu}, \tag{97}$$

where n_A, n_B, n_L etc. are the moles of each constituent in the initial reactant mixture, $r_B = b/a$, $r_L = l/a$, $r_m = m/a$ and N is the total number of moles in the equilibrium mixture including inert as well as active components. It is equal to the sum of the 4 terms in the parentheses (or brackets) of Eq. (97) plus n_I. This equation is merely Eq. (28) combined with mass balances. Given K_p and the number of moles of each constituent in the initial mixture, x can be calculated by trial.

The use of Eq. (97) will be illustrated by the following case: An initial mixture of 25 mole % CO, 55% H_2 and 20% inert gas undergoes the following reaction

$$CO + 2H_2 = CH_3OH \tag{III}$$

and equilibrium is reached at 300 atm and 350° C. What percentage of CO will be converted? A rigorous solution would be quite complex and time-consuming and it would require PVT data on the mixture in order to calculate K_p from K_a. To simplify the solution it will be assumed that the equilibrium mixture is an ideal solution. K_a at this temperature is taken as 4.9×10^{-5} (Dodge, 1944). From Fig. 2, $K_v = 0.35$ and using Eq. (60), $K_p = 1.4 \times 10^{-4}$. Let $A = CO$, $B = H_2$ and $L = $ methanol; then $n_A = 25$ (basis of 100 moles total), $n_B = 55$, $n_L = 0$, $n_M = 0$, $r_L = 1$, $r_M = 0$, $r_B = 2$, $\sum v = -2$, $N = 100 - 50x$. Substituting these values in Eq. (97) one gets

$$\frac{(25x)(100 - 50x)^2}{25(1 - x)(55 - 50x)^2} = 1.4 \times 10^{-4}(300)^2 = 12.6.$$

Solving by trial, $x = 0.61$ or 61.0% CO converted. If ideal gases had been assumed the result would have been 44.1%.

It is not difficult to prove that the maximum concentration of any reacting constituent in the equilibrium mixture is obtained when the reactants are mixed in the stoichiometric proportions. Naturally this is not the condition for maximum conversion.

IX. ANOTHER APPROACH TO THE TREATMENT OF GAS EQUILIBRIA

The treatment of chemical equilibrium given above, based on the equilibrium constant, may be said to be the classical approach. Some authors advocate another approach which does not involve an equilibrium constant but deals directly with the effect of pressure, temperature and composition on the degree of advancement or extent of the reaction. The change in mass of any component due to reaction is proportional to its molecular weight and to the stoichiometric number or

$$m_i - m_i^\circ = v_i M_i \xi, \tag{98}$$

and

$$d\xi = \frac{dm}{v_i M_i}. \tag{99}$$

The quantity ξ, defined by these equations, is the " extent of reaction " or " degree of advancement " and is merely one variable for representing changes in composition. It is simply the number of moles of any component formed or disappearing divided by the respective stoichiometric number. It is related to the fraction of a reactant converted, x, by

$$\xi = \frac{n_0}{v} x, \tag{100}$$

where n_0 = number of moles of the reactant initially present. With the aid of the usual thermodynamic relations, the quantity ξ can be related to pressure and temperature.

The author finds this method of treating chemical equilibrium less easy to understand than the conventional method and the advantages are not very apparent. For further details of the method, the book by Prigogine and Defay (1954) and a paper by Pings (1961) are suggested.

X. HEAT EFFECTS

So far we have ignored the heat effect which accompanies any reaction and have considered only the conditions at the exit from the reactor. Let us now consider the situation from the standpoint of entrance conditions. In addition to the equilibrium- and mass-balance equations an energy balance can be added, namely

$$\sum_r n_i H_i + Q = \sum_p n_j H_j, \tag{101}$$

where $\sum_r$ represents a summation over all reactants, of which i represents any one and $\sum_p$ is a summation for all reaction products of which j represents any one. Q is heat added (positive) or removed (negative). H_i and H_j are functions of p, t and y and the rigorous use of Eq. (101), though possible if the needed data are available, becomes complicated. For reactions at moderate or low pressures one can usually assume ideal gases which makes H a function of t only and greatly simplifies the use of Eq. (101). For higher pressures one might assume an ideal solution which makes H a function of p and t but independent of composition. Another procedure is to correct the values of H from low pressure to high pressure by the use of the generalized enthalpy correction, $(H - H^*)/T_c$.

In using Eq. (101) the H of all elements can be taken equal to zero at some p_0 and t_0 but the H of all compounds must be taken as greater than zero at p_0, t_0 by the heat of formation.

There are two limiting cases in the use of Eq. (101) namely (1) when the reaction is isothermal and Q is equal to the heat of reaction at the given temperature, and (2), when $Q = 0$ and the reaction is adiabatic. An infinite number of intermediate cases is possible depending on the extent of the heat transfer between the reacting system and its surroundings.

Given the pressure (usually assumed constant through the reactor) and initial temperature, t_i, one wishes to know the final temperature, t_f, and the conversion x, for any specified Q or if both t_i and the conversion x are specified one can calculate Q and of course t_f. A few calculated figures will be presented to show the magnitude of the effect of heat evolution. If a synthesis gas containing 2 moles H_2 to 1 of CO were reacted isothermally at 275° C and 200 atm over a good methanol catalyst, the maximum or equilibrium conversion would be 84%. If the same reaction with these inlet conditions were carried out adiabatically the exit temperature would rise to 429° C and the maximum conversion would be only 14%.

The equilibrium-conversion equation (97) and the energy-balance equation (101), for a given Q may be expressed in the following very general forms:

$$x = \phi_1(t_f) \quad \text{[equilibrium]} \tag{102}$$

$$x = \phi_2(t_f) \quad \text{[energy balance].} \tag{103}$$

Simultaneous solution of these two equations enables one to calculate x and t_f. This is illustrated graphically in Fig. 3 for an exothermic

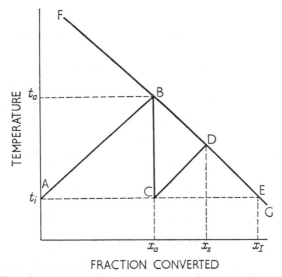

FIG. 3. Fraction converted *vs.* temperature for an exothermic reaction.

reaction. Point A represents the condition at entrance to the reactor and AB is the graph of Eq. (101) for the case of $Q = 0$. FG is the graph of the equilibrium equation (102) and the intersection at B gives the solution for final temperature and fraction converted. Point E represents the conversion that would have been obtained had the reaction been carried out isothermally. An intermediate case is that of a reaction run in stages with inter-cooling (or inter-heating in the case of endothermic reactions). AB represents the first-stage conditions, BC is the inter-cooling line (constant pressure and perfect inter-cooling assumed) and CD represents second-stage conditions. The conversion is greatly improved by the use of two stages, and three stages would give a significant increase, but beyond that the gain is small and economic considerations would dictate a maximum of two or perhaps three stages in practice. The contact process for SO_3 generally uses two stages with a conversion of about 75–80% in the first stage and a final over-all conversion of about 97–98%.

The methane–steam reaction for hydrogen production has been carried out in three stages to obtain a high-purity hydrogen. This is an endothermic reaction and its graphical representation is similar to that in Fig. 3 but with slopes of both heat balance and equilibrium lines of opposite sign. Figure 3 is for the case of a fixed pressure and fixed initial temperature but a series of lines AB can be plotted for different values of t_i and likewise one can plot a family of equilibrium lines FG, one for each pressure desired.

XI. Equilibrium in the Case of Simultaneous Reactions

A. *Systems of Two Reactions*

Up to this point only a single reaction has been considered but in the vast majority of practical cases more than one reaction may occur and often does. This is especially true in the organic field. In the simple case of CO and H_2 as reactants many different products are possible and the same is true of combustions when the oxygen concentration is insufficient for complete burning to CO_2 and H_2O. What actually occurs may be controlled as much by the kinetics as by equilibrium considerations but in this chapter we are concerned only with the latter. In the case of methanol synthesis, for example, the reaction

$$CO + 2H_2 = CH_3OH \tag{IV}$$

can be made to go almost to the exclusion of all other possible reactions by suitable choice of a catalyst. In fact if equilibrium were assumed with respect to the reaction

$$CO + 3H_2 = CH_4 + H_2O \tag{V}$$

as well as (IV) the yield of methanol would be very small.

The treatment of a system of any number of reactions under the assumption that equilibrium is reached with respect to all of them involves no new principles but there are a number of short-cuts that can be made and some pitfalls to be avoided which make it desirable to enter into a little detail about the procedures.

Even reaction (IV) undoubtedly takes place in the following two steps

$$CO + H_2 = HCOH \tag{VI}$$

$$HCOH + H_2 = CH_3OH \tag{VII}$$

and, in principle, one should treat it as a case of two simultaneous equilibria. If one does this one finds that the equilibrium concentration of formaldehyde is so small that it is negligible and so one can treat this case as a single reaction which is the sum of (VI) and (VII). One can take it as a general rule that if any reaction proceeds in a series of steps, simultaneous equilibria in all the reaction steps should be considered unless the concentration of intermediate products is small enough to be neglected and then only the over-all reaction need be considered. One can often reach a good judgment on this point just by observing the order of magnitude of the equilibrium constants.

Another interesting and important case is the synthesis of ethanol from C_2H_4 and H_2O. Most investigators have assumed that the reaction

$$C_2H_4 + H_2O = C_2H_5OH \tag{VIII}$$

was the only one that need be considered. This is far from true under some conditions where the reaction

$$2C_2H_5OH = (C_2H_5)_2O + H_2O \tag{IX}$$

must also be considered. This has been discussed by Cope and Dodge (1959) whose paper is referred to for details. Their work was with the two-phase, liquid–vapour system and not a purely gaseous system but a few figures will be cited to show how great an error can be made by ignoring reaction (IX). The following figures are calculated ones but they are at least qualitatively supported by a few experimental measurements:

TABLE III. Effect of Neglecting Reaction (IX) When Calculating Concentration of Ethanol Obtained in the Hydration of Ethylene

p atm	t° C	Concentration, Mole per cent			
		EtOH in liquid	EtOH in vapour	Ether in vapour	
200	200	39·0	38·1	—	Ether formation neglected
200	200	5·5	14·2	54·1	Ether formation not neglected
200	250	12·1	25·0	—	Ether neglected
200	250	5·2	14·6	26·9	Ether not neglected

The simple case of two simultaneous equations with one or more reactants and/or products in common will now be treated quantitatively. Consider the two reactions

E

$$aA + bB = cC + dD \tag{D}$$

$$aA + eE = fF + gG \tag{E}$$

and let K_D and K_E be the two equilibrium constants in terms of partial pressures, i.e. K_p. Taking a basis of 1 mole and letting x_1 and x_2 be the fractions of A converted in (D) and (E) respectively, one has from Eq. (97)

$$K_D = \frac{(n_c + r_c n_A x_1)^c (n_D + r_D n_A x_1)^d}{[n_A(1 - x_1 - x_2)]^a (n_B - r_B n_A x_1)^b} p^{\Sigma \nu} (N)^{-\Sigma \nu} \tag{104}$$

$$K_E = \frac{(n_F + r_F n_A x_2)^f (n_G + r_G n_A x_2)^g}{[n_A(1 - x_1 - x_2)]^a (n_E - r_E n_A x_2)^e} p^{\Sigma \nu} (N)^{-\Sigma \nu} . \tag{105}$$

$$N = \sum n = \text{the sum of the 7 terms which are raised to the}$$
powers of stoichiometric numbers.

At an elevated pressure where one would not wish to assume ideal gases, K_p should be replaced by K_{p*}/K_ϕ or K_{p*}/K_ν.

The two equations can readily be solved by a graphical method as follows: take trial values of x_1 and solve for x_2 by both equations and then plot x_1 *vs* x_2 and the solution is given by the intersection of the 2 lines. (See Fig. 4.) If $x_1 + x_2$ approaches $1 \cdot 0$, this method of solution is unsatisfactory. It is suggested that a new equation be generated by dividing Eq. (104) by Eq. (105), which will not contain the term $(1 - x_1 - x_2)$.

Consider the special case of the two reactions

$$C_3H_8 = C_3H_6 + H_2 \tag{X}$$

$$C_3H_8 = C_2H_4 + CH_4 \tag{XI}$$

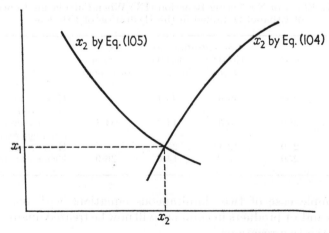

FIG. 4. Solution of Eqs. (104) and (105).

Let $A = C_3H_8$, $C = C_3H_6$, $D = H_2$, $F = C_2H_4$ and $G = CH_4$. Eliminate B and E. Let $n_A = 1$. $n_C = n_D = n_F = n_G = 0$ if the initial gas is pure propane, $r_C = r_D = r_F = r_G = 1$. $\sum \nu = 1$, $\sum n = 1 + x_1 + x_2$. Equations (104) and (105) reduce to

$$\frac{x_1^2}{(1 - x_1 - x_2)(1 + x_1 + x_2)} = K_D/p, \tag{106}$$

$$\frac{x_2^2}{(1 - x_1 - x_2)(1 + x_1 + x_2)} = K_E/p. \tag{107}$$

In this case, an analytical solution is possible and, one gets

$$x_2 = \left[\frac{1}{(1/K_D) + \{(K_D/K_E)^{\frac{1}{2}} + 1\}^2} \right]^{\frac{1}{2}} \tag{108}$$

and

$$x_1 = x_2 \left(\frac{K_D}{K_E} \right)^{\frac{1}{2}} \tag{109}$$

An interesting case is that of the two reactions

$$CH_4 + \tfrac{1}{2}N_2 = HCN + \tfrac{3}{2}H_2 \tag{XII}$$
$$CH_4 = C + 2H_2 \tag{XIII}$$

Assume the reactants in stoichiometric proportion in (XII).

The two equilibrium equations can be obtained directly from Eqs. (104) and (105) by putting in the special conditions. Note that D and G are the same product in this case and the terms to the powers d and g both become $(n_D + r_D x_1 n_A + r_G x_2 n_A)$

The two equations become

$$p^{-1}K_{XII} = \frac{(x_1)(\tfrac{3}{2}x_1 + 2x_2)^{\frac{3}{2}}}{(1 - x_1 - x_2)(\tfrac{1}{2} - \tfrac{1}{2}x_1)^{\frac{1}{2}}(\tfrac{3}{2} + x_1 + x_2)} \tag{110}$$

$$p^{-1}K_{XIII} = \frac{(\tfrac{3}{2}x_1 + 2x_2)^2}{(1 - x_1 - x_2)(\tfrac{3}{2} + x_1 + x_2)}. \tag{111}$$

From known values of the two equilibrium constants, one can calculate, using these two equations, that at $2\,000°$ K and 1 atm about 2% of the methane would be converted to HCN. If one considered only reaction XII a conversion of about 96% would be predicted. This is a very striking illustration of the gross errors that one can make if some reactions are neglected in considering a chemical equilibrium.

B. *Application to Production of Synthesis Gas*

There are many important cases where equilibrium in a large number of possible reactions must be considered, and to illustrate one method of treating such a case the production of synthesis gas from natural gas and oxygen has been chosen. This is an important step in many processes for the synthesis of ammonia, alcohols, fuels, etc. by high-pressure processes. One may write the over-all reaction as

$$CH_4 + \tfrac{1}{2}O_2 = CO + 2H_2. \tag{XIV}$$

This is clearly not the only reaction that is possible and furthermore the initial reactant mixture will certainly contain some nitrogen and higher hydrocarbons. The problem is to predict the composition of the product gas for a given set of conditions or to predict a composition of the feed gas to give a product of specified composition.

The first step in the solution is to list what one considers to be the likely products of such a reaction. A tentative list might include: CH_4, C_2H_6, C_2H_2, H_2, H, O_2, O, N_2, N, CO, H_2O, OH^-, CO_2, NO, and C. Some judgment has already been exercised in limiting this list. One could obviously list others such as NH_3, HCN, CN, NO_2, HCOH, and many others. These have been omitted on the assumption that their concentrations at equilibrium are so small as to be negligible. This assumption for any particular component can always be checked by calculation if one can estimate an equilibrium constant for the reaction or reactions that could yield the compound in question.

An approximate knowledge of the temperature and pressure conditions for this process will enable one to eliminate some of the substances in the above list. For example, assuming that the final temperature will be in the range of 813–1 372° C (1 500–2 500° F) and that the pressure will not exceed 20 atm, one can eliminate C_2H_6, C_2H_2, H, O_2, OH^-, and NO. They could exist only in negligible quantities at equilibrium or, as in the case of N_2, no reaction occurs, and it is present only as a diluent. In the case of O_2, this implies that the proportion in the initial mixture is insufficient for complete combustion. The only reason for elimination of some constituents at the start is to simplify the problem; if there is any doubt they can be carried along.

The following six products are left: CH_4, H_2, CO, H_2O, CO_2, and C. A number of reactions can be written which involve these six constituents, but not all of them will be independent. The next step is to write the least number of independent reactions which will involve all of the six substances. One possible set is:

$$CH_4 + H_2O = CO + 3H_2 \tag{XV}$$
$$H_2 + CO_2 = H_2O + CO \tag{I}$$
$$C + CO_2 = 2CO. \tag{XVI}$$

This is not the only set that could be chosen, but it is obvious that since we are dealing with equilibrium the final state is independent of the steps by which it is achieved, so that all sets of independent reactions we choose will lead to the same end result.

It is of interest to note that what is probably the initiating reaction of the whole process, namely

$$CH_4 + 2O_2 = CO_2 + 2H_2O \qquad \text{(XVII)}$$

does not appear because O_2 was eliminated as a product on the basis that the amount that could be present at equilibrium is quite negligible. This is easily verified by calculation but, of course, it assumes that the molal ratio of O_2 to CH_4 in the initial gas is less than 2.

The next step is to write equations from which to solve for the number of moles of each of the six components. For this we need six simultaneous equations and these are readily obtained in the following way. After an initial gas composition and quantity has been chosen we can write three mass balances, one for each of C, H, and O. It is obvious that only elements can be balanced, as these are the only species that retain their identity through a series of chemical changes. In addition we have one equilibrium or mass-action equation for each reaction and this gives us the required total of six. The answer, which is the composition of the gas issuing from the reaction, is then obtained by solution of the six equations. This is a trial or iteration process which can readily be done manually but becomes very tedious if many different conditions are to be investigated and in that case it is advantageous to use a computer.

One assumes equilibrium at a final temperature and pressure, both of which can be arbitrarily chosen or one may assume an initial temperature and calculate the final temperature through an energy balance as previously explained. One also notes that one of the products is a solid and hence the equilibrium-gas composition is fixed if one can solve for only five numbers of moles. Because of this we may be able to simplify the solution of the problem by omitting carbon from consideration and the reaction (XVI) which involves it, and solving only five simultaneous equations. In doing this one is assuming that no carbon will be produced under the conditions chosen because although the carbon does not enter into the mass-action equations or the gas composition, it does affect one of the mass balances. Consequently when the calculation is completed one must test the answer by using the equilibrium relation

$$\frac{y_{CO}^2}{y_{CO_2}} = \frac{K_a}{p}. \qquad (112)$$

If $y_{CO}^2/y_{CO_2} < K_a/p$ no carbon will be formed. If, on the other hand, $y_{CO}^2/y_{CO_2} > K_a/p$ the solution will be incorrect and one must either repeat with the carbon included or change conditions to avoid carbon formation.

When the equality of Eq. (112) is satisfied we have a limiting condition. A slight change in one direction will cause carbon formation and a slight change in the other will bring us into the field of no carbon. On a suitable diagram a carbon-deposition boundary line can be established and from this one knows what conditions to choose to avoid carbon formation. We note, in passing, that all thermodynamic properties of carbon are based on graphite but the carbon that would deposit from a hydrocarbon would not be graphite but a form of carbon that is less stable and hence with a higher free energy of formation. This has the effect of introducing a small factor of safety into the calculation.

In making the calculation on production of synthesis gas from natural gas and O_2, one can either start (1) with a fixed initial gas composition which may contain only CH_4 and O_2 or may have CO_2 or H_2O added to shift the ratio of H_2 to CO in the product and calculate the product composition, or (2) one can start with a desired ratio of H_2/CO in the product gas and calculate the initial gas composition to attain it.

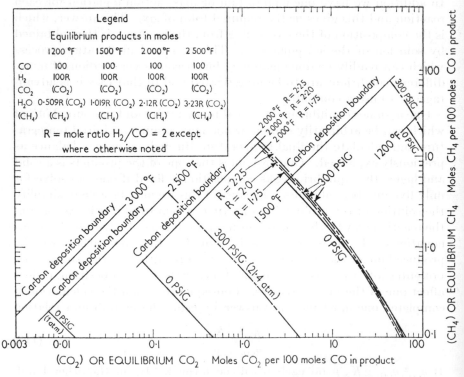

FIG. 5. Equilibrium compositions at various temperatures and pressures in the production of synthesis gas (CO and H_2) by the oxidation of methane. (Reproduced with permission from Mayland and Hayes, 1949.)

Some results of calculations of the latter kind are shown in Fig. 5. This shows results for final temperatures of $1\,200°$, $2\,000°$, $2\,500°$ and $3\,000°$ F, for pressure of 1 and 21·4 atm and for a ratio R (H_2/CO) in the product of 2·0 for all cases except at $2\,000°$ F where three values of R are shown. Each isobar ends at a carbon-deposition boundary line. In the field above this line, carbon formation is to be expected and below it no carbon should form. The ordinate is moles $CH_4/100$ moles CO and the abscissa is moles $CO_2/100$ moles CO. The H_2 content of the product is fixed by R and the H_2O by the relation

$$\text{moles } H_2O = K_2R \text{ (moles } CO_2)$$

where K_2 is the equilibrium constant for reaction (I). The initial gas may now be calculated from material balances.

A brief discussion of the results shown in Fig. 5 may be in order. Since the ratio of H_2 to CO is fixed in the product, it is clear that CO_2 or H_2O must be added to the feed gas to maintain this ratio. Maximum yield of synthesis gas and minimum consumption of CO_2 and steam are favoured by high temperatures and low pressures.

C. More Complex Systems

The simplest case is that of isomerization when several isomers exist. If one assumes at equilibrium one mole of a given isomer which was the starting material, the moles of all the other isomers in the equilibrium mixture will equal the equilibrium constants of the reactions for the formation of each isomer from the starting one.

In more complex systems such as arise in connection with the combustion of special fuels or rocket propellants, somewhat more sophisticated methods of analysis are desirable and the analysis should be made with a view to the use of a digital computer for numerical solution. One problem that arises is the choice of independent components once the total number of probable constituents present in more than negligible proportions has been chosen. This was simple enough in the example chosen where the number of constituents was only 6. In cases where there may be 10 or more, it is not so simple but Brinkley (1946) has developed an analytical criterion which he later applied (1947) in the development of a procedure for solving two general cases of equilibrium in systems of many constituents. Kandiner and Brinkley (1950) applied this procedure to the specific case of the combustion of propane at a pressure of 40 atm where 10 constituents were assumed to be present. Brinkley and Lewis (1952) developed the general method further for combustion in carbon, hydrogen, oxygen, nitrogen systems.

Another useful reference with a clear and simple discussion of methods and several numerical examples is a report by Kobe and Leland (1954). A NACA report by Huff *et al.* (1951) develops a method for determination of both temperature and composition of a reacting system of many constituents and applies it to the case of three processes involving a reaction between diborane and oxybifluoride where 16 reaction products are considered. Marynowski *et al.* (1962) have very recently treated equilibrium in the carbon–hydrogen–nitrogen system at the high temperatures obtainable in a plasma jet (2 000–6 000° K). In this case 20 species were considered and the treatment was focused on the determination of conditions for maximum yield of HCN.

Denbigh (1955) gives the following simple rule for determining the number of independent reactions: Write reactions for forming all compounds (including molecules of elements) from the atoms and then by combination of equations eliminate those atoms not assumed to be present in the equilibrium mixture. The remaining equations will be the number sought.

In recent years the thermodynamics of gas equilibria at high temperatures has been extensively developed because of its importance to rocket propellants and a good review of the subject may be obtained from the book edited by Bahn and Zukoski (1960).

D. *Another Procedure*

Another approach to the problem of simultaneous equilibria that may have some advantages over the method just discussed is one based directly on free-energy minimization. One starts, as before, with an assumption of the total list of chemical species likely to be present at equilibrium in significant amounts, but then instead of writing a series of equations and finding the least number of independent equations that will produce all the species postulated, one develops an equation for the free energy of the whole system of species (including those in condensed phases if a heterogeneous equilibrium is being treated) and then by the usual techniques of partial differentiation and setting the partial derivatives with respect to numbers of moles of the various constituents, equal to zero one has a collection of simultaneous equations to be solved. This yields a composition of the system corresponding to that for a minimum of the total free-energy which would be that composition for chemical equilibrium. In principle this is simple enough but in practice it can get rather complex. For further details with examples, papers by White *et al.* (1958) and by Oliver *et al.* (1962) are suggested. A technique of minimization based on the gradient method which is well-adapted to machine computation is briefly discussed by Naphtali (1961).

Note that in this method it is not necessary to write any chemical reactions, determine the minimum number of independent equations or deal with mass-action expressions. This is presumably its main advantage.

NOMENCLATURE

A,B,C,D,E,F,G	Components in a reaction, constants in heat-capacity equations
a,b,c,d,e,f,g	Stoichiometric numbers
a	Activity
$A,A_0,B,B_0,a,b,$	
$C_0,c,D,h,\alpha,\gamma,\epsilon$	Equation-of-state constants
C_p	Heat capacity at constant pressure
E	Energy (internal)
f	Fugacity
$\bar{f}$	Fugacity of a component of a solution
G	Total free energy (Gibbs potential) of a system
$\bar{G}$	Molal free energy
H	Molal enthalpy
K_a	Equilibrium constant in terms of activities
K_f	Equilibrium constant in terms of fugacities
K_p	Equilibrium constant in terms of partial pressures
K_{p*}	Equilibrium constant K_p at limit where $p \to 0$
K_γ	Equilibrium constant defined by Eq. (59)
K_ϕ	Equilibrium constant defined by Eq. (31)
M	Molecular weight
m	Mass
N	Total number of moles
n	Number of moles of any component
p	Total pressure
Q	Heat transferred
R	Gas constant
r	Ratio of stoichiometric numbers
S	Total entropy of a system
$\bar{S}$	Molal entropy
T	Absolute temperature
t	Temperature on Fahrenheit or Centigrade scale
V	Total volume
v	Molal volume
$\bar{v}_i$	Partial molal volume of any component $= \left(\dfrac{\partial n_i}{\partial V}\right)_{P,T,n_j}$
x	Fraction converted in a reaction
y	Mole fraction

E*

| Z | Compressibility factor based on total volume |
| z | Molal compressibility factor |

Greek Letters

α	Residual volume
γ	Fugacity coefficient, f/p
μ	Chemical potential
ν	Generalized stoichiometric number
ξ	Degree of advancement of a reaction
$\prod$	Operator for a progressing product
ρ	Density
$\sum$	Operator for summation
ϕ_0,ϕ_1, etc.	Function of ...
ϕ	Function of, or fugacity coefficient of a component in a solution $=\bar{f}_i/y_i p$
ω	Acentric factor

Subscripts and Superscripts

A,B,L,M	Components of a reaction system
B	Boiling point
c	Critical state
F	Freezing point
f	Formation of a compound from the elements, final state
I	Inert gas
i	Initial state
i,j	Any components
m	Mixture
n_j	Indicates that the numbers of moles of all components except i are held constant
p	Constant pressure, products of a reaction
r	Reduced state, initial reactant mixture
T	Constant temperature
$','',''', \ldots$	Phases
$\circ$	Standard state (This refers to a fixed state of pressure and state of aggregation but not to fixed temperature)
$*$	Ideal gas state

REFERENCES

American Petroleum Institute Research Project No. 44, " Selected Values of Properties of Hydrocarbons and Related Compounds " (1945 to date).

Aston, J. G., and Fritz, J. J. (1959). " Thermodynamics and Statistical Thermodynamics," John Wiley, New York.

Bahn, G. S., and Zukoski, E. E., editors (1960) " Kinetics, Equilibria and Performance of High Temperature Systems," Butterworths, London.

Beattie, J. A. (1949). *Chem. Rev.* 44, 141.

Benedict, M., Webb, G. B., and Rubin, L. C. (1951). *Chem. Engng. Progr.* 47, 449.

Bloomer, O. T., and Rao, K. N. (1952). Institute of Gas Technology Research Bulletin 18.

Brinkley, S. R. (1946). *J. chem. Phys.* 14, 563; 686.

Brinkley, S. R. (1947). *J. chem. Phys.* 15, 107.

Brinkley, S. R., and Lewis, B. (1952). U.S. Bureau of Mines Report of Investigations 4806.

Comings, E. W. (1956). " High-Pressure Technology," p. 410, McGraw-Hill, New York.

Cope, C. S., and Dodge, B. F. (1959). *Amer. Inst. chem. Engrs. J.* 5, 10.

Curl, R. F. Jr., and Pitzer, K. S. (1958). *Industr. Engng. Chem.* 50, 265.

Denbigh, K. G. (1955). " Principles of Chemical Equilibrium," Cambridge University Press.

Dodge, B. F. (1944). " Chemical Engineering Thermodynamics ", p. 504, McGraw-Hill, New York.

Dole, M. (1954). " Introduction to Statistical Thermodynamics ", Prentice-Hall, New York.

Gillespie, L. J., and Beattie, J. A. (1930). *Phys. Rev.* 36, 743.

Harrison, R. H., and Kobe, K. A. (1953). *Chem. Engng. Progr.* 49, 349.

Hougen, O. A., Watson, K. M., and Ragatz, R. A. (1959). " Chemical Process Principles," Part II, " Thermodynamics," John Wiley, New York.

Huff, V. N., Gordon, S., and Morrell, V. E. (1951). National Advisory Committee for Aeronautics Report 1037.

Janz, G. J. (1958). " Estimation of Thermodynamic Properties of Organic Compounds ", Academic Press, New York.

Joffe, J. (1947). *Industr. Engng. Chem.* 39, 837.

Joffe, J. (1948). *Industr. Engng. Chem.* 40, 1738.

Kandiner, H. J., and Brinkley, S. R. (1950). *Industr. Engng. Chem.* 42, 850; 1526.

Kay, W. B. (1936). *Industr. Engng. Chem.* 28, 1014.

Kobe, K. A., and Leland, T. W. (1954). University of Texas, Bureau of Engineering Research, Special Publication No. 26.

Luft, N. W. (1957). *Chem. Engng.* Nov. 235.

Marinowski, C. W., Phillips, R. C., Phillips, J. R., and Hiester, K. (1962). *Industr. Engng. Chem.* Fundamentals 1, 52.

Mayland, B. J., and Hays, G. E. (1949). *Chem. Engng. Progr.* 45, 452.

Naphtali, L. M. (1961). *Industr. Engng. Chem.* 53, 387.

Newton, R. H. (1935). *Industr. Engng. Chem.* 27, 302.

Newton, R. H., and Dodge, B. F. (1935). *Industr. Engng. Chem.* 27, 577.

Oliver, R. C., Stephanon, S. E., and Baier, R. W. (1962). *Chem. Engng.* Feb. 19, p. 121.

Pings, C. J. (1961). *Chem. Engng. Sci.* 16, 181.

Pitzer, K. S. (1953). " Quantum Chemistry," Prentice-Hall, New York.

Pitzer, K. S., Lippman, D. Z., Curl, R. F., Huggins, C. M., Petersen, D. E. (1955). *J. Amer. chem. Soc.* **77**, 3433.

Prausnitz, J. M., and Gunn, R. D. (1958). *Amer. Inst. chem. Engrs. J.* **4**, 430.

Prigogine, I., and Defay, R. (1954). " Chemical Thermodynamics," Longmans, Green, London.

Redlich, O., and Kwong, J. N. S. (1949). *Chem. Rev.* **44**, 233.

U.S. National Bureau of Standards (1952). Circular 500, " Selected Values of Chemical Thermodynamic Properties," 1268 pages.

White, W. B., Johnson, S. M., and Dantzig, G. B. (1958). *J. chem. Phys.* **28**, 751.

Winchester, L. J., and Dodge, B. F. (1957). *Amer. Inst. chem. Engrs. J.* **2**, 431.

Chapter 7.ii

CHEMICAL EQUILIBRIA IN CONDENSED SYSTEMS

S. D. HAMANN

*C.S.I.R.O. Division of Physical Chemistry,
Melbourne, Victoria, Australia*

I. HISTORICAL INTRODUCTION

The first statement of the role of pressure in displacing chemical equilibria was made by Le Chatelier (1884) in citing some applications of his general principle. He remarked that " the increase of condensation of the whole of a system maintained at constant temperature leads to modifications [of chemical equilibrium] which tend to reduce the condensation of the system such as . . . the combination of the dissociation products of CO_2 ". This statement becomes clearer when we note that by " condensation " Le Chatelier meant either pressure or the number of molecules per unit volume.

A few years later Braun (1887) expressed the principle more specifically in relation to the solubility of salts in liquids: " substances which dissolve in their nearly saturated solutions with contraction are more strongly dissolved by increasing the pressure."

It seems that at that time van't Hoff, also, was well aware of the relationship between the effect of pressure and the volume change for a reaction. In fact Spring and van't Hoff (1887) demonstrated the principle convincingly in an experimental study of the influence of pressure on the double salt, copper-calcium acetate:

$$Ca.Cu(CH_3CO_2)_4.8H_2O.$$

They noted that the volume of the double salt is greater than that of its components:

$$Ca(CH_3CO_2)_2.H_2O + Cu(CH_3CO_2)_2.H_2O + 6H_2O,$$

and predicted that the salt should therefore be decomposed by an increase in hydrostatic pressure. Experimentally, they found that the decomposition proceeds rapidly at a pressure of about 6 000 atm at 40° C. On the other hand Spring had earlier observed that compression favoured the *formation* of substances whose volumes were smaller than those of their components.

Le Chatelier's principle is, of course, no more than a qualitative statement of the way in which chemical systems respond to changes in pressure; it says nothing about the degree of the effect. But soon after Le Chatelier propounded his theorem, Planck (1887) derived an exact quantitative relationship between the volume change accompanying a reaction and the influence of pressure on its equilibrium constant (Eq. 19). Planck's formula remains one of the most important in the field of high pressure chemistry, and it has been amply verified by experiment. The first direct confirmation was given by some measurements of Fanjung (1894) on the influence of pressure on the ionization constants of weak acids in water. Fanjung showed that his results were entirely consistent with the predictions of Planck's formula, based on Ostwald's (1878) measured values of the changes in volume for ionization of the acids.

It is clear from this brief review that the foundations of high pressure chemistry were laid in the decade following 1884. Subsequent work has followed two principal lines. The first, an experimental one, has been concerned with extending our knowledge of the behaviour of chemical equilibria over as wide a range of pressures and of different systems as possible. Tammann (1910) and Cohen (1926) were prominent in the early work in this field. The second line of attack has been a theoretical one which attempts to interpret the pressure effects on a molecular basis by postulating a plausible model for a particular reaction and using this to calculate the volume change accompanying the reaction. The first use of this method was Drude and Nernst's (1894) application of the theory of electrostriction to the ionization of weak electrolytes.

II. Some General Thermodynamic Relations

Consider a homogeneous liquid-phase system in which the following chemical equilibrium exists

$$aA + bB + \ldots \rightleftharpoons lL + mM + \ldots \tag{1}$$

Here $a, b, \ldots l, m \ldots$ denote the stoichiometric number of molecules of the type $A, B \ldots L, M \ldots$ taking part in the reaction.

The molar chemical potential of any component J of the system can be written in the form

$$\mu_J = \mu°_J + RT \ln a_J, \tag{2}$$

where $\mu°_J$ denotes the molar chemical potential of J in its standard state (which need not be specified at this stage). R is the gas constant, T the absolute temperature, and a_J is called the activity of the component J.

The condition for thermodynamic equilibrium is that

$$a\mu_A + b\mu_B + \ldots = l\mu_L + m\mu_M + \ldots, \tag{3}$$

and it follows from Eq. (2) that

$$RT \ln \frac{(a_L)^l (a_M)^m \ldots}{(a_A)^a (a_B)^b \ldots} = a\mu°_A + b\mu°_B + \ldots - l\mu°_L - m\mu°_M \ldots \tag{4}$$

Defining an equilibrium constant K by

$$K = \frac{(a_L)^l (a_M)^m \ldots}{(a_A)^a (a_B)^b \ldots}, \tag{5}$$

we may rewrite Eq. (4) as

$$RT \ln K = a\mu°_A + b\mu°_B + \ldots - l\mu°_L - m\mu°_M \ldots \tag{6}$$

Introducing the relationship

$$\left(\frac{\partial \mu°_J}{\partial p}\right)_T = V°_J, \tag{7}$$

where $V°_J$ is the molar volume of the component J in its standard state, we find that

$$\left(\frac{\partial RT \ln K}{\partial p}\right)_T = aV°_A + bV°_B + \ldots - lV°_L - mV°_M - \ldots = -\Delta V°, \tag{8}$$

where $\Delta V°$ denotes the excess of the molar volumes of the products over those of the reactants, all in their standard states.

A. *Concentrated Solutions*

If the components of a liquid mixture are present in comparable amounts, it is convenient to express the concentration of each in terms of its mole fraction x_J, defined by

$$x_J = \frac{n_J}{n_A + n_B + \ldots + n_L + n_M + \ldots}, \tag{9}$$

where the n's denote the number of moles of each molecular species in the mixture.

If, now, we define an activity coefficient f_J

$$f_J = a_J / x_J, \tag{10}$$

such that it approaches unity as x_J tends to unity, it follows from Eq. (2) that $\mu°_J$ is the molar chemical potential (or the Gibbs free energy) of the pure component J. If, similarly, we take the standard states of the other components to be their pure states, then $\Delta V°$ in Eq. (8) becomes equal to the difference between the molar volumes of the products and the reactants, all in their *pure* states.

Experimentally it is rather difficult to measure the "activity" equilibrium product K_x,

$$K_x = \frac{(x_L)^l (x_M)^m \cdots}{(x_A)^a (x_B)^b \cdots} \times \frac{(f_L)^l (f_M)^m \cdots}{(f_A)^a (f_B)^b \cdots} \tag{11}$$

under pressure. It is more convenient to measure K'_x, the product of the mole fractions of the components at equilibrium:

$$K'_x = \frac{(x_L)^l (x_M)^m \cdots}{(x_A)^a (x_B)^b \cdots}. \tag{12}$$

Since the variation of the activity coefficients with pressure is given by relationships of the type

$$\frac{\partial RT \ln f_J}{\partial p} = \overline{V}_J - V°_J, \tag{13}$$

where $\overline{V}_J$ denotes the partial molar volume of the component J in the actual solution,

$$\overline{V}_J = \frac{\partial V}{\partial n_J}, \tag{14}$$

V being the total volume of the solution, it follows that

$$\left(\frac{\partial RT \ln K'_x}{\partial p} \right)_T = -\Delta\overline{V}, \tag{15}$$

where the operator Δ has the same significance as it has in Eq. (8). This formula shows that, whilst the pressure dependence of K_x is determined by the volumes of the pure components, that of K'_x is governed by their partial molar volumes in the equilibrium mixture. In nearly ideal solutions the difference will be small.

It may be mentioned here that Eq. (15) applies quite generally since it is independent of the choice of standard states. For example, it applies to dilute solutions in which the conventional standard states are quite different from the pure states (see next section).

B. *Dilute Solutions*

In dilute solutions and particularly in electrolyte solutions it is customary to define the activity coefficient f_J of a *solute* component J

in such a way that it approaches unity as the mole fractions of all the solute species approach zero.

In the standard state $\mu_J = \mu°_J$, so that from Eq. (2) $a_J = 1$, and hence the standard state is a state in which the solute is at unit activity.

Equation (2) can be rewritten

$$\mu_J = \mu°_J + RT \ln x_J + RT \ln f_J,$$

from which

$$\left(\frac{\partial \mu_J}{\partial p} \right)_{x,T} = \left(\frac{\partial \mu°_J}{\partial p} \right)_T + \left(\frac{\partial RT \ln f_J}{\partial p} \right)_{x,T}, \tag{16}$$

that is,

$$\overline{V}_J = \overline{V}°_J + \left(\frac{\partial RT \ln f_J}{\partial p} \right)_{x,T}, \tag{17}$$

where $\overline{V}_J$ is the partial molar volume of J, and $\overline{V}°_J$ is its partial molar volume in the standard state.

By definition, $f_J = 1$ at infinite dilution, at all temperatures and pressures, so that

$$\overline{V}°_J = \overline{V}_J^\infty. \tag{18}$$

That is, the value of the partial molar volume in the standard state is the same as that at infinite dilution, $\overline{V}_J^\infty$.

It follows that Eq. (8) can be rewritten

$$\left(\frac{\partial RT \ln K_x}{\partial p} \right)_T = a\overline{V}_A^\infty + b\overline{V}_B^\infty \ldots - l\overline{V}_L^\infty - m\overline{V}_M^\infty - \ldots = -\Delta \overline{V}^\infty, \tag{19}$$

where it is to be understood that the $\overline{V}^\infty$ refer to the *solute* species. If the *solvent* enters into the reaction it contributes a term proportional to its molar volume $V°_S$, since the standard state for the solvent is the pure state.

Corresponding to Eq. (15) we have, for the pressure dependence of the " equilibrium function " K'_x (defined in formula (12)),

$$\left(\frac{\partial RT \ln K'_x}{\partial p} \right)_T = -\Delta \overline{V} \tag{20}$$

where the $\overline{V}$ refer to the partial molar volumes of the solute species (and where necessary of the solvent) at the actual concentration of the solution.

For several reasons it has become the practice to express the composition of a dilute solution, not in terms of the mole fractions x_J of its components, but in terms of their molalities m_J, or volume concentrations c_J. These quantities are defined by

$$m_J = \frac{1\ 000\ n_J}{n_S M_S}, \tag{21}$$

$$c_J = \frac{n_J}{V},$$ (22)

where n_J denotes the number of moles of the component J, n_S denotes the number of moles of the solvent, M_S is the gramme molecular weight of the solvent, and V is the volume of the solution. The molality m_J is the number of moles of J dissolved in 1 kg of solvent; the volume concentration c_J is usually expressed as the number of moles of J per litre of solution (molarity).

In the limit of very dilute solutions m_J and c_J are related to x_J by the formulae (see, for instance, Guggenheim, 1950):

$$m_J = \frac{1\,000 x_J}{M_S},$$ (23)

$$c_J = \frac{x_J}{V_S},$$ (24)

where V_S is the molar volume of the pure solvent. Since, by definition, $f_J \rightarrow 1$ at infinite dilution, at all temperatures and pressures, it follows from Eq. (11) that the equilibrium constants for the new concentration scales are

$$K_m = K_x \left(\frac{1\,000}{M_S}\right)^{l+m+\ldots-a-b-\ldots},$$ (25)

$$K_c = K_x (V_S)^{a+b+\ldots-l-m-\ldots}.$$ (26)

Clearly M_S is independent of the pressure, so that

$$\left(\frac{\partial RT \ln K_m}{\partial p}\right)_T = \left(\frac{\partial RT \ln K_x}{\partial p}\right)_T = -\Delta \overline{V}^\infty,$$ (27)

(cf. formula 19). On the other hand V_S varies with pressure, the derivative

$$-\left(\frac{\partial \ln V_S}{\partial p}\right)_T = \kappa_S$$ (28)

being termed the compressibility coefficient of the solvent. It follows that

$$\left(\frac{\partial RT \ln K_c}{\partial p}\right)_T = \left(\frac{\partial RT \ln K_x}{\partial p}\right)_T + (l+m+\ldots-a-b-\ldots)RT\kappa_S$$
$$= -\Delta \overline{V}^\infty + (l+m+\ldots-a-b-\ldots)RT\kappa_S.$$ (29)

At 25° C and 1 atm, the factor $RT\kappa_S$ is 1·1 cm³/mole for water, and 3·2 cm³/mole for methanol. These values are by no means negligible in comparison with the partial molar volumes of the solute species and, for non-zero values of $(l+m+\ldots-a-b-\ldots)$ it is unjustifiable to neglect the term in κ_S. This point was first emphasized by Guggenheim (1937).

It is clear from this discussion that, in high pressure chemistry, it is more convenient and more rational to use the mole fraction or molality scales than the molar scale of concentrations.

The formulae presented above show how equilibrium constants defined in various ways depend upon the effective volumes of the initial reactants and the final products. With the exception of Eq. (29) the relationships all have the general form

$$\left(\frac{\partial RT \ln K}{\partial p} \right)_T = - \Delta V. \tag{30}$$

If ΔV were independent of pressure, Eq. (30) could be integrated to give

$$\ln \frac{K(p_2)}{K(p_1)} = - \frac{\Delta V(p_2 - p_1)}{RT}, \tag{31}$$

where $K(p_1)$ and $K(p_2)$ denote the values of the equilibrium constant at the pressures p_1 and p_2, both at the temperature T. In reality ΔV often varies considerably with the pressure and in extreme instances it may change by as much as a factor of two over a pressure interval of 1 000 atm.† Nevertheless it is sometimes convenient to use Eq. (31) to define an " average " volume change over a finite range of pressures

$$(\Delta V_{av})_1^2 = - \frac{RT \ln [K(p_2)/K(p_1)]}{p_2 - p_1}, \tag{32}$$

TABLE I. The Effect of Pressure on Equilibrium Constants for Various Average Changes in Volume, at 25° C.

$(\Delta V_{av})_1^2$ (cm³/ mole)	$K(p_2)/K(p_1 = 1 \text{ atm})$					
	p_2 (atm): 1	1 000	2 000	5 000	10 000	20 000
+20	1·00	0·44	0·19	$1·7 \times 10^{-2}$	$2·8 \times 10^{-4}$	$7·9 \times 10^{-8}$
+10	1·00	0·67	0·44	0·13	$1·7 \times 10^{-2}$	$2·8 \times 10^{-4}$
0	1·00	1·00	1·00	1·00	1·00	1·00
−10	1·00	1·50	2·26	7·71	60	$3·6 \times 10^3$
−20	1·00	2·26	5·13	60	$3·6 \times 10^3$	$1·3 \times 10^7$
−30	1·00	3·40	11·6	$4·6 \times 10^2$	$2·1 \times 10^5$	$4·5 \times 10^{10}$

† The order of change that may occur in ΔV is illustrated by Gonikberg and Vereshchagin's (1949) measurements of the densities of cyclopentadiene and its dimer at pressures between 1 atm and 1 000 atm, at 40° C. These authors found that $\Delta V°$ for the dimerization reaction is − 33·2 cm³/mole at 1 atm, − 31·1 at 500 atm, and − 27·6 at 1 000 atm. Similarly, Kobeko et al. (1950) have shown that the change of volume for the polymerization of styrene is − 23 cm³ per mole of styrene at 1 atm, − 15 at 2 000 atm, and − 11 at 6 000 atm.

At this point it is informative to present some numerical examples of the manner in which $K(p_2)/K(p_1)$ depends upon $(\Delta V_{av})_1^2$ and on $p_2 - p_1$. This is done in Table I, where p_1 has been taken to be 1 atm.

III. DISCUSSION OF SOME EXPERIMENTAL DATA ON LIQUID–PHASE SYSTEMS

This section will outline our knowledge of the behaviour under pressure of chemical equilibria in homogeneous liquid systems. It will also attempt to provide molecular interpretations of the volume changes which accompany the reactions. These interpretations will be based on considerations of the changes in size and packing of the reacting molecules and in the degree of electrostriction of the surrounding liquid.

For convenience the data will be reviewed in order of increasing polarity of the reacting molecules, starting with reactions between nearly non-polar molecules and proceeding to reactions between polar molecules and finally to reactions involving ions.

A. *Reactions Between Nearly Non-Polar Molecules*

Very few direct measurements have been made of the influence of pressure on equilibria between nearly non-polar molecules. But since these molecules usually form almost ideal mixtures, it is possible to predict the pressure effects quite accurately from knowledge of the molar volumes of the pure reactants (Eq. 8).

One of the simplest chemical reactions between completely non-polar molecules is the isotopic exchange of hydrogen with deuterium:

$$\tfrac{1}{2}H_2 + \tfrac{1}{2}D_2 \rightleftharpoons HD \qquad (33)$$

The equilibrium constant for this reaction has been measured in the gas phase at atmospheric pressure (Gould *et al.* 1934) and in principle it could be determined in the liquefied gases as a function of the hydrostatic pressure. But if we compare the molar volumes of liquid H_2, D_2 and HD at $20°$ K (28.37, 23.53 and 25.57 cm³, respectively (Woolley *et al.*, 1948)), we find that the value of $\Delta V°$ for reaction (33) is only -0.38 cm³/mole and it follows that the change of equilibrium constant with pressure will be rather small. It is doubtful whether it could be detected at pressures below the freezing pressure of the mixture.

It is difficult to find other instances of chemical reactions in *entirely* non-polar systems. But there are many in which the components are only slightly polar. Perhaps the simplest of these is the conversion of liquid oxygen into liquid ozone:

$$\tfrac{3}{2}O_2 \rightleftharpoons O_3. \tag{34}$$

Oxygen has no dipole moment and ozone has only a small one (Lewis and Smyth, 1939). The molar volume of O_2 at $77 \cdot 6°$ K is $26 \cdot 61$ cm³, whilst that of O_3 at the same temperature is $29 \cdot 76$ cm³ (Jenkins and di Paolo, 1956). It follows from this that the formation of one mole of ozone from oxygen in the liquid state involves a contraction of $10 \cdot 2$ cm³, and the equilibrium (34) will be shifted to the right by an increase in pressure. It must be admitted that this prediction is a rather academic one since the equilibrium concentration of ozone in liquid oxygen is so

TABLE II. Volume Changes for Reactions between Pure Liquids at 20° C

Reactions	Net increase in number of covalent bonds	$\Delta V°$ (cm³/mole)*
Dimerizations:		
2(1-butene)→1-octene	1	− 33
2(1-pentene)→1-decene	1	− 30
2(1-hexene)→1-dodecene	1	− 28
2(1-octene)→1-hexadecene	1	− 27
2(1-decene)→1-eicosene	1	− 26
Trimerization:		
3(1-hexene)→1-octadecene	2	− 36
Cyclizations:		
1-pentene→cyclopentane	1	− 15
1-hexene→cyclohexane	1	− 17
1-heptene→cycloheptane	1	− 20
1-octene→cyclo-octane	1	− 23
1-dodecene→cyclododecane	1	− 27
1-pentyne→cyclopentene	1	− 10
1-hexyne→cyclohexene	1	− 14
3(acetaldehyde)→paraldehyde	3	− 36
Isomerizations:		
n-pentane→2-methyl butane	0	+ 1·2
„ →2:2-dimethyl propane	0	+ 6·8
n-hexane →2-methyl pentane	0	+ 1·2
„ →3-methyl pentane	0	− 1·0
„ →2:2-dimethyl butane	0	+ 2·0
„ →2:3-dimethyl butane	0	− 0·4
cis-2-butene→trans-2-butene	0	+ 2·6
cis-1:2-dichlorethylene→trans-1:2-dichlorethylene	0	+ 1·6
Exchange:		
n-octane + n-decane→2(n-nonane)	0	0·0

* The values of $\Delta V°$ are based on densities listed in the American Petroleum Institute Tables.

small as to be quite immeasurable (Briner, 1942). Nevertheless the negative sign of $\Delta V°$ has a theoretical significance which will be referred to later in this section in connection with some other reactions.

The hydrocarbons constitute the largest class of nearly non-polar molecules and it is highly informative to consider the changes in volume which occur when they undergo simple transformations. Some of these are listed in Table II, where $\Delta V°$ denotes the increase in volume accompanying the formation of one mole of the pure liquid product from the pure liquid reactants. The data are typical of a great many more which can readily be extracted from the American Petroleum Institute's tables of the molar volumes of pure hydrocarbons. It should be emphasized that the table is intended merely to illustrate the magnitude of the volume changes for certain classes of reactions, and it is not to be supposed that all the listed reactions occur measurably in practice. For instance the main product formed in the dimerization of 1-butene is not 1-octene but 2-ethyl-1-hexene (Ziegler, 1956), for which the volume change is -34 cm³/mole.

The following points emerge from Table II:

(a) The reactions which involve the formation of new carbon–carbon covalent bonds (the polymerizations and cyclizations) are all accompanied by substantial contractions.

(b) The reverse reactions in which carbon bonds are broken involve equal and opposite expansions.

(c) Reactions in which no new carbon–carbon bonds are formed (the branched-chain isomerizations and the exchange reaction) occur with relatively small volume changes.

We shall now examine these generalizations from the standpoint of the probable changes in volume of the individual molecules. Let us consider first the combination of a terminal $-CH=CH_2$ group with a terminal CH_3- group to form the arrangement $-\overset{\alpha}{C}H_2-\overset{\beta}{C}H_2-\overset{\gamma}{C}H_2-$. In the initial state the $\overset{\beta}{C}$ and $\overset{\gamma}{C}$ atoms can be assumed to be separated by the normal van der Waals distance between non-bonded $-CH_3$ and $=CH_2$ groups, 4Å (Pauling, 1960) and in the final state by the normal $-C-C-$ covalent bond distance, 1.54 Å. There is thus a linear contraction of 2.5 Å in forming the $-\overset{\beta}{C}-\overset{\gamma}{C}-$ bond. But at the same time the transformation of the $\overset{\alpha}{C}-\overset{\beta}{C}$ bond from double to single order increases its distance from 1.33 Å to 1.54 Å. The initial and final states of the carbon skeletons can therefore be represented diagramatically as

The final $C\text{---}C$ distance in these configurations is $2\cdot12$ Å less than the
α   γ
initial distance and if we assume for simplicity that this linear contraction occurs along the axis of a cylinder whose radius is the same as the van der Waals radius of a methyl or methylene group (2 Å) we find that it causes a *volume* contraction of $26\cdot6$ Å^3 per molecule, that is, $\Delta V° = -16\cdot0$ cm^3/mole. This value is of the same order as those for the bond-forming reactions in Table II, and it would be unreasonable to expect more precise agreement since the model takes no account of the detailed packing of the molecular groups, reflected in the rather wide range of experimental values (Table II, reactions 1–14). The agreement is close enough to justify the belief that in this class of reactions the volume change arises principally from the replacement of the van der Waals radii of the terminal groups by the very much smaller covalent radii of carbon atoms. A converse situation occurs, of course, in the reverse reactions.

The contraction which accompanies the formation of liquid O_3 from liquid O_2 (reaction (34)) is also understandable on this basis.

When we consider branched-chain isomerizations of the type

$$CH_3(CH_2)_3CH_3 \rightarrow C(CH_3)_4 \quad , \qquad (35)$$
$$n\text{-pentane} \qquad \text{neo-pentane}$$

or *cis→trans* isomerizations:

$$(36)$$

we see that no extra covalent bonds are formed in these reactions. The value of $\Delta V°$ is therefore determined simply by the effect of molecular geometry on the excluded volumes of the isomers. At present there is no way of estimating this effect theoretically but the experimental evidence in Table II shows that it is small[†] in comparison with the effect of bond formation.

The last reaction listed in Table II consists simply in the transference of a $\text{---}CH_2\text{---}$ group from one hydrocarbon to another. Although one

† It would be zero if Kopp's (1889) hypothesis of the additivity of the volumes of constituent groups were valid.

might expect there to be a geometrical effect here, it is evidently extremely small. This is confirmed by the data for a great many other analogous reactions, both between hydrocarbons and between more complex molecules containing hydrocarbon chains. It seems that the —CH_2— group contributes a remarkably constant volume increment (about 16 cm³/mole at 20° C) to whatever molecule it is in.

To summarize this section; although we lack direct information about the influence of pressure on equilibria between nearly non-polar molecules in the liquid phase, it is apparent that large effects can only be expected for reactions in which covalent bonds are formed or broken. On a molecular scale these effects arise from the large differences between the van der Waals radii of atoms and their covalent radii.

B. *Reactions Involving Polar Molecules*

Since the reactions to be discussed in this section are rather diverse, it will be helpful to systematize them by grouping them into two classes, (*a*) those which result in the association of molecules or molecular groups through the formation of new bonds, and (*b*) those in which there is a re-arrangement of existing groups without any increase in the number of bonds. Class (*a*) would include for example the first fourteen of the reactions listed in Table II, and class (*b*) would include the remainder.

1. *Association Reactions*

One of the simplest association reactions is the dimerization of nitrogen dioxide

$$2NO_2 \rightleftharpoons N_2O_4 \qquad K'_x = \frac{x^2_{NO_2}}{x_{N_2O_4}}, \tag{37}$$

whose equilibrium constant can be measured both in the gaseous and liquid phases. Ewald (1956) has made some high pressure measurements of K'_x in carbon tetrachloride solution at 22 and 51·5° C and at 1,750, and 1500 atm. He found that an increase in pressure shifted the equilibrium to the right; the value of K'_x being about four times greater at 1500 atm than at 1 atm. Applying Eq. (20) to his results we find that $\Delta \overline{V} \approx -23$ cm³/mole at 1 atm.

There is no doubt that a substantial part of this contraction must be caused by the formation of the new N—N bond of the dimer, and in fact the magnitude of $\Delta \overline{V}$ is quite close to those of $\Delta V°$ for the dimerization reactions listed in Table II. But as Ewald (1956) pointed out, it is considerably greater than we should expect from the difference in the molecular dimensions of N_2O_4 and NO_2. It is possible that the discrepancy arises from interactions between the solute species and the solvent and from the formation of auto-complexes between pairs of N_2O_4 molecules (Addison and Sheldon, 1957). On this point it is significant that density measurements (Addison and Smith, 1958) show that the partial molar volume of N_2O_4 at infinite dilution is less by 5 cm³ in carbon tetrachloride than in cyclohexane, indicating that there is a specific interaction between N_2O_4 and CCl_4. This may well contribute to the negative value of $\Delta \overline{V}$ for reaction (37).

Sapiro and Shu-lin P'eng (1938) examined the effect of pressure on the self-condensation of cyclohexanone, catalysed by an equi-molar quantity of aniline,

$$
2 \left\langle \right\rangle C{=}O \rightleftharpoons \left\langle \right\rangle \begin{array}{c} C{-}C \\ O{\diagup}^{\displaystyle C} \end{array} \left\langle \right\rangle + H_2O \tag{38}
$$

$$\text{I} \qquad\qquad \text{II} \qquad\qquad\qquad \text{III}$$

They found that, at 120° C, the equilibrium product

$$K'_x = \frac{x_{\mathrm{II}} x_{\mathrm{III}}}{x_{\mathrm{I}}^2}$$

increased by a factor of 4·5 when the pressure was raised from 2 000 to 5 000 atm. This increase corresponds to an " average " volume change (Eq. (32)) of − 12 cm³/mole, which is, perhaps fortuitously, close to the difference of − 11 cm³/mole between the volumes of the products and the reactant in their pure states at atmospheric pressure (Hamann, 1957). The contraction is rather less than it is for simple dimerizations (Table II) as we might have expected from the fact that a molecule of water is released during the condensation.

2. Cyclizations

Fawcett and Gibson (1934) have made some rough measurements of the influence of pressure on the equilibrium between pure 5-methyl-4-heptenoic acid and its δ-lactone

$$
\begin{array}{c} CH_3 \\ {>}C \\ CH_3 \diagup \end{array} \begin{array}{c} CH{-}CH_2 \\ \diagdown \\ HO{-}CO \end{array} CH_2 \rightleftharpoons \begin{array}{c} CH_3 \\ {>}C \\ CH_3 \diagup \end{array} \begin{array}{c} CH_2{-}CH_2 \\ \diagdown \\ O{\rule{1.2em}{0.5pt}}CO \end{array} CH_3 . \tag{39}
$$

Although their results are not detailed enough to yield reliable values for the equilibrium constant, they show clearly that at high pressures there is a substantial shift towards the lactone. This accords with the fact that the molar volume of the lactone is normally less by 7·6 cm³ than the molar volume of the acid. The contraction on cyclization, here, is notably less than for the hydrocarbon cyclizations listed in

Table II and it is likely that the difference arises from the existence of strong hydrogen bonds between molecules of the original acid. The breaking of these bonds in forming the lactone must contribute a substantial positive term to ΔV°.

3. *Polymerizations of Alcohols by Hydrogen Bonding*

It is known that, in inert solvents, alcohols associate into polymers by forming hydrogen bonds and that in general the polymers may be of all orders from two to infinity (Kretschmer and Wiebe, 1954)

$$nA \rightleftharpoons A_n, \qquad K'_x = \frac{x_{A_n}}{x_A^n}. \tag{40}$$

The molar volumes of hydrogen-bonded compounds are always smaller than those of non-associated compounds of similar molecular size (Pimentel and McClellan, 1960), and it is possible to make a rough theoretical estimate of the contraction for the formation of each hydrogen bond in the following way. In the absence of hydrogen bonding the minimum distance between the α and β oxygen atoms in the linear arrangement $\underset{\alpha}{O}—H\cdots\underset{\beta}{O}$ is the sum of the O—H bond distance, 0·96 Å, and the van der Waals radii of the H and $\underset{\beta}{O}$ atoms, 1·2 Å and 1·4 Å respectively, making a total of 3·6 Å. The corresponding distance in the presence of hydrogen bonding is less than this by about 0·9 Å and if we assume that this contraction occurs along the axis of a cylinder of radius equal to the van der Waals radius of the oxygen atoms, we find that the decrease of volume is about 3·8 cm³/mole.

There are two sets of experimental data concerning the influence of pressure on the formation of hydrogen-bonded polymers.

Shishkin and Novak (1953) made some extensive measurements, to 3 000 atm, on the infra-red spectra of several alcohols and of phenol, both in their pure states and in carbon tetrachloride solution. They found that an increase in pressure had the same effect as a decrease in temperature, decreasing the number of free —OH groups and favouring the formation of polymers. They found that a pressure rise of 90–130 atm had the same effect as a temperature drop of 1° C. From this fact, together with the known enthalpies of formation of hydrogen bonds (Pimentel and McClellan, 1960), we can estimate that the polymerization involved a contraction of 4·5–6 cm³ per mole of hydrogen bonds.

Later, Fishman and Drickamer (1956) examined the infra-red spectrum of 1-butanol in carbon disulphide solution at 25° C and found that the characteristic hydrogen-bond absorption was increased by a factor of 2·4 between 1 and 5 820 atm. Since, in their experiments, there was a large excess of monomer over polymer molecules the change corresponded to an " average " contraction (Eq. (32)) of $3 \cdot 7$ cm³ per mole of polymer produced. If the polymers were of low order, which is likely, this contraction would be close to that for the formation of a mole of singly-bonded dimers. It is remarkably close to the theoretical value calculated above.

4. *Isomerization Reactions*

One of the simplest isomerizations is that between the *cis*- and *trans*-forms of 1 : 2 dichlorethylene

$$ \underset{Cl}{\overset{H}{>}}C=C\underset{Cl}{\overset{H}{<}} \rightleftharpoons \underset{Cl}{\overset{H}{>}}C=C\underset{H}{\overset{Cl}{<}} , \quad K'_x = \frac{x_{\text{trans}}}{x_{\text{cis}}} . \tag{41} $$

Although the *cis*- isomer possesses a dipole moment the two modifications form approximately ideal mixtures and it is justifiable to assume that their activity coefficients in the equilibrium mixture are close to unity and independent of the pressure. It follows that $\Delta \bar{V}$ in Eq. (15) can be replaced by ΔV° the difference in molar volume between the pure isomers. This difference has the value $+ 1 \cdot 6$ cm³ at 20° C (cf. Table II), so that a rise in pressure should suppress the formation of the *trans*-isomer. Some direct measurements by Ewald *et al.* (1957) have shown that the value of K'_x for the isomerization of liquid dichlorethylene (with a trace of iodine added as a catalyst) decreases by 15% between 20 and 3 000 atm, at 185° C. The change corresponds to an average volume change of $+ 2$ cm³/mole, which is close to the value of ΔV° at 20° C and 1 atm.

Kiyama and Minomura (1952) have observed that an increase in pressure favours the transformation of liquid maleic acid into fumaric acid at 175° C:

$$ \begin{array}{c} H-C-CO_2H \\ \parallel \\ H-C-CO_2H \\ \text{\small maleic acid} \end{array} \rightleftharpoons \begin{array}{c} H-C-CO_2H \\ \parallel \\ HO_2C-C-H \\ \text{\small fumaric acid} \end{array} \tag{42} $$

Their measurements were too scanty to yield equilibrium constants for the isomerization and, in addition, it is possible that the system was a heterogeneous one containing a solid phase. However, the observed effect certainly accords with the fact that the density of fumaric acid is greater than that of maleic acid under ordinary conditions.

Kabachnik *et al.* (1954) have examined the effect of compression to 3 000 atm on the keto–enol tautomerism of aceto-acetic ester at 20° C:

$$ \begin{array}{c} CH_3-C-CH_2CO_2C_2H_5 \\ \parallel \\ O \\ \text{\small keto} \end{array} \rightleftharpoons \begin{array}{c} CH_3-C=CHCO_2C_2H_5 \\ | \\ OH \\ \text{\small enol} \end{array} , \quad K'_x = \frac{x_{\text{enol}}}{x_{\text{keto}}} \tag{43} $$

They found that in the absence of solvent the equilibrium was independent of the pressure. In non-polar solvents it was shifted slightly towards the keto-form and in polar solvents towards the enol-form. In every solvent except water the average volume change derived from Eq. (32) was small, but in water it amounted to $-7 \cdot 5$ cm³/mole. This comparatively large contraction suggests that the enolic isomer interacts much more strongly with water than does the keto-isomer and the simplest explanation is that the hydroxy group forms strong hydrogen bonds with the surrounding water molecules.

C. Reactions Involving Ions

The interactions between solute and solvent species, which could be discerned in some of the reactions of polar molecules discussed in the last section, are much more pronounced in reactions involving free ions. And so, of course, are the interactions between the ions themselves. Since these interactions give rise to quite large volume effects, they play an important part in the chemistry of electrolyte solutions at high pressures.

A measure of the degree of specific interaction between a solute and its solvent is given by the difference between the molar volume of the solute in its pure state $V°$ and its partial molar volume in an infinitely dilute solution $\bar{V}^\infty$. For unionized solutes this difference is seldom† more than a few cm³ but for ionized solutes it may be very much larger. This was strikingly demonstrated by Kohlrausch and Hallwachs's (1894) measurements of the densities of aqueous solutions of $ZnSO_4$. These authors found that although the molar volume of solid $ZnSO_4$ is $+45$ cm³, its partial molar volume in very dilute solutions has the *negative* value of -11 cm³.

It is natural to look for an explanation of this large contraction in the influence of the electrical charges of the ions on the structure and density of the surrounding water, and this was first done by Drude and Nernst (1894) who used the classical theory of the electrostriction of a homogeneous dielectric around a charged sphere to derive the relation

$$\Delta V_{el} = \frac{V \kappa_S z^2 e^2}{2r\epsilon^2} \frac{\partial \epsilon}{\partial V}, \qquad (44)$$

where ΔV_{el} denotes the contraction (electrostriction) of a medium of dielectric constant ϵ around a sphere of radius r carrying a charge ze, e

† Two instances of exceptionally large values of $\bar{V}^\infty - V°$ are those of $+7 \cdot 6$ cm³ for the solution of methanol in n-heptane (Staveley and Spice, 1952), and $-7 \cdot 7$ cm³ for the solution of butyric acid in water (Hamann and Lim, 1954). These large changes are almost certainly caused by the breaking and formation respectively of hydrogen-bonded polymers.

being the electronic charge and z an integral number. V denotes the volume of the dielectric and κ_S its compressibility (Eq. (28)). The derivative $\partial\epsilon/\partial V$ is nearly always negative and the compressibility coefficient is always positive.

It may be mentioned here that the assumptions and approximations used in deriving Eq. (44) are precisely those which underlie Born's (1920) formula for the free energy of solvation of spherical ions of radius r. In fact Krichevsky (1938) rediscovered Eq. (44) in an equivalent form:

$$\Delta V_{el} = -\frac{z^2 e^2}{2r\epsilon^2}\frac{\partial\epsilon}{\partial p}, \tag{45}$$

by differentiating Born's formula with respect to pressure, and Hamann (1957) later introduced an additional term to allow for the change of r with pressure:†

$$\Delta V_{el} = -\frac{z^2 e^2}{2r\epsilon^2}\frac{\partial\epsilon}{\partial p} + \frac{z^2 e^2}{2r^2}\left(1 - \frac{1}{\epsilon}\right)\frac{\partial r}{\partial p}. \tag{46}$$

Despite the theoretical weaknesses of Born's model there is experimental evidence that it gives a fair description of the thermodynamic properties of electrolyte solutions (see, for instance, La Mer and Brescia, 1940; Robinson and Stokes, 1959), and it should provide at least a rough estimate of the magnitude of ΔV_{el}. Applied to monatomic singly charged ions in water it yields a value $\Delta V_{el} \approx -10$ cm³/mole, so that the total electrostriction for the two ions of a 1:1 electrolyte should be about -20 cm³/mole. This is certainly of the same order as the experimental value of $\bar{V}^\infty - V^\circ$ for the alkali halides if we take for V° the extrapolated volumes of the liquid salts.

To make a more detailed comparison between theory and experiment it is desirable to consider the numerical values of $\bar{V}^\infty$ for electrolytes in water, determined from density measurements. Since $\bar{V}^\infty$ is an additive property of the partial molar volumes of the separate ions of the electrolyte $\bar{V}_i^\infty$, the data can be presented conveniently by listing values of $\bar{V}_i^\infty$ based on the convention that $\bar{V}_{H^+} = 0$, which is analogous to the convention commonly used in tabulating molar ionic entropies. Some values of $\bar{V}_i^\infty$ are listed in Table III. It appears likely that $\bar{V}_{H^+}$ is actually, and not merely by convention, close to zero (Fajans and Johnson, 1942, Mukerjee, 1961), so that the relative values of $\bar{V}_i^\infty$ in the table are probably near the true partial molar volumes of the individual ions.

† In formula (46) V_{el} denotes the change of volume for the transfer of a fully charged ion from a medium of dielectric constant unity to one of dielectric constant ϵ. It should be distinguished from the volume change accompanying the charging of an ion in the medium ϵ, for which the factor $(1 - 1/\epsilon)$ is replaced by $-1/\epsilon$.

TABLE III. Partial Molar Volumes of Ions at Infinite Dilution in Water at 25° C and 1 atm (relative to H+)

Cation	$\bar{V}_i^\infty$ (cm³)	Reference	Anion	$\bar{V}_i^\infty$ (cm³)	Reference
H+	0	a	F⁻	−2·1	a
Li+	−1·0	a	Cl⁻	+18·1	a
Na+	−1·5	a	Br⁻	+25·0	a
K+	+8·7	a	I⁻	+36·6	a
Rb+	+13·7	a	OH⁻	−3·2	d
Cs+	+21·1	a	NO₃⁻	+29·3	a
Ag+	−1·0	a	ClO₃⁻	+35†	b
OH₃+	+18·1	a	BrO₃⁻	+36†	b
Be²+	−14	b	IO₃⁻	+25	b
Mg²+	−21·8	b	ClO₄⁻	+44	b
Ca²+	−19·4	b	MnO₄⁻	+43	a
Sr²+	−18·8	b	HSO₄⁻	+26·5	b
Ba²+	−13·6	b	HCO₃⁻	+24	a
Fe²+	−18	b	CNS⁻	+40	b
Zn²+	−26	b	CO₃²⁻	−3·7	a
Al³+	−43	b	SO₄²⁻	+14·5	a
Fe³+	−30	b	CrO₄²⁻	+19·7	a
La³+	−38	a	Cr₂O₇²⁻	+73	b
NH₄+	+17·9	a	HCO₂⁻	+26·3	c
CH₃NH₃+	+37·4	c	CH₃CO₂⁻	+39·5	c
(CH₃)₂NH₂+	+55·0	c	C₂H₅CO₂⁻	+54·2	c
(CH₃)₃NH+	+73·6	c	C₃H₇CO₂⁻	+71·0	c
C₆H₅NH₃+	+83·8	c	C₆H₅O⁻	+69·0	c

† Owen and Brinkley's compilation (reference a) erroneously lists the values of $\bar{V}^\infty$ for the *potassium salts* of these two ions.

REFERENCES TO TABLE III

a B. B. Owen and S. R. Brinkley (1941).
b K. Fajans and O. Johnson (1942).
c S. D. Hamann and S. C. Lim (1954).
d A. Bodanszky and W. Kauzmann (1962).

It is informative to consider these experimental data in the light of electrostrictive theory. If we disregard the compressibility of the ion (Eq. (46)), electrostriction contributes to $\bar{V}_i^\infty$ a term proportional to $-z^2e^2/r$, and the volume of the unsolvated ion contributes a term proportional to r^3. We can thus write an equation of the general form:

$$\bar{V}_i^\infty = Ar^3 - Bz^2/r. \tag{47}$$

Hepler (1957) has shown that this relation applies well to the monatomic ions listed in Table III, the proportionality constants A and B being 5·3 and 4·7 respectively for cations and 4·6 and 19 for anions, r being expressed in Å, and $\bar{V}_i^\infty$ in cm³/mole. The values of A correspond to volumes almost twice as great as the actual volumes of the ions $4\pi r^3/3$, for which $A = 2·5$, but Stokes and Robinson (1957) have pointed out that the voids which exist between packed spheres increase the theoretical value of A to 4·35, which is satisfactorily close to the experimental values if we bear in mind that the ionic radii in solution may be larger than the crystal radii used in fitting Eq. (47). The theoretical value of B for aqueous solutions at 25° C and 1 atm, based on Eq. (45), is 5·3, which is close to the experimental value found for cations but considerably smaller than that for anions. The difference might be explained by the known fact that anions interact more strongly with water than do cations of the same radius (Verwey, 1942), or it could arise in part from the neglect of ionic compressibility (Eq. (46)). Unfortunately, there is no way of determining the compressibilities of individual ions but it is likely that anions are much more compressible than cations.

We shall now review some of the effects of pressure on ionic equilibria and discuss them in the light of the electrostrictive theory outlined above.

1. Ionization of Weak Electrolytes in Water

Ostwald (1878) was the first to recognize that the ionization of a weak electrolyte in water involves a substantial contraction. He based his conclusion on measurements of the changes in volume which accompany the neutralization of acids by bases. His experiments showed that when both acid and base were strong, e.g.:

$$K^+ + OH^- + H_3O^+ + Cl^- \rightarrow K^+ + Cl^- + 2H_2O \qquad (48)$$

$$\equiv H_3O^+ + OH^- \rightarrow 2H_2O, \qquad (49)$$

the neutralization occurred with a constant expansion of about $+19·5$ cm³/mole. But if one of the electrolytes were weak, and at a concentration high enough to ensure that it was almost completely unionized, then the expansion was much smaller and varied from one weak electrolyte to another. For example, the neutralizations:

$$K^+ + OH^- + CH_3CO_2H \rightarrow K^+ + CH_3CO_2^- + H_2O, \qquad (50)$$

$$NH_3 + H_3O^+ + Cl^- \rightarrow NH_4^+ + Cl^- + H_2O, \qquad (51)$$

occurred with volume changes of $+9·5$ and $-6·6$ cm³/mole respectively. Subtracting (48) from (50) and (51), we find that the ionization reactions

$$CH_3CO_2H + H_2O \rightarrow CH_3CO_2^- + H_3O^+ \qquad (52)$$

$$NH_3 + H_2O \rightarrow NH_4^+ + OH^- \qquad (53)$$

must involve volume changes of $-10·0$ and $-26·1$ cm³/mole respectively, and in confirmation of this Ostwald showed that the volume change for the mutual neutralization of the two weak electrolytes,

TABLE IV. The Effect of Pressure on the Ionization of Weak Electrolytes in Water at 25° C

Electrolyte	K_1 (mole/kg)	K_p/K_1 p(atm): 1000	2000	3000	$\Delta \bar{V}^\infty$ (I)[†] (cm³/mole)	$\Delta \bar{V}^\infty$ (II)[‡] (cm³/mole)	Ref. for (I)	Ref. for (II)
Water (1st ionization	1.01×10^{-14}					-21.3		q
Acids:								
Formic Acid	1.74×10^{-4}	1.40	1.87	2.40	-8.8	-8.0	a,b	c
Acetic Acid	1.75×10^{-5}	1.56	2.24	3.15	-12.2	-12.5	a,b,g,j,o	c,m
Propionic Acid	1.34×10^{-5}	1.63	2.49	3.52	-12.9	-13.7	a	c
Butyric Acid	1.52×10^{-5}					-13.7		c
Benzoic Acid	6.2×10^{-5}	1.55	2.27	3.10	-10.9		f,p	
o-NO₂-Benzoic Acid	6.1×10^{-3}	1.53	2.10	2.93	-10.2		f	
m-NO₂-Benzoic Acid	3.2×10^{-4}	1.41	1.94	2.60	-8.7		f,p	
p-NO₂-Benzoic Acid	3.5×10^{-4}	1.45	1.96	2.60	-8.8		f,p	
m-F-Benzoic Acid	1.37×10^{-4}	1.48	2.09	2.82	-9.8		p	
p-F-Benzoic Acid	7.0×10^{-5}	1.51	2.16	2.96	-10.5		p	
o-OH-Benzoic Acid	1.01×10^{-3}	1.35	1.81	2.30	-7.2		f	
m-CH₃O-Benzoic Acid	8.2×10^{-5}	1.50	2.14	2.93	-10.3		p	
p-CH₃O-Benzoic Acid	3.1×10^{-5}	1.56	2.29	3.19	-11.3		p	
Phenylacetic Acid	4.9×10^{-5}	1.66	2.51	3.60	-12.7		p	
m-NO₂-Phenylacetic Acid	1.1×10^{-4}	1.54	2.25	3.11	-11.1		p	
p-NO₂-Phenylacetic Acid	1.2×10^{-4}	1.54	2.23	3.11	-10.9		p	
m-F-Phenylacetic Acid	7.4×10^{-5}	1.61	2.40	3.42	-12.0		p	
p-F-Phenylacetic Acid	6.0×10^{-5}	1.64	2.48	3.54	-12.4		p	
m-Cl-Phenylacetic Acid	7.8×10^{-5}	1.59	2.38	3.40	-11.8		p	
p-Cl-Phenylacetic Acid	6.6×10^{-5}	1.62	2.41	3.43	-12.2		p	
p-CH₃-Phenylacetic Acid	4.4×10^{-5}	1.65	2.52	3.63	-12.6		p	
d-CH₃O-Phenylacetic Acid	4.4×10^{-5}	1.63	2.51	3.56	-12.4		p	
Phenol	1.12×10^{-10}					-17.0		c
p-NO₂-Phenol (40° C)	7.2×10^{-8}	1.40	1.90		-10.3		o	
Fumaric Acid (20° C) (1st ionization)	9.9×10^{-4}	1.46	2.03		-10.8		o	
" Carbonic " Acid (1st ionization)	4.2×10^{-7}	2.86	7.9	16.9	-26.5	-29	d,o	e
" Sulphurous " Acid (1st ionization)	1.4×10^{-2}	2.23	4.60		-19.7		g	
Phosphoric Acid (1st ionization)	7.1×10^{-3}	1.87	2.96		-15.5	-16.2	g	h
Hydrogen Sulphide (1st ionization)	1.5×10^{-7}	1.79	2.76		-15.0		n	
HCO₃⁻	4.7×10^{-11}					-27.8		e
HSO₄⁻	1.2×10^{-2}					-20.2		i
H₂PO₄⁻	6.2×10^{-8}					-28.1		h
Bases:								
Ammonia	1.75×10^{-5}	2.94	6.97	13.9	-28.9	-29.4	k	k
Monomethylamine	4.19×10^{-4}	2.82	6.13	11.3	-26.4	-27.5	k	c
Dimethylamine	5.89×10^{-4}	2.75	6.21	12.8	-27.2	-27.4	b	c
Trimethylamine	6.28×10^{-5}	2.87	6.89	14.6	-28.1	-28.1	b	c
Aniline						-28.6		c
Pyridine						-28.1		c
Piperidine						-24.3		c
Salts:								
(Mg²⁺+SO₄²⁻)ion pairs	5.0×10^{-3}	1.29	1.79		-7.3		l	

† From the pressure dependence of K ‡ From density measurements at $p=1$ atm.

$$CH_3CO_2H + NH_3 \rightarrow CH_3CO_2^- + NH_4^+ \tag{54}$$

was $-16\cdot3$ cm³/mole, which is very close to the value obtained by adding the changes for reactions (48), (52) and (53). It follows that ionizations of the type (52) and (53) should be favoured by an increase in pressure (here, it should be noted that although subsequent density measurements have shown that Ostwald's values were wrong by several cm³/mole, they have confirmed this general conclusion).

Later, at Ostwald's suggestion, Fanjung (1894) measured the influence of pressure, to 260 atm, on the electrical conductivities of aqueous solutions of weak carboxylic acids, HA. He found that a given increase of pressure raised the conductivities much more than it did those of solutions of strong electrolytes and from this he was able to show that the ionization quotients

$$K'_c = \frac{c_{H_3O^+} c_{A^-}}{c_{HA}} \tag{55}$$

increased, on the average, by 12% between 1 and 260 atm. For acetic acid the change corresponded to $\partial RT \ln K'_c / \partial p \approx +10\cdot6$ cm³/mole and it follows from Eq. (29), that $\Delta \bar{V}^\infty \approx -9\cdot5$ cm³/mole, which is quite close to the contraction measured by Ostwald.

Fanjung's work was followed by more extensive measurements by Tammann and his colleagues, in the pressure range 1–3 000 atm. The results (reviewed by Brander, 1932) are qualitatively interesting but unfortunately they have little quantitative value because they were based on conductivity measurements made at quite high concentrations, where the interionic effects were important and difficult to allow for.

During the last ten years a large number of measurements have been made of the ionization constants of weak electrolytes under pressure, using improved methods that permit extrapolation of the results to concentrations where the interionic forces are negligible. In nearly all this work the conductance technique has been employed because of its experimental convenience, and the conductivity data have been

---

REFERENCES TO TABLE IV

[a] S. D. Hamann (1957, p. 151).
[b] S. D. Hamann, and W. Strauss (1955).
[c] S. D. Hamann, and S. C. Lim (1954).
[d] A. J. Ellis (1959).
[e] B. B. Owen, and R. B. Brinkley (1941).
[f] R. J. H. Clark, and A. J. Ellis (1960).
[g] A. J. Ellis, and D. W. Anderson (1961).
[h] J. S. Smith (1943).
[i] I. M. Klotz, and C. F. Eckert (1942).
[j] A. Distèche (1959).
[k] J. Buchanan, and S. D. Hamann (1953).
[l] F. H. Fisher (1962).
[m] O. Redlich, and J. Bigeleisen (1942).
[n] A. J. Ellis (1961).
[o] E. Brander (1932).
[p] A. Fisher, B. R. Mann, and J. Vaughan. (1961).
[q] A. Bodanszky and W. Kauzmann (1962).

analyzed by the method of Davies (1925) and of MacInnes and Shedlovsky (1932), or by the simpler method outlined by Robinson and Stokes (1959, p. 338). Recently, however, Distèche (1959) has succeeded in using a glass electrode at high pressures and his directly-measured values of the pH of acetic acid solutions agree very well with those calculated from conductivity data. It may be mentioned also that Gibson and Loeffler (1941) demonstrated the increase in acidic and basic strengths at high pressures by an entirely independent method based on the use of cresol red and bromophenol blue as indicators in a high-pressure optical cell.

Table IV presents a critical summary of recent measurements on weak acids and bases and on the ion-pair $Mg^{2+}SO_4^{2-}$. In this table K represents the *molality* scale equilibrium constant at infinite dilution, K_m (Eq. (25)), and the subscripts 1 and p denote the values at 1 atm and p atm. The sixth and seventh columns list values of the standard partial molar volume changes $\Delta \bar{V}^\infty$ for ionization calculated, I, from the pressure dependence of K extrapolated to 1 atm (Eq. (27)) and, II, from density measurements at atmospheric pressure.

There have been no direct density measurements of $\Delta \bar{V}_p^\infty$ at high pressures, but some indirect estimates by Owen and Brinkley (1941) show that it should tend to decrease in magnitude with increasing pressure. This is borne out by the high pressure measurements of K, which invariably yield plots of log K against p whose slopes decrease as p increases. To illustrate this, Table V lists some values of $\Delta \bar{V}_p^\infty$

TABLE V. Ionization of Ammonia in Water at 45° C

p (atm)	1	3 000	6 000	9 000	12 000
$10^5 \times K_p$ (mole/kg)	1·93	13	78	255	520
$\Delta \bar{V}_p^\infty$ (cm³/mole)†	− 28·5	− 18	− 13	− 8	− 6

† Calculated from $\Delta \bar{V}_p^\infty = - \partial RT \ln K_p / \partial p$

calculated from the pressure dependence of K for the ionization of ammonia in water at 45° C (Hamann and Strauss, 1955). It will be seen that there is a very substantial decrease in $\Delta \bar{V}_p^\infty$ between 1 and 12 000 atm.

Referring to Section III, C, we see that the most likely explanation of the universal contraction for these ionizations lies in the electrostriction of water around the free ions. Expressed in another way, the reason why pressure increases the ionization of weak electrolytes is that it enhances the hydration of the ions (principally, by increasing the dielectric constant of the solution) and in this way lowers their free energy with respect to that of the relatively unhydrated parent molecules.

Considering the individual electrolytes in Table IV, we find that it is possible to make a number of generalizations:

(i) With only a few exceptions the carboxylic acids ionize with a contraction of about 12 cm³/mole. The exceptions include formic acid, for which the initial unionized molecule is probably more strongly "hydrated" by hydrogen bonding than are the other acids. Another exception is o-hydroxy-benzoic acid (salicylic acid), and here Clark and Ellis (1960) have suggested that the abnormality arises from internal hydrogen-bonding between the carboxyl and hydroxyl groups. The low values of $\Delta \bar{V}^{\infty}$ for the nitrobenzoic acids might be explained by the electron-withdrawing capacity of the $-NO_2$ group, which will tend to disperse the negative charge of the anion and so reduce the electrostrictive field strength.

(ii) The average value of $-\Delta \bar{V}^{\infty}$ for the carboxylic acids, in which the negative charge of the anion is shared by two oxygen atoms

$$\left. R-C \begin{array}{c} \diagup O \\ \diagdown O \end{array} \right\}^{-}$$

is notably less than for acids (H_2O, H_2S, phenol) in which the charge is located on a single atom.

(iii) The second ionization of the anions HCO_3^-, HSO_4^- and $H_2PO_4^-$ involves rather large contractions. For instance, whereas $\Delta \bar{V}^{\infty}$ for the first ionization of phosphoric acid is -16 cm³/mole, it is $-28 \cdot 1$ cm³/mole for the second ionization. This is understandable since, in theory, the electrostriction of solvent around an ion is proportional to the *square* of the ionic charge (Eqs. 44–46).

(iv) The values of $-\Delta \bar{V}^{\infty}$ for the amine bases are considerably larger than those of the acids, possibly because the positive charges of the cations are localized on the small nitrogen atoms. Ellis (1959) and Ellis and Anderson (1961) have suggested that another contributing factor may be the existence of a preliminary hydration equilibrium for ammonia-type bases, e.g.:

$$NH_3 + H_2O \rightleftharpoons NH_3.H_2O; \quad K_1 = \frac{[NH_3.H_2O]}{[NH_3]}, \tag{56}$$

in addition to the ionization equilibrium

$$NH_3.H_2O \rightleftharpoons NH_4^+ + OH^-; \quad K_2 = \frac{[NH_4^+][OH^-]}{[NH_3.H_2O]}. \tag{57}$$

The equilibrium constants K listed in Table IV are based on the total concentration of amine, both free and hydrated, so that

$$K = \frac{[NH_4^+][OH^-]}{[NH_3] + [NH_3.H_2O]} = \frac{K_1 K_2}{1 + K_1}. \tag{58}$$

It follows that, when K_1 is very small, $K = K_1 K_2$ and $\Delta \overline{V}^\infty = \Delta \overline{V}_1^\infty + \Delta \overline{V}_2^\infty$, where the subscripts 1 and 2 refer to the hydration and ionization reactions (56) and (57). Ellis correctly pointed out that the abnormally large values of $-\Delta \overline{V}^\infty$ for " carbonic " acid and " sulphurous " acid can be ascribed to the contribution of $\Delta \overline{V}_1^\infty$ since, at atmospheric pressure, CO_2 and SO_2 are only slightly hydrated in solution ($K_1 < 0.003$).

On the other hand, ammonia and the methylamines are quite extensively hydrated. For instance, Moore and Winmill (1912) estimated that $K_1 = 15.3$ for monomethylamine at $25°$ C and 1 atm, and it follows that K is within a few per cent of K_2 and that $\Delta \overline{V}^\infty$ must be very close to $\Delta \overline{V}_2^\infty$.

(v) The last equilibrium listed in Table IV:

$$(Mg^{2+}SO_4^{2-})_{\text{ion pairs}} \rightleftharpoons Mg^{2+} + SO_4^{2-}, \tag{59}$$

is the only dissociation of ion pairs which has been measured under pressure. But there are indications from density measurements that the dissociations of $CuSO_4$ and $ZnSO_4$ ion pairs also involve contractions of the order of 5 to 10 cm^3/mole. The small magnitude of $\Delta \overline{V}^\infty$ for these reactions reflects the fact that the ions are already extensively solvated in the associated state; there may in fact be one or two water molecules between them when they are still within the Bjerrum critical distance of each other.

It is interesting to note, in passing, that the rather strong absorption of sound in sea-water is thought to arise from the influence of pressure waves on the magnesium sulphate equilibrium (59) (Leonard, 1948).

2. *The Self-Ionization of Water*

The influence of pressure on the ionic product of water K_w has considerable practical importance in fields as diverse as geophysics and marine biology. Surprisingly there have been no measurements of the effect at normal temperatures. The reason probably lies in the difficulties of measuring K_w by conductance methods in conditions where water is only slightly ionized. Alternative EMF methods requiring the use of hydrogen electrodes are feasible (Hainsworth *et al.*, 1924) but inconvenient. Distèche's (1959) successful use of glass electrodes at high pressures offers a more promising approach to the problem, and it is being explored in the writer's laboratory.†

Owen and Brinkley (1941) attempted an indirect estimate of the change of K_w with pressure by integrating Eq. (27), starting with the value of $\Delta \bar{V}^\infty$ at 1 atm and allowing for its variation under pressure by invoking the "partial molar compressibilities" of the H^+ and OH^- ions, defined by

$$\bar{\kappa}_i{}^\infty = - \frac{1}{\bar{V}_i{}^\infty} \frac{\partial \bar{V}_i{}^\infty}{\partial p}. \tag{60}$$

They calculated that, at 25° C, K_w increases by a factor of 2·36 between 1 and 1 000 atm. However, it was subsequently shown that their selected value of $\Delta \bar{V}^\infty$ at 1 atm was wrong by about 2 cm³/mole (Bodanszky and Kauzmann, 1962), and the reliability of the method is in any case questionable, since similar calculations failed to predict correctly the ionization constant of acetic acid under pressure (compare Table 5 of Owen and Brinkley (1941) with Table IV of this chapter).

At higher temperatures the ionization of water increases sufficiently to make conductivity methods feasible, and Franck (1956) succeeded in measuring K_w at temperatures between 400 and 700° C at static pressures to 3 000 atm, and to a maximum density of 0·8 g/cm³. Subsequently David and Hamann (1959) measured the electrical conductance of water compressed by strong shock waves from explosions. They found that the conductivity rises steadily from its normal value of $10^{-7} \Omega^{-1} cm^{-1}$ at 1 atm and 25° C, to a value of about $1 \Omega^{-1} cm^{-1}$ at 127 000 atm and 770° C. Their results have been confirmed by Brish *et al.* (1960).

By making plausible assumptions about the mobilities of the H^+ and OH^- ions, David and Hamann (1959) concluded that K_w had increased by a factor of about 10^{12} in their strongest shock wave (at a pressure of 127 000 atm, at 770° C, and at a density of 1·72 g/cm³). Two of their results are shown in Fig. 1, together with the results of Franck's static measurements, shown as solid curves, and with the extrapolations of an empirical formula which Franck (1961) fitted to his data at densities below 0·8 g/cm³ (the dotted curves). The shock-wave results are a few powers of ten higher than Franck's extrapolated isotherms. The line A in the diagram shows the limiting effect of a weak shock wave driven into water initially at 25° C and 1 atm (David and Hamann 1959). It

† *Note added in proof*: Measurements of K_w by a glass electrode at high pressures have now been completed and the results will be published in *J. phys. Chem.* **67**, No. 9 (1963).

was calculated by the method of Owen and Brinkley (1941), allowing for the effects of the increases in both pressure and temperature behind the shock front. The strong-shock results are consistent with this slope (Hamann 1959).

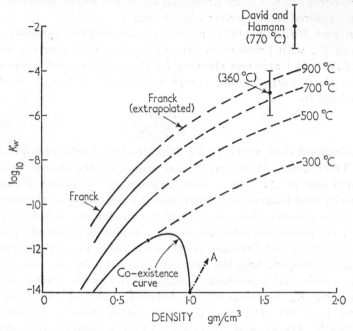

FIG. 1. The ionization product of water at high temperatures and high pressures.

David and Hamann (1960) later produced rather higher pressures, of the order of 300 000 atm, by the head-on collision of pairs of shock waves in water. Under these conditions the conductivity approached $10 \, \Omega^{-1} \, cm^{-1}$, indicating a very high degree of ionization. Similar measurements on methanol and some pure carboxylic acids showed that they, too, became highly ionized. This evidence seems to support the thesis that any weak electrolyte will become strong at sufficiently high pressures.†

3. *Ionic Complexes in Aqueous Solution*

Ewald and Hamann (1956) observed that an increase in pressure favours the formation of the I_3^- complex ion from iodide ions and iodine in water:

† From the theory of weak shocks in water (David and Hamann, 1959) it appears that most of the increase in K_w arises from the *pressure* jump rather than the *temperature* jump.

$$I_2 + I^- \rightleftharpoons I_3^-. \tag{61}$$

At 25° C the molality scale equilibrium constant increased from 620 kg/mole at 1 atm to 830 kg/mole at 1 500 atm, corresponding to a volume change $(\varDelta V_{av})_1^{1500} = -5 \cdot 4$ cm^3/mole (Eq. 32). This is a much smaller change than those discussed in Section III, C, 1, which is understandable since the equilibrium involves no alteration in the number of ionic charges and consequently no large change in electrostriction. In fact, the magnitude of $(\varDelta V_{av})_1^{1500}$ can be accounted for quite well by ignoring solvation effects and considering only the change of internuclear distances between the initial linear arrangement I---I—I and the final linear I_3^- ion (Hamann, 1957).

When, however, complexing occurs not between an ion and a neutral molecule but between ions of opposite sign, we may expect a large increase in volume due to the release of bound solvent molecules. In confirmation of this, Ewald and Hamann (1956) found that an increase of pressure reduces the concentration of the blue complex form of cobaltous chloride in a solvent consisting of a mixture of i-propyl alcohol with $2 \cdot 9\%$ (wt) of water. They attributed the effect to a displacement of the equilibrium

$$\underset{\text{pink}}{Co^{2+}.6H_2O} + 4Cl^- \rightleftharpoons \underset{\text{blue}}{CoCl_4^{2-}} + 6H_2O \tag{62}$$

But recent work (Libus $et\ al.$, 1960) makes it seem more likely that the principal equilibria concerned are

$$Co^{2+}.6H_2O + 3Cl^- + S \rightleftharpoons CoCl_3S^- + 6H_2O \tag{63}$$

$$\underset{\text{pink}}{Co^{2+}.6H_2O} + 2Cl^- + 2S \rightleftharpoons \underset{\text{blue}}{CoCl_2S_2} + 6H_2O, \tag{64}$$

where S denotes a solvent molecule. All three reactions involve some cancellation of electric charges and so the observed effect of pressure remains explicable in terms of solvation changes.

By polarographic methods Ewald and Lim (1957) have shown that the free energy change for the reaction

$$Cu^{2+} + 3Cl^- + Hg \rightarrow CuCl_2^- + \tfrac{1}{2}Hg_2Cl_2 \tag{65}$$

in water, is increased by raising the pressure. This means that the neutralization of the ionic charges of the initial species is inhibited by pressure as we might expect from the fact that the Cu^{2+} and $3Cl^-$ ions are much more strongly solvated than the complex $CuCl_2^-$ ion.

4. Micelle Formation in Aqueous Solution

An extreme example of the aggregation of ions in solution is the formation of micelles, which are large clusters of anions or cations surrounded by a nearly equal number of oppositely charged ions (*gegen* ions). This aggregation should release a considerable amount of bound solvent, so that the transition to a micellar state should increase the volume of the solution and therefore be suppressed by an increase in the pressure. In agreement with this it has been found, from density measurements, that the partial molar volumes of electrolytes are greater by about 10 cm³/mole in the micellar state than in the free ion state (for references, see Hamann, 1962), and this implies that an increase in pressure should raise the critical concentration (CMC) for the formation of micelles. Hamann (1962) has shown that this happens in aqueous solutions of sodium dodecyl sulphate at pressures below 1 000 atm. But surprisingly the CMC begins to drop above 1 000 atm, suggesting that the micelles are then more dense than the free ions. This effect is hard to explain, but it could arise from the partial freezing of the hydrocarbon chains within the micelles or from the fact that the hydrocarbon interior of the micelles is more compressible than the hydrocarbon chains of the free ions in water. Or it could reflect the inadequacy of our knowledge of the mechanism and thermodynamics of micelle formation.

5. Zwitter-*Ion Formation in Aqueous Solution*

By simple arithmetic, it is easy to show from the data in Table IV that reactions which involve the simultaneous formation of $-CO_2^-$ and $\equiv NH^+$ ionic groups from neutral molecules are all accompanied by substantial contractions. For instance we find:

$$NH_3 + CH_3CO_2H \rightleftharpoons NH_4^+ + CH_3CO_2^- \qquad \Delta \overline{V}^\infty (cm^3/mole) = -19 \cdot 8,$$
$$CH_3NH_2 + C_2H_5CO_2H \rightleftharpoons CH_3NH_3^+ + C_2H_5CO_2^- \qquad ,, \qquad = -18 \cdot 0,$$
$$C_6H_5NH_2 + C_6H_5CO_2H \rightleftharpoons C_6H_5NH_3^+ + C_6H_5CO_2^- \qquad ,, \qquad = -18 \cdot 2.$$

By analogy we might expect the formation of the *zwitter*-ions of amino-acids to be accompanied by a contraction, possibly less than 18 cm³/mole when the ionic groups are close together and partially shield each other, but approaching this value when they are far apart. Cohn *et al.* (1934) found experimentally, by density measurements, that the formation of the *zwitter*-ions of α-amino acids in water involves a contraction of 13 cm³/mole, but that this value increases to 18 cm³/mole for the ε-acids.

There have been no direct measurements of the effect of pressure on the ionization of amino-acids, but it must clearly be large and it probably plays an important part in the behaviour of proteins and of biological systems at high pressures (Johnson *et al.*, 1954).

6. *Ionization of Weak Electrolytes in Non-Aqueous Solutions*

It is almost universally true that the value of the derivative $\epsilon^{-2} \partial\epsilon/\partial p$, which enters into the theoretical formulae for electrostriction (Eqs. 44–46), is greater for organic liquids than for water. From this it follows that the partial molar volumes of ions in water should be smaller in these liquids than in water. The data in Table VI show that this is the case.

TABLE VI. The Partial Molar Volumes (cm³) of Salts at Infinite Dilution at 25° C and 1 atm.

Salt	Solvent				
	water	*methanol*	*ethanol*	*acetic acid*	*acetone*
LiBr	24·0[a]	5·7[c]			
NaBr	23·5[a]	5·1[b]			
NaI	35·1[a]	16·2[c]			−12[e]
KI	45·3[a]	21·5[d]	27[e]		
NH₄NO₃	47·2[a]	31·0[b]			
piperidinium Br	114·2[b]	91·2[b]	100·4[b]	103·1[b]	
$10^7 \times \epsilon^{-2} \partial\epsilon/\partial p$ for solvent (atm⁻¹)	7·4	31·5	35·8		67·8

[a] Owen and Brinkley (1941);   [b] Hamann and Lim (1954);
[c] Gibson and Kincaid (1937);   [d] MacInnes and Dayhoff (1953);
[e] found by extrapolating the data of Gonikberg *et al.* (1956) to infinite dilution.

It follows that the values of $\Delta\bar{V}^\infty$ for the ionization of weak electrolytes in organic solvents will generally be more negative than they are in water, and the ionization equilibria will be more strongly affected by pressure. In confirmation of this Hamann and Lim (1954) showed from density measurements that $\Delta\bar{V}^\infty$ for the basic ionization of piperidine in methanol at 25° C:

$$C_5H_{10}NH + CH_3OH \rightleftharpoons C_5H_{10}NH_2^+ + CH_3O^- \qquad (66)$$

is more negative by 25 cm³/mole than $\Delta\bar{V}^\infty$ for the corresponding ionization in water.

Subsequently Hamann and Strauss (1956) made some direct measurements of the effect of pressure on the equilibrium constant for reaction (66) in methanol at 45° C and found that K_m increased from $2\cdot8 \times 10^{-6}$ at 1 atm to $3\cdot1 \times 10^{-3}$ at 12 000 atm. Since the ionization constant of piperidine in *water* at atmospheric pressure is $1\cdot3 \times 10^{-3}$ mole/kg at 45° C (Bates and Bower, 1956) it could be said that methanol at 12 000 atm is a better " ionizing " solvent than water at 1 atm.

160   S. D. HAMANN

REFERENCES

Addison, C. C., and Sheldon, J. C. (1957). *J. chem. Soc.* 1937.
Addison, C. C., and Smith, B. C. (1958). *J. chem. Soc.* 3664.
Bates, R. G., and Bower, V. E. (1956). *J. Res. nat. Bur. Stand.* **57**, 153.
Bodanszky, A., and Kauzmann, W. (1962). *J. phys. Chem.* **66**, 177.
Born, M. (1920). *Z. Phys.* **1**, 45.
Brander, E. (1932). *Comment. phys.-math., Helsingf.* **6** (8), 21, 42.
Braun, F. (1887). *Ann. Phys. Chem.* **30**, 250.
Briner, E. (1942). *Helv. chim. acta* **25**, 1515.
Brish, A. A., Tarasov, M. S., and Tsukerman, V. A. (1960). *J. exp. theor. Phys.* **38**, 22.
Buchanan, J., and Hamann, S. D. (1953). *Trans. Faraday Soc.* **49**, 1425.
Clark, R. J. H., and Ellis, A. J. (1960). *J. chem. Soc.* 247.
Cohen, E. (1926). " Physico-Chemical Metamorphoses and Some Problems in Piezochemistry ", McGraw-Hill, New York.
Cohn, E. J., McMeekin, T. L., Edsall, J. T., and Blanchard, M. H. (1934). *J. Amer. chem. Soc.* **56**, 784.
David, H. G., and Hamann, S. D. (1959). *Trans. Faraday Soc.* **55**, 72.
David, H. G., and Hamann, S. D. (1960). *Trans. Faraday Soc.* **56**, 1043.
Davies, C. W. (1925). *J. phys. Chem.* **29**, 977.
Distèche, A. (1959). *Rev. sci. Instrum.* **30**, 474.
Drude, P., and Nernst, W. (1894). *Z. phys. Chem.* **15**, 79.
Ellis, A. J. (1959). *J. chem. Soc.* 3689.
Ellis, A. J. (1961). *J. chem. Soc.* 4678.
Ellis, A. J., and Anderson, D. W. (1961). *J. chem. Soc.* 1765.
Ewald, A. H. (1956). *Disc. Faraday Soc.* **22**, 138.
Ewald, A. H., and Hamann, S. D. (1956). *Austr. J. Chem.* **9**, 54.
Ewald, A. H., and Lim, S. C. (1957). *J. phys. Chem.* **61**, 1443.
Ewald, A. H., Hamann, S. D., and Stutchbury, J. E. (1957). *Trans. Faraday Soc.* **53**, 991.
Fajans, K., and Johnson, O. (1942). *J. Amer. chem. Soc.* **64**, 668.
Fanjung, I. (1894). *Z. phys. Chem.* **14**, 673.
Fawcett, E. W., and Gibson, R. O. (1934). *J. chem. Soc.* 386.
Fisher, A., Mann, B. R., and Vaughan, J. (1961). *J. chem. Soc.* 1093.
Fisher, F. H. (1962). *J. phys. Chem.* **66**, 1607.
Fishman, E., and Drickamer, H. G. (1956). *J. chem. Phys.* **24**, 548.
Franck, E. U. (1956). *Z. phys. Chem.* **8**, 92, 107, 192.
Franck, E. U. (1961). *Angew. Chemie* **73**, 309.
Gibson, R. E., and Kincaid, J. F. (1937). *J. Amer. chem. Soc.* **59**, 579.
Gibson, R. E., and Loeffler, O. H. (1941). *Trans. Amer. geophys. Un.* 503.
Gonikberg, M. G., and Vereshchagin, L. F. (1949). *J. phys. Chem., Moscow* **23**, 1447.
Gonikberg, M. G., Miller, V. B., Neiman, M. B., D'yachkovsky, F. S., Likhtenshtein, G. I., and Opekunov, A. A. (1956). *J. phys. Chem., Moscow* **30**, 784.
Gould, A. J., Bleakney, W., and Taylor, H. S. (1934). *J. chem. Phys.* **2**, 48.
Guggenheim, E. A. (1937). *Trans. Faraday Soc.* **33**, 607.
Guggenheim, E. A. (1950). " Thermodynamics ", p. 291. North Holland Publ. Co., Amsterdam.

Hainsworth, W. R., Rowley, H. J., and MacInnes, D. A. (1924). *J. Amer. chem. Soc.* **46**, 1437.

Hamann, S. D. (1957). " Physico-Chemical Effects of Pressure ". Butterworths, London.

Hamann, S. D. (1959). " Proc. XVII IUPAC Congress, Munich ", Vol. II, p. 277. Butterworths, London.

Hamann, S. D. (1962). *J. phys. Chem.* **66**, 1359.

Hamann, S. D., and Lim, S. C. (1954). *Austr. J. Chem.* **7**, 329.

Hamann, S. D., and Strauss, W. (1955). *Trans. Faraday Soc.* **51**, 1684.

Hamann, S. D., and Strauss, W. (1956). *Disc. Faraday Soc.* **22**, 70.

Hepler, L. G. (1957). *J. phys. Chem.* **61**, 1426.

Jenkins, A. C., and di Paolo, F. S. (1956). *J. chem. Phys.* **25**, 296.

Johnson, F. H., Eyring, H., and Polissar, M. J. (1954). " Kinetic Basis of Molecular Biology ", pp. 286–368. Wiley & Sons, New York.

Kabachnik, M. I., Yakushkina, S. E., and Kislyakova, N. V. (1954). *C. R. Acad. Sci. U.R.S.S.* **96**, 1169.

Kiyama, R., and Minomura, S. (1952). *Rev. phys. Chem. Japan* **22**, 4.

Klotz, I. M., and Eckert, C. F. (1942). *J. Amer. chem. Soc.* **64**, 1878.

Kobeko, P. P., Kuvshinsky, P. P., and Semenova, A. S. (1950). *J. phys. Chem., Moscow* **24**, 345.

Kohlrausch, F., and Hallwachs, W. (1894). *Ann. Phys. Chem.* **53**, 1, 14.

Kopp, H. (1889). *Ann. Phys.* **250**, 1.

Kretschmer, C. B., and Wiebe, R. (1954). *J. chem. Phys.* **22**, 1697.

Krichevsky, I. R. (1938). *Acta phys. chim. U.R.S.S.* **8**, 181.

La Mer, V. K., and Brescia, F. (1940). *J. Amer. chem. Soc.* **62**, 617.

Le Chatelier, H. (1884). *C. R. Acad. Sci. Paris* **99**, 786.

Leonard, R. W. (1948). *J. acoust. Soc. Amer.* **20**, 254.

Lewis, G. L., and Smyth, C. P. (1939). *J. Amer. chem. Soc.* **61**, 3063.

Libus, W., Ugniewska, A., and Minc, S. (1960). *Roczn. Chem.* **34**, 29.

MacInnes, D. A., and Dayhoff, M. O. (1953). *J. Amer. chem. Soc.* **59**, 579, 5219.

MacInnes, D. A., and Shedlovsky, T. (1932). *J. Amer. chem. Soc.* **54**, 1429.

Moore, T. S., and Winmill, T. F. (1912). *J. chem. Soc.* **101**, 1635.

Mukerjee, P. (1961). *J. phys. Chem.* **65**, 740.

Ostwald, W. (1878). *J. prakt. Chem.* **18**, 328.

Owen, B. B., and Brinkley, S. R. (1941). *Chem. Rev.* **29**, 461.

Pauling, L. (1960). " Nature of the Chemical Bond ", p. 261. Cornell University Press.

Pimentel, G. C., and McClellan, A. L. (1960). " The Hydrogen Bond ", Table 2–XVI, p. 53. Freeman & Co., San Francisco.

Planck, M. (1887). *Ann. Phys. Chem.* **32**, 462.

Redlich, O., and Bigeleisen, J. (1942). *Chem. Rev.* **30**, 171.

Robinson, R. A., and Stokes, R. H. (1959). " Electrolyte Solutions ", pp. 255–257. Butterworths, London.

Sapiro, R. H., and Shu-Lin P'eng (1938). *J. chem. Soc.* 1171.

Shishkin, N. I., and Novak, I. I. (1953). *J. tech. Phys., Moscow* **23**, 1485.

Smith, J. S. (1943). Dissertation Yale, quoted by B. B. Owen, " Electrochemical Constants ", *Nat. Bur. Stand. Circular* 524, p. 193.

Spring, W., and van't Hoff, J. H. (1887). *Z. phys. Chem.* **1**, 227.

Staveley, L. A. K., and Spice, B. (1952). *J. chem. Soc.* 406.

Stokes, R. H., and Robinson, R. A. (1957). *Trans. Faraday Soc.* **53**, 301.

Strauss, W. (1957). *Austr. J. Chem.* **10**, 277.

Tammann, G. (1910). *Z. Elektrochem.* **16**, 592.

Verwey, E. J. W. (1942). *Rec. Trav. Chim., Pays-Bas* **61**, 127.

Woolley, H. W., Scott, R. B., and Brickwedde, F. G. (1948). *J. Res. nat. Bur. Stand.* **41**, 379.

Ziegler, K. (1956). U.S. Pat. 2695327, *Chem. Abs.* **50**, 1073.

Chapter 8

CHEMICAL KINETICS

S. D. HAMANN

*C.S.I.R.O. Division of Physical Chemistry,
Melbourne, Victoria, Australia*

I. INTRODUCTION

FOR many years chemists have been familiar with the effects of temperature on the rates of chemical reactions and with its influence on their course. But it is only recently, since high pressure equipment has become cheap and readily available, that they have begun to study the analogous effects of hydrostatic pressure. These effects can be just as great and as varied as those caused by changes in temperature; in fact there are reasons to believe that very high pressures will cause the spontaneous breaking of covalent bonds (Hirschfelder *et al.* 1954) and in this way bring about extremely fast reactions. The pressures needed to do this are probably above a million atmospheres, and they have not yet been reached under static conditions. This chapter will be concerned with the effects of more moderate pressures in the range 1–40 000 atm.

Understandably, the influence of pressure is greatest when one or more of the reactants is a gas, since compression then produces large changes in the concentrations of the components. There have been several experimental studies of the kinetics of gas-phase and heterogeneous systems at high pressures (see, e.g., Laird *et al.*, 1956; Mills and Bennett, 1959; Gonikberg, 1960), but they have nearly all been concerned with complex reactions whose mechanisms are obscure. The interpretation of the results is difficult and any specifically chemical effects tend to be masked by the gross physical effect of the changed concentrations. For these reasons the discussion in this chapter will be restricted to the kinetics of homogeneous liquid-phase reactions.

II. Molecular Theory of Reaction Rates at High Pressures

A. *General*

The writer (Hamann, 1957) has previously pointed out that although the collision theory and the transition state (or activated complex) theory of reaction rates are essentially equivalent (Hinshelwood, 1937; Frost and Pearson, 1961) the transition state approach is much the better suited to an analysis of the role of pressure in chemical kinetics.

In the transition state theory, a reaction of the general type

$$aA + bB + \ldots \rightarrow X^{\ddagger} \rightarrow lL + mM + \ldots \tag{1}$$

is assumed to proceed through a state of maximum energy $X^{\ddagger}$ which can be regarded as a definite molecular species in equilibrium with the reactants and the products. On this assumption it is possible to separate the factors constituting a rate constant into kinetic and thermodynamic terms. In this way, Glasstone *et al.* (1941) obtained the relation

$$k = \kappa \frac{kT}{h} (K^{\ddagger})', \tag{2}$$

where k is the specific rate constant, k is Boltzmann's constant, h is Planck's constant and κ is a factor, close to unity, which defines the probability that the transition state $X^{\ddagger}$ will decompose into the products $lL + mM + \ldots$ rather than revert to the original species $aA + bB + \ldots$ The quantity $(K^{\ddagger})'$ is defined by

$$(K^{\ddagger})' = \frac{[X^{\ddagger}]}{[A]^a [B]^b \ldots}, \tag{3}$$

where $[A]$, $[B]$ ... denote the *concentrations* of A, B, ..., not their activities. $(K^{\ddagger})'$ is thus an equilibrium product for the formation of the transition state, uncorrected by the activity coefficients of A, B ... and $X^{\ddagger}$. It is important to note at this point that k and $(K^{\ddagger})'$ must be based on the same concentration scale.

If we follow Eyring and assume that κ is independent of the temperature and the pressure we find that

$$\ln k = \ln (K^{\ddagger})' + \ln T + \text{const.,} \tag{4}$$

and so

$$\frac{\partial \ln k}{\partial p} = \frac{\partial \ln (K^{\ddagger})'}{\partial p}. \tag{5}$$

In considering this derivative we need to be explicit in our choice of concentration scales. If we select the *mole fraction* x or *molality* m scales, then from Eqs. (15) and (27) of Chapter 7.ii, and remembering that the activity coefficients on the mole fraction and molality scales are proportional to each other (Robinson and Stokes, 1959), we find

$$\frac{\partial\ RT \ln k_x}{\partial p} = \frac{\partial\ RT \ln k_m}{\partial p} = -\Delta \bar{V}^{\ddagger}, \tag{6}$$

where

$$\Delta \bar{V}^{\ddagger} = \bar{V}_{X\ddagger} - a\bar{V}_A - b\bar{V}_B - \ldots . \tag{7}$$

Thus, the influence of pressure on k_x and k_m is determined by the excess of the partial molar volume of the transition state over the partial molar volumes of the initial species, all at the composition of the mixture.

Unfortunately, in work on liquid-phase chemical kinetics it has become the practice to express the composition of a solution in terms of the *molar* concentrations of its components. This convention would be acceptable if we were interested only in results at a particular temperature and pressure but it is inconvenient in the study of pressure effects. Even if we make the simplifying assumption that the solution is nearly infinitely dilute and the activity coefficients of the solute species are unity, we find from Eq. (29) of Chapter 7.ii that the derivative (Eq. 5) assumes the form

$$\left(\frac{\partial RT \ln k_c}{\partial p}\right)_{c=0} = -(\Delta \bar{V}^{\ddagger})^{\infty} + (1 - a - b - \ldots)RT\kappa_S, \tag{8}$$

where the operator Δ has the same meaning as in Eq. (6), and κ_S denotes the compressibility coefficient of the solvent. Only for a first-order reaction $(a = 1; b, c \ldots = 0)$ does formula (8) reduce to (6). Although Guggenheim (1937) drew attention to this fact many years ago it has remained common practice to discuss experimental data on the basis of an assumed relationship:

$$\frac{\partial RT \ln k_c}{\partial p} = -\Delta V^{\ddagger}. \tag{9}$$

The quantity $\Delta V^{\ddagger}$ is usually called a " volume of activation " although it is clear that it is really a composite function. The only justification for identifying it with $\Delta \bar{V}^{\ddagger}$ or with $(\Delta \bar{V}^{\ddagger})^{\infty}$ lies in the fact that the errors involved in measuring rate constants under pressure are sufficient to introduce an uncertainty of a few cm³/mole into $\Delta V^{\ddagger}$, and this is usually greater than the factor $RT\kappa_S$ in Eq. (8). In the remainder of this chapter we shall, perforce, assume that there is only a small difference between the quantity $\Delta V^{\ddagger}$, defined by Eq. (9) and the true volume change for activation $\Delta \bar{V}^{\ddagger}$. For simplicity the symbol $\Delta V^{\ddagger}$ will be used for both.

Formula (9) was first suggested by Evans and Polanyi (1935). It is sometimes wrongly ascribed to van't Hoff (1901) who merely proposed a " possible " relation of the form

$$\frac{\partial \ln k}{\partial p} = \frac{V}{RT} + A, \tag{10}$$

where A is a term of undefined magnitude, independent of the pressure, and V denotes an unspecified volume. As Evans and Polanyi (1937) pointed out, even if one were to identify V with some physically significant volume change, such as $\Delta V^{\ddagger}$, the presence of the term A would still make it impossible to derive $\Delta V^{\ddagger}$ from $\partial \ln k / \partial p$.

B. Molecular Models of Transition States

Evans and Polanyi (1935) pointed out that from the theoretical standpoint it is convenient to split $\Delta V^{\ddagger}$ into two terms: $\Delta_1 V^{\ddagger}$, which is the change in volume of the reacting molecules aA, bB ... when they form the transition state; and $\Delta_2 V^{\ddagger}$, which is the accompanying change in volume of the surrounding liquid, arising principally from changes in electrostriction. We shall consider $\Delta_1 V^{\ddagger}$ and $\Delta_2 V^{\ddagger}$ separately.

1. Terms Contributing to $\Delta_1 V^{\ddagger}$

The principal terms contributing to $\Delta_1 V^{\ddagger}$ are those associated with the partial formation of new chemical bonds and with the stretching and partial breaking of existing bonds during the activation process. There may be minor contributions from the relaxation of parts of the molecules remote from the reacting centres.

(a) The Breaking of Covalent Bonds. It was pointed out in Chapter 7.ii that the breaking of a covalent bond in a molecule causes a large increase in the total molecular volume. It is reasonable to suppose that at least part of this expansion occurs during the activation process. For example, in the unimolecular dissociation of dinitrogen tetroxide

$$N_2O_4 \rightarrow 2NO_2 \tag{11}$$

there is little doubt that the N—N bond must be stretched in order to form the transition state, and since it is unlikely that there is any compensating decrease in the van der Waals radii of the nitrogen atoms in directions perpendicular to the bond, the transition state will have a larger volume than the initial state. But just how much larger is a question that is not easily answered.

The principal piece of information needed to estimate $\Delta_1 V^{\ddagger}$ for this kind of dissociation is the degree to which the initial bond becomes stretched in the transition state. In 1940 Ri and Eyring (1940) stated, without quoting their sources, that " calculations of potential surfaces for activated complexes indicate that those atomic distances which are changing are often around 10 per cent larger than the normal distances ". Stearn and Eyring (1941a, b) later incorporated this idea in a treatment of pressure effects in which they assumed that the transition state for a unimolecular dissociation

$$AB \rightarrow A + B \qquad (12)$$

can be regarded as being formed when the A—B bond has become stretched by 10 per cent of its original length.

This hypothesis of 10 per cent stretching has become widely and uncritically accepted, although its validity is by no means obvious. In fact Eyring, himself, had earlier suggested that the Cl—Cl distance in the transition state for dissociating Cl_2 may be about $2 \cdot 5$ Å (Gerschinowitz and Eyring, 1935), that is, 25 per cent greater than the initial bond length. It is pertinent to consider this question in some detail.

If we examine, first, the simple dissociation of a diatomic molecule AB into two atoms A and B, we find that when the process is adiabatic† the potential energy proper has no maximum except at infinite separation of the atoms. But from the point of view of kinetics it is more appropriate to consider an " effective potential energy " (Hirschfelder et al., 1954, p. 49; Glasstone et al. 1941, p. 127) which takes account of the decrease of rotational kinetic energy as the A—B bond is stretched, and which does have a very slight hump at a distance several times greater than the normal bond length. The hump is usually negligible in comparison with kT, and it is doubtful whether it can properly be regarded as representing a transition state.

In the dissociation of more complex molecules it is possible for a redistribution of energy within the separating fragments to lead to the appearance of quite a pronounced saddle-point in the potential energy surface (Slater, 1960). This is demonstrated by the fact that the experimental activation energy for the dissociation of hexaphenyl ethane into triphenyl methyl radicals is 75 per cent greater than the final dissociation energy (Waters, 1946). Unfortunately the theory of this type of dissociation has not yet reached the stage where it is possible to predict the transition state configuration, even approximately.

There is, however, one instance in which the transition state for a

---

† This term implies that the stretching of the A—B bond involves no abrupt jump from one electronic state to another.

unimolecular dissociation is known with some certainty. It is the thermal decomposition of nitrous oxide

$$N_2O(^1\Sigma) \rightarrow N_2(^1\Sigma) + O(^3P), \qquad (13)$$

in which the N—O bond of the ground state becomes stretched until the energy of the system reaches that of the excited (triplet) state; a transition then occurs and the triplet state breaks into the final products with a release of energy (Stearn and Eyring, 1935; Reuben and Linnett, 1959). Calculations show that the transition occurs at an N—O distance of $1 \cdot 73$ Å, which is 45 per cent greater than the initial bond length.

Bimolecular exchanges of the type

$$C + AB \rightarrow CA + B \qquad (14)$$

also involve partial breaking of the A—B bond in the activation process. For these reactions it is comparatively easy to calculate transition state distances, although the results depend rather critically on the approximations made in setting up the theoretical models. Table I shows some transition state configurations that have been calculated for a variety of reactions by different authors using different methods. It will be seen that the degrees of bond stretching vary from 11 to 100 per cent and have an average value of 35 per cent. Without placing too much reliance on these figures, we can nevertheless infer that Eyring's estimate of 10 per cent is a good deal too low. For what they are worth, the potential surface calculations suggest that there is no justification for making *any* general rule about the amount of elongation of breaking bonds in their transition states.

For a given elongation δl of a bond whose initial length was l, we can attempt a rough calculation of its contribution to $\Delta_1 V^{\ddagger}$ by assuming that the stretching occurs along the axis of a cylinder of constant cross-section. An appropriate cross-sectional area for a diatomic molecule can be taken to be the mean of the van der Waals cross-sectional areas of the separating atoms, and if the van der Waals radii of the atoms are r_A and r_B it follows that

$$\Delta_1 V_b{}^{\ddagger} = \pi(r_A{}^2 + r_B{}^2)\delta l/2, \qquad (15)$$

where the subscript b denotes the contribution of a bond-breaking term. It is more difficult to select an appropriate cross-sectional area for polyatomic molecules, but for the relatively simple molecules in Table I it is again reasonable to take the mean of the van der Waals areas of the atoms whose bond is being broken. Applying formula (15) to these reactions we find the values of $\Delta_1 V_b{}^{\ddagger}$ listed in Table II.

(b) *The Formation of Covalent Bonds.* The contribution which the

TABLE I. Transition State Distances Calculated from Potential Energy Surfaces†

	Reaction	Transition State	Degree of bond stretching (%)	Reference
1	$N_2O \rightarrow N_2 + O$	N—N---O 1·73 (1·19)	45	Stearn and Eyring (1935)
2	$H + CH_4 \rightarrow CH_4 + H$	H H \\/ H------C------H | 1·30 H (1·09)	19	Gorin et al. (1939)
3	$H_3C + H_2 \rightarrow CH_4 + H$	H\\ H—C---H---H H/ 0·92 (0·74)	24	Johnston (1961)
4	$H + CH_4 \rightarrow CH_3 + H_2$	H / H---H---C—H 1·27 \\H (1·09)	17	Johnston (1961)
5	$Cl + H_2 \rightarrow HCl + H$	Cl---H---H 1·40 (0·74)	90	Wheeler et al. (1936)
6	$Br + H_2 \rightarrow HBr + H$	Br---H---H 1·5 (0·74)	100	Wheeler et al. (1936)
7	$R_3C^- + HCR_3 \rightarrow$ $R_3CH + {}^-CR_3$	$[R_3C---H---CR_3]^-$ 1·35 (1·09)	24	Bell (1941)
8	$RO^- + HCR_3 \rightarrow$ $ROH + {}^-CR_3$	$[RO---H---CR_3]^-$ 1·5 (1·09)	45	Bell and Lidwell (1940)
9	$I^- + CH_3I \rightarrow$ $ICH_3 + I^-$	H H \\/ I------C------I | 2·6 H (2·10)	24	Evans (1946)
10	$H_2 + I_2 \rightarrow 2HI$	(0·74) 0·97 H------H / \\ I············I 2·95 (2·66)	31 11	Wheeler et al. (1936)
11	1:3-butadiene $+ Br_2 \rightarrow$ 1:4-dibromo-2-butene	C—C / \\ C C \\ / Br---Br 2·61 (2·28)	14	Eyring et al. (1933)

† The first number below each bond denotes its length, in Å, in the transition state; the number in parenthesis denotes its length, in Å, in the initial state.

TABLE II. Contributions to $\Delta_1 V^{\ddagger}$ of Bond Breaking in the Reactions Listed in Table I, and of Bond Formation in the Reverse Reactions†

Reaction number	$\Delta_1 V_b{}^{\ddagger}$ (cm³/mole)	$\Delta_1 V_f{}^{\ddagger}$ (cm³/mole)
1	+2·2	− 4·8
2	+1·1	−10·0
3	+0·5	− 4·2
4	+0·9	− 9·7
5	+1·8	− 2·7
6	+2·1	− 2·5
7	+1·3	− 9·5
8	+2·1	− 8·7
9	+4·1	−12·7
10 (H—H bond)	+0·6	− 3·7
10 (I—I bond)	+2·5	−11·6
11	+2·4	− 9·4

† The CH_3- group has been treated as if it were an atom of van der Waals radius 2 Å (Pauling, 1960).

partial formation of a covalent bond makes to $\Delta_1 V^{\ddagger}_!$ can be judged by considering the reactions which are the reverse of those listed in Table I. For example, in the converse of reaction 1

$$O + N_2 \rightarrow N_2O$$

the initial O---N separation can be taken to the the sum of the van der Waals radii of the O and N atoms (2·9 Å), whilst the transition state distance is the same as it is for the forward reaction (1·73 Å). This shrinkage must contribute to $\Delta_1 V^{\ddagger}$ a negative term which we shall designate $\Delta_1 V_f{}^{\ddagger}$, the subscript f denoting bond *formation*. Employing the same approximations that underlie Eq. (15), we obtain the relation:

$$\Delta_1 V_f{}^{\ddagger} = - \pi(r_A{}^2 + r_B{}^2)(r_A + r_B - l - \delta l)/2, \qquad (16)$$

which gives the values listed in the third column of Table II.

(c) *Combination of Bond-Forming and Bond-Breaking.* Although the approximations used in deriving Eqs. (15) and (16) are rather crude they are certainly no worse, and are probably a lot better, than some that have been employed in other calculations (Stearn and Eyring, 1941a, b). It is likely that the values of $\Delta_1 V_b{}^{\ddagger}$ and $\Delta_1 V_f{}^{\ddagger}$ are at least of the right order. Comparing them, we see that $-\Delta_1 V_f{}^{\ddagger}$ is invariably greater than $\Delta_1 V_b{}^{\ddagger}$, which means that when the activation step for a reaction involves the simultaneous formation of one bond and the breaking of another the first term will predominate and $\Delta_1 V^{\ddagger}$ will be negative. As an example of this, the figures in Table II show that the net value of $\Delta_1 V^{\ddagger}$ for the symmetrical exchanges 2, 7 and 9 is about

$- 9$ cm³/mole and, of course, it is the same for the forward and reverse reactions.

For reaction 10, which involves the simultaneous formation of two bonds and the breaking of another two, the calculated net value of $\Delta_1 V^{\ddagger}$ is $- 15$ cm³/mole (based on the theoretical H---I distance of 1·75 Å).

2. *Terms Contributing to $\Delta_2 V^{\ddagger}$*

We turn now to the second term $\Delta_2 V^{\ddagger}$ which represents the change in volume of the solvent during the activation process. This change can arise either because the solvent molecules rearrange their packing for purely steric reasons, to accommodate the changed shape of the reacting molecules, or because there is a tightening or loosening of the electrostatic bonds between the solvent and the reactant species. The first effect seems to be quite unimportant in liquid systems although it may play a role in solid-phase reactions; here we shall ignore it. The second effect can be extremely important in reactions in which electrical charges are developed or are neutralized.

In Chapter 7.ii it was shown, from experimental data, that the dissociation of a neutral molecule into two free ions involves a contraction which may be as great as 28 cm³/mole in water, 45 cm³/mole in methanol solution. On a molecular scale the contraction arises because the ionic charges exert strong attractive forces on the permanent and induced dipoles of the solvent molecules. The magnitude of the effect can be calculated theoretically on this basis by using, for instance, Bernal and Fowler's (1933) model for the hydration of ions (Buchanan and Hamann, 1953; Buchanan, 1953) or it can be estimated from the macroscopic theory of electrostriction (Equations (44)–(46) of Chapter 7.ii). The two approaches agree in the prediction that the contraction accompanying the development of a single electronic charge on a small spherical molecule is between 10 and 30 cm³/mole in most solvents.

It is therefore to be expected that the solvation term $\Delta_2 V^{\ddagger}$ may be quite as important as $\Delta_1 V^{\ddagger}$ in reactions which produce or remove electrical charges. This point was emphasized by Polanyi (1937), when he remarked that " bimolecular reactions [are] association reactions primarily leading to the fusion of the reacting molecules into a transition state. One might expect, therefore, all bimolecular reactions to be accelerated by pressure. It is true that this is confirmed by experience, so far [that is, in 1937]. Nevertheless, this consideration cannot hold strictly, and can be formulated quantitatively, only if A and B unite to the transition state (AB) without any change in the solvation forces and changes in the density of the solution arising from this cause."

Despite this clear statement of the importance of solvation, the term $\Delta_2 V^\ddagger$ was ignored in some later discussions of the influence of pressure on reaction rates in solution (Stearn and Eyring, 1941b).

A question which arises here is that of the relative importance of $\Delta_1 V^\ddagger$ and $\Delta_2 V^\ddagger$ for any particular reaction. Unfortunately it is impossible to answer this theoretically since we have no reliable way of knowing how fully developed are the electrical charges in the transition state. However there are at least two classes of reactions for which the experimental results show unambiguously that $\Delta_2 V^\ddagger$ is the predominant term. The first is the group of unimolecular dissociations which proceed through a slow step involving the formation of ions

$$AB \rightarrow X^\ddagger \rightarrow A^+ + B^-. \tag{17}$$

There is considerable evidence that the transition state $X^\ddagger$ has the configuration $A^{-\delta}\text{---}B^{\delta+}$, where the A—B bond has been stretched and the separating fragments have acquired partial charges, δ (Ingold, 1953). It is clear that the stretching of the bond must increase the volume of the molecule (cf. Table II); $\Delta_1 V^\ddagger$ is therefore positive and if it were the only term in $\Delta V^\ddagger$, then by Eq. (6) the reaction should be retarded by an increase in pressure. On the other hand the development of the partial charges, δ, attracts solvent molecules around the transition state and compresses them locally to a higher density than they had around the initial AB molecule. It follows that $\Delta_2 V^\ddagger$ is negative and will tend to counteract the effect of $\Delta_1 V^\ddagger$. Experimentally it is found that these dissociations are strongly accelerated at high pressures (see Section III, B, 1, (a)) proving that $\Delta_2 V^\ddagger$ is numerically greater than $\Delta_1 V^\ddagger$.

The second instance of the predominance of $\Delta_2 V^\ddagger$ occurs in bimolecular associations of the type

$$A^+ + B^- \rightarrow X^\ddagger \rightarrow \text{products}. \tag{18}$$

These reactions are retarded by an increase in pressure (see Section III, B, 2, (a)), despite the fact that the partial formation of a covalent bond between the A and B groups must cause a considerable contraction of the system. Evidently the increase in volume $\Delta_2 V^\ddagger$ arising from the partial desolvation of the initial ions more than balances $\Delta_1 V^\ddagger$.

In more complex reactions the experimental evidence is often ambiguous, especially in instances where $\Delta_1 V^\ddagger$ and $\Delta_2 V^\ddagger$ have the same sign. It is tempting to make the generalization that the solvation term will always be the dominant one in reactions which produce or remove ionic charges (Buchanan and Hamann, 1953) and this principle seems to apply quite well to a wide range of reactions (Hamann, 1957). But it should be regarded only as a working hypothesis, with no real theoretical basis.

III. DISCUSSION OF EXPERIMENTAL RESULTS

From the foregoing discussion of the factors contributing to $\Delta V^{\ddagger}$ for a chemical reaction in solution (and hence to the influence of pressure on its rate) it is clearly helpful to consider spearately those reactions in which the solvent plays little part, and those in which it participates strongly. We shall therefore follow the procedure adopted in Chapter 7.ii and discuss the experimental results in order of increasing polarity of the reactants and their transition states.

A. *Reactions of Non-Polar and Slightly Polar Molecules*

1. *Homolytic Unimolecular Dissociations: $AB \rightarrow A + B$*

This class of reactions includes the decomposition of molecules into either free radicals or into other molecules. An example of a free radical decomposition is the dissociation of pentaphenyl ethane (Bachmann and Osborn, 1940):

$$\phi_3C\text{—}CH\phi_2 \rightarrow \phi_3C^{\bullet} + \phi_2HC^{\bullet}, \tag{19}$$

where $\phi = $ phenyl (C_6H_5—).

An instance of a molecular decomposition is the depolymerization of α-dicyclopentadiene (Khambata and Wassermann, 1939):

$$\tag{20}$$

Both kinds of reactions have been studied under pressure.

(a) *Free Radical Dissociations.* The results for free radical dissociations are summarized in Table III where, under the heading " Method ", the term " direct " means that the reactions were followed by measuring the rate of disappearance of the original substance in the absence of a free radical scavenger (e.g. I_2 or diphenylpicrylhydrazyl). The term " scavenger " in the table indicates that the reactions were followed by observing the disappearance of an added scavenger.

It will be seen that all the reactions were retarded by an increase in the pressure. The values of $\Delta V^{\ddagger}$ are considerably greater than those of $\Delta_1 V_b^{\ddagger}$ calculated for simple molecules and listed in Table II, but this is understandable since the separating groups are rather bulky and we should expect the difference between the excluded volumes of their initial and transition states to be greater than it is for the simpler molecules. Attempts have been made to explain the observed values of $\Delta V^{\ddagger}$, quantitatively, in terms of molecular models, but in the writer's opinion this exercise is profitless and will remain so until we learn more about the actual degree of bond stretching in the transition states and about the effective cross-sectional areas around the breaking bonds.

TABLE III. The Kinetics of Some Unimolecular Free Radical Decompositions under Pressure

Substance	Solvent	Temp. (° C)	Method	10^5k (sec^{-1})		$\Delta V\ddagger$ $(cm^3/mole)$ at 1 atm	Reference
				1 atm	1 500 atm		
Pentaphenyl ethane	toluene	70	scavenger	2·5	1·2	+ 13	Ewald (1956a)
AZBN†	,,	62·5	,,	0·89	0·55	+ 9	Ewald (1956a)
,,	,,	62·5	direct	1·87	1·52	+ 4	Ewald (1956a)
Benzoyl peroxide	,,	60	scavenger	0·25	0·18	+ 7	Ewald (1956b)
,, ,,	CCl₄	60	direct	0·14	0·078	+10	Nicholson and Norrish (1956a)
,, ,,	ϕCOCH₃	80	,,	5·6	4·6	+ 5	Walling and Pellon (1957b)
t-Butyl peroxide††	toluene	120	,,	1·34	1·05	+ 5	Walling and Metzger (1959)
,, ,, ,,	cyclo-C₆H₁₀	120	,,	0·83	0·60	+ 7	Walling and Metzger (1959)
,, ,, ,,	C₆H₆	120	,,	1·39	0·83	+13	Walling and Metzer (1959)
,, ,, ,,	CCl₄	120	,,	0·9	0·45	+13	Walling and Metzger (1959)

† 2: 2′azo-*bis-iso*butyronitrile.
†† Laird's (1956) measurements on this substance appear to be unreliable.

A matter which calls for comment is the large difference between the values of $\Delta V\ddagger$ for the dissociation of t-butyl peroxide in toluene and cyclohexene solution on the one hand, and in benzene and carbon tetrachloride on the other. Walling and Metzger (1959) suggested that the difference arises because toluene and cyclohexene are readily attacked by the freshly formed t-butoxy radicals (with the abstraction of hydrogen atoms) so that the reaction is completed within the solvent " cage " (Walling, 1957). The measured value $\Delta V_{obs}\ddagger$ therefore applies to the initial dissociation

$$\overset{1}{\underset{slow}{ROOR \rightarrow 2RO^{\cdot}}}$$

$$\overset{2}{\underset{fast}{SH + RO^{\cdot} \rightarrow ROH + S^{\cdot}}}$$

On the other hand, in benzene and carbon tetrachloride the $RO^•$ radicals must escape from the cage or else they will recombine, and there is therefore a competition between the two processes 3 and 4:

$$ROOR \xrightarrow{1} 2RO^•$$

$$2RO^• \xrightarrow{3} ROOR$$

$$2RO^• \xrightarrow{4} RO^• + RO^• \text{ (separated)}$$

and $\Delta V^{\ddagger}$ becomes a composite quantity. If the rate of reaction 3 is fast compared with that of 4, as it is likely to be at high pressures, then $\Delta V_{obs}^{\ddagger} \approx \Delta V_1^{\ddagger} + \Delta V_4^{\ddagger} - \Delta V_3^{\ddagger}$. Of these quantities, $\Delta V_1^{\ddagger}$ is known to be positive (from the reactions in toluene and cyclohexene); it is very likely that $\Delta V_3^{\ddagger}$ is negative, and that $\Delta V_4^{\ddagger}$ is positive (since diffusion processes invariably involve an expansion during their activation steps). The contribution of the last two terms accounts for the larger values of $\Delta V_{obs}^{\ddagger}$.

Ewald (1956a) and Walling and Metzger (1959) pointed out that the difference between the results given by the " direct " and " scavenger " methods for the dissociation of 2:2′azo-*bis*-isobutyronitrile (AZBN) is probably due also to a " cage " effect. The direct method gives the correct value of $\Delta V^{\ddagger}$ for the dissociation, and the scavenger method gives a larger value because the radicals must diffuse out of their cages before they can react with scavenger molecules.

(b) *Molecular Dissociations.* There have been no accurate measurements of the rate of the unimolecular decomposition of α-dicyclopentadiene into cyclopentadiene molecules (reaction (20)) under pressure. But some qualitative experiments by Raistrick *et al.* (1939) suggest that it falls with increasing pressure. The following figures show the amount of dimer decomposed after 21 hours at 138° C:

p (atm)	1	2 000	3 000	5 000	10 000
dimer decomposed (%)	21	26	15	13	4 to 5

The reason for the apparent initial rise in rate between 1 and 2 000 atm is not clear; it could lie in experimental errors or in the possible existence of complicating reactions (Gonikberg, 1960, p. 135). The evidence at higher pressures certainly suggests that the transition state is more bulky than the initial state.

Another reaction involving the production of two neutral molecules from one is the Curtius re-arrangement of acyl azides, in which the slow step is the dissociation

$$\underset{\underset{\displaystyle O}{\|}}{R\text{---}C\text{---}N_3} \quad \rightarrow \quad \underset{\underset{\displaystyle O}{\|}}{R\text{---}C\text{---}N\!:} \quad +N_2.$$

Brower (1961) has found that an increase in pressure from 68 to 1 400 atm retards the re-arrangement of benzazide in both ligroin and alcohol–water solutions, the respective volumes of activation being about $+5$ and $+2$ cm^3/mole. These values are similar to those for free radical dissociations (cf. Table III).

To conclude this section, it is worthwhile to point out that the general reduction in rate of decomposition of substances at high pressures might be put to some practical use in organic chemistry, since it means that compressed materials can be kept stable at much higher temperatures than their normal decomposition temperatures. For example, Bridgman (1938) found that the thermal decompositions of carbon tetrabromide and urea are almost completely suppressed at high pressures.

2. *Homopolar Bimolecular Associations:* $A+B\rightarrow AB$

From the discussion in Section II, B, 1, and from the theoretical values of $\varDelta_1 V_b{}^{\ddagger}$ and $\varDelta_1 V_f{}^{\ddagger}$ listed in Table II, we should expect these reactions to be accelerated by an increase in pressure, to a more marked degree than the reverse dissociations are retarded.

(a) *Free Radical Combinations.* The combination of two free radicals in solution is an extremely fast process requiring only a small energy of activation. In fact the rate of reaction is often determined, not by the combination itself, but by the rate at which the combining radicals can diffuse together (Burnett, 1954). Since the viscosities of organic liquids rise with an increase in pressure, the diffusion rate must decrease correspondingly. In agreement with this Nicholson and Norrish (1956b) have found that the rate of self-neutralization of growing polymer radicals (i.e. the termination step) in the polymerization of styrene decreases rapidly up to 1 000 atm, and then more slowly. The same conclusion was reached independently by Walling and Pellon (1957a).

To the writer's knowledge, no high pressure measurements have yet been made on reactions for which the slow step is actually the formation of a covalent bond between two radicals.

(b) *Attack of Radicals on Olefins.* These reactions are very much slower than the free radical combinations discussed above (they usually have activation energies of about 10 kcal/mole) and in consequence their rates are independent of the diffusion process except in solvents of very high viscosity.

A relatively simple reaction of this type is the *cis*$\rightleftharpoons$*trans* isomerization of 1:2 dichlorethylene catalysed by iodine, which almost certainly occurs by the mechanism

$$I_2 \rightleftharpoons 2I\cdot$$

where 1 and 4 are the rate-determining steps. Ewald *et al.* (1957) have studied the influence of pressure on the forward and reverse isomerizations in the liquid phase at 150° C and found that the over-all rates of both were doubled by raising the pressure from 10 to 3 000 atm. It is likely that the rate constants k_1 and k_4 were increased even more than this, since the rise in pressure presumably reduced the stationary concentration of $I\cdot$ atoms by suppressing the dissociation of I_2 (cf. some analogous equilibria discussed in Chapter 7.ii, Sections III, A, III, B).

Another reaction of this class is the propagation step in the free radical polymerization of olefins

$$C—C\cdot + C{=}C \rightarrow C—C—C—C\cdot. \tag{21}$$

By using the " rotating sector " method, Nicholson and Norrish (1956b) were able to show that the rate constant for chain propagation in styrene increased by a factor of 5·5 between 1 and 2 900 atm at 30° C, and their results yield an activation volume $\Delta V^{\ddagger} = -13\cdot4$ cm³/mole (Whalley, 1956). Later Walling and Pellon (1957a) measured the same rate constant by an entirely different emulsion technique and found that it increased by a factor of 3·9 between 1 000 and 3 700 atm at 40° C, corresponding to an activation volume $\Delta V^{\ddagger} = -11\cdot5$ cm³/mole, which is satisfactorily close to Nicholson and Norrish's value. Whalley (1956) has pointed out that since the volume of polystyrene is less than that of styrene by 22·7 cm³ per mole of styrene units, the activation volume amounts to about 50 per cent of the total decrease in volume in going from the initial to the final states for reaction (21). This is consistent with the results of some potential energy calculations (Evans *et al.*, 1948) which indicate that, in the transition state, the distance between the centres of the attacking and the attacked carbon atoms is close to the mean of their van der Waals and covalent separations, whilst the length of the original C=C bond remains almost unaltered.

(c) *Molecular Associations.* It has become generally accepted that diene addition reactions (Diels-Alder condensations) proceed through homopolar transition states which are essentially cyclic (see, e.g., Ingold, 1953, p. 718):

$$
\begin{array}{ccc}
\underset{\text{C}}{\overset{\text{C}}{\text{C}}} + \underset{\text{C}}{\overset{\text{C}}{\text{C}}} & \rightarrow & \left[\;\right] & \rightarrow & \\
\end{array}
\tag{22}
$$

If this model is correct, then the simultaneous partial formation of the two new C—C bonds should involve a substantial contraction and the reactions should be more strongly accelerated by pressure than those which form only one bond (Section III, A, 2, b).

In agreement with this Raistrick *et al.* (1939) found that pressure has a very marked effect on the rate of the Diels Alder dimerization of cyclopentadiene (the reverse of reaction (20)), the bimolecular rate constant increasing by a factor of 41 between 1 and 4 000 atm at 30° C. Their results at 20° C are summarized in Table IV, where k_p/k_1 denotes the ratio of the second-order rate constant at the pressure p to that at 1 atm; $\Delta V_p^{\ddagger}$ is the activation volume at the pressure p (formula (6)), and $\Delta H_p^{\ddagger}$ and $\Delta S_p^{\ddagger}$ are enthalpies and entropies of activation calculated from the transition state theory.

TABLE IV. The Effect of Pressure on the Dimerization of
Cyclopentadiene at 20° C

p (atm)	1	1 000	2 000	3 000	4 000
k_p/k_1†	1·00	3·36	8·77	18·45	41·1
$\Delta V_p^{\ddagger}$ (cm³/mole)	−31·0	−24·9	−21·0	−18·3	−16·6
ΔH_p (kcal/mole)	16·4	17·0	17·6	18·0	18·3
$\Delta S_p^{\ddagger}$ (cal/deg mole)	−31	−27	−23	−20	−18

† These values of k_p/k_1 are based on the mole fraction scale, not the molarity scale used by Raistrick *et al.* (1939).

Several features of the data call for comment. First, the values of $\Delta V^{\ddagger}$ are very close to the total changes in volume which occur when two moles of the monomer dimerize (Gonikberg and Vereshchagin, 1949). This is true both at atmospheric pressure and at high pressures, and it provides strong evidence for the hypothesis that the transition state has a cyclic structure very similar to the final state. Secondly, the large negative values of $\Delta S^{\ddagger}$ suggest that the reacting monomer molecules must assume a very specific and rigid configuration in the transition state, and this again is compatible with a cyclic structure. Finally, the increase of both $\Delta S^{\ddagger}$ and $\Delta H^{\ddagger}$ with increasing pressure can be explained by the loss of some of the rotational freedom of the monomer molecules in their initial states: a restriction of rotation is to be expected on theoretical grounds, and it would have the effect of reducing the entropy and enthalpy in much the way that freezing does.

Walling and Peisach (1958) later examined the influence of pressure to 8 000 atm on the Diels-Alder dimerization of isoprene at 60 and 75° C. They found that this reaction, like the dimerization of cyclopentadiene is strongly accelerated by pressure. But in contrast to the results for cyclopentadiene, their data suggested that the value of the activation volume at 1 atm, $\Delta V_1^{\ddagger}$, was only about half the over-all volume change ΔV_1° for complete reaction (at 60° C they found $\Delta V_1^{\ddagger} = -24\cdot3$ cm^3/mole, while $\Delta V_1^{\circ} = -45\cdot5$ cm^3/mole). From this they concluded that the transition state could not be cyclic, but might be one leading to the formation of an open-chain biradical. That is, they ruled out the mechanism (22) and proposed instead

$$\text{(23)}$$

The principal reason for their favouring the mechanism (23) was that the measured value of $\Delta V_1^{\ddagger}$ was closer to the contraction for the formation of one C—C bond than of two (cf. Table II of Chapter 7.ii). Thus their conclusion rests heavily on the numerical accuracy of $\Delta V_1^{\ddagger}$.

At first sight there seems little cause to doubt the reliability of $\Delta V_1^{\ddagger}$ because, as Fig. 1 shows, the plot A of $\log_{10}(k_p/k_1)$ against pressure is very nearly linear between 1 and 4 000 atm and it is easy to make an accurate estimate of the slope of this initial part of the curve, which is what Walling and Peisach did in order to find the value $\Delta V_1^{\ddagger} = -24\cdot3$ cm^3/mole. But the existence of such a long straight section followed by rather steep curvature is in itself slightly suspicious, since most (although not all) other data on reaction rates under pressure yield plots which, from the beginning, curve towards the pressure axis indicating that $|\Delta V^{\ddagger}|$ decreases with increasing pressure (see, e.g., Table IV). On this ground Benson and Berson (1962) have recently suggested that Walling and Peisach's estimate of $-\Delta V_1^{\ddagger}$ may be much too low.

Benson and Berson advanced the hypothesis that, because many organic liquids conform closely to Tait's empirical equation of state, it can be assumed that the transition states for non-ionic reactions also obey this equation. In its integrated form (see, e.g., Rowlinson, 1959) the isothermal Tait equation can be written

$$V_p = V_1\left[1 - C\log_{10}\left(\frac{B+p}{B+1}\right)\right], \qquad \text{(24)}$$

where V_p and V_1 denote the volumes of the substance at the pressures p atm and 1 atm respectively; C is a dimensionless constant, and B is a

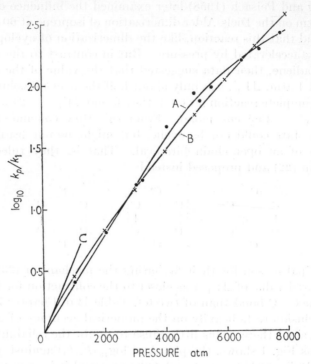

FIG. 1. Variation in the rate of dimerization of isoprene with pressure at 60° C. The dots are the experimental points; the curve A is the one drawn by Walling and Peisach (1958); the curve B is the " Tait Equation " curve fitted by Benson and Berson (1962).

constant in units of atm. Both B and C are positive quantities. Applying Eq. (24) to the initial (i) and transition ($\ddagger$) states for a reaction, we find that

$$\Delta V_p{}^{\ddagger} = V_p{}^{\ddagger} - V_p{}^i = \Delta V_1{}^{\ddagger} - V_1{}^{\ddagger}C^{\ddagger} \log_{10}\left(\frac{B^{\ddagger}+p}{B^{\ddagger}+1}\right)$$

$$+ V_1{}^i C^i \log_{10}\left(\frac{B^i+p}{B^i+1}\right). \qquad (25)$$

Benson and Berson further proposed that since the values of C for different organic liquids are very nearly independent of their structures $C^{\ddagger}$ can be assumed to be the same as C^i and to have the value 0·216 which is close to the actual value of C for a wide range of liquids. To this approximation Eq. (25) *demands* that if $V_1{}^{\ddagger} \neq V_1{}^i$ then $\Delta V_p{}^{\ddagger}$ must vary with the pressure in a particular way. It says in fact that if the rate of a reaction is at all affected by pressure then the plot of $\log_{10}(k_p/k_1)$ against p can never be straight.

Let us now consider the specific application of Eq. (25) to the dimerization of isoprene. Of the quantities in this formula V^i and B^i can be derived from density and compressibility measurements at low pressures; for two moles of isoprene at $60°$ C they have the values $V^i = 213$ cm³/mole (Walling and Peisach, 1958), $B^i = 319$ atm (Peisach, 1958). If we accept Benson and Berson's assumption that $C^{\ddagger} = C^i = 0.216$ we are left with a relation involving the two unknown quantities $B^{\ddagger}$ and $V_1^{\ddagger}$, which can be adjusted to fit the experimental data. Benson and Berson developed an approximation method to simplify the process of fitting, but apparently they found that two adjustable parameters were not enough and were forced to change B^i slightly. Their final values for the parameters were $V_1^{\ddagger} = 175.5$ cm³/mole (whence, $\Delta V_1^{\ddagger} = -36.5$ cm³/mole), $B^{\ddagger} = 508$ atm, $B^i = 290$ atm. With these values the integrated form of Eq. (25)

$$\int_1^p \Delta V_p^{\ddagger}\, \mathrm{d}p = \int_1^p - RT \frac{\partial \ln k}{\partial p}\, \mathrm{d}p = - RT \ln (k_p/k_1) \qquad (26)$$

yields the curve B in Fig. 1.

The activation volumes obtained in this way were -36.5 cm³/mole at $60°$ C and -38.4 cm³/mole at $75°$ C which are considerably more negative than the values -24.3 and -25.6 cm³/mole estimated by Walling and Peisach. Benson and Berson suggested that if any mechanistic inference is to be drawn from the new values it is that they are at least as consistent with a cyclic transition state (22) as with Walling and Peisach's biradical mechanism (23). However there are several reasons for distrusting the more negative values. They are,

(i) Equation (25) has no basis in theory. It was derived from an empirical equation of state which unrealistically predicts negative volumes at very high pressures (Eq. (24)). Moreover there is no real justification for supposing that a transition state obeys the same kind of equation of state as stable molecules. In particular there is no reason why the compressibility of a transition state along its " reaction co-ordinate " should resemble any ordinary molecular compressibility.

(ii) The curve B in Fig. 1 is certainly not as good a representation of the experimental results as is A. If we accept B in preference to A it means that we discount the experiments in favour of an empirical formula. The fact is that the limiting slope C, corresponding to $\Delta V^{\ddagger} = -36.5$ cm³/mole is simply not consistent with the experimental data as they stand; it has been forced on us by the particular form of Tait's equation. It is the writer's opinion that until the experiments have been disproved it is more justifiable to accept them than the requirements of an arbitrary " theory ".

Nevertheless Benson and Berson were right in pointing out that, in the past, too little attention has been paid to the way in which the activation volume for a reaction varies with the pressure. This variation depends directly on the compressibility of the transition state and it could very well give useful information about the structure and properties of the transition state. It is an effect which should certainly be examined in the future, from both the theoretical and experimental angles.

3. Homopolar Exchange Reactions $A + BC \rightarrow AB + C$

Ewald (1959) has measured the effect of pressure on the rates of abstraction of hydrogen atoms from thiols RSH by diphenylpicryl-hydrazyl (DPP$^{\cdot}$) radicals:

$$\begin{array}{c} \phi_2 N \\ \diagdown \\ \diagup \quad N^{\cdot} + HSR \\ (NO_2)_3C_6H_2 \\ (DPP) \end{array} \xrightarrow{\text{slow}} \begin{array}{c} \phi_2 N \\ \diagdown \\ \diagup \quad NH + {}^{\cdot}SR. \\ (NO_2)_3C_6H_2 \\ (DPPH) \end{array} \qquad (27)$$

He used Russell's (1954) method of following the reactions by observing the rate of disappearance of DPP$^{\cdot}$. Unfortunately this rate (k_{obs}) is not a direct measure of the rate (k_{ex}) of hydrogen exchange (27) because the subsequent reactions of the $^{\cdot}$SR radical remove some additional DPP$^{\cdot}$. Brook et al. (1958) have suggested that the principal of these reactions are

$$2 \,{}^{\cdot}SR \;\rightarrow\; RSSR \qquad (28)$$

and
$$DPP^{\cdot} + {}^{\cdot}SR \;\rightarrow\; DPPSR, \qquad (29)$$

which remove one and two molecules of DPP$^{\cdot}$ respectively for each molecule of RSH attacked. The stoicheiometry shows that (28) and (29) occur concurrently and in varying relative amounts under different conditions, so that the ratio k_{obs}/k_{ex} can vary between 1 and 2; usually it seems to be about 1·8 (Hazell and Russell, 1958; Godsay et al., 1959). Although this ratio may depend upon the pressure it is unlikely to change very much if the competing reactions are both free radical combinations, (28) and (29). Here we shall assume that it is constant and that the pressure dependence of k_{obs} is a good indication of the true behaviour of k_{ex}.

Ewald found that the second-order rate constants for the reaction of a number of alkyl thiols with DPP$^{\cdot}$ increased rapidly with increasing pressure. Some of his results are listed in Table V, where the values of

k_p/k_1 and of $\Delta V_1^{\ddagger}$ have been averaged over the temperature range of the experiments.

TABLE V. Second-Order Rate Constants for the Reaction of DPP* with Thiols in Toluene

Thiol	Temp. range (°C)	$10^3 \times k$ at 1 atm and 35°C (kg/mole sec.)	k_p/k_1						$\Delta V_1^{\ddagger}$ (cm³/mole)
						p (atm)			
			1	1500	2700	5000	8000	10000	
C_4H_9SH	35–75	18	1	2·1	4·5				− 13
$C_6H_{13}SH$	30–50	27	1	3·0	6·1	26	52	83	− 20
t-octyl-SH	35	1·0	1	1·8	9·1				− 21

The acceleration of the reactions can reasonably be attributed to the contraction caused in the transition state by the partial formation of the N---H bond, the accompanying increase in length of the H---S bond being quite small (cf. Section II, B, 1, (c)).

The Claisen re-arrangement of allyl vinyl ethers and allyl phenyl ethers is essentially an *intra-molecular* exchange reaction which proceeds through a slow step involving the simultaneous breaking of an O—C bond and formation of a C—C bond (Ingold, 1953, p. 600):

$$
\begin{array}{ccc}
\text{O—CH}_2 & \left[\text{O---CH}_2 \right] & \text{O} \quad \text{CH}_2 \\
\diagdown \quad \diagdown & \diagdown \quad \diagdown & \diagdown \quad \| \\
\text{C} \quad \text{CH} \rightarrow & \text{C} \quad \text{CH} \rightarrow & \text{C} \quad \text{CH} \\
\| \quad \| & \vdots \quad \vdots & \diagdown \\
\text{C} \quad \text{CH}_2 & \text{C---------CH}_2 & \text{C—CH}_2 \\
\diagup \diagdown \quad \diagdown & \diagup \diagdown & \diagup \diagdown
\end{array}
\qquad (30)
$$

Brower (1961) has examined several of these reactions in different solvents under pressure. He found that they were accelerated by pressure in a remarkably uniform way, all their rate constants increasing by a factor of about 1·7 between 68 and 1400 atm at 130–190° C. The values of $\Delta V_1^{\ddagger}$ were − 14 to − 18 cm³/mole, which are again consistent with the view that the contraction due to the partial formation of the new C—C bond outweighs the stretching of the O—C bond.

The " chain transfer " step in vinyl polymerizations is another exchange reaction of this general class. The transfer can occur either by the attack of a polymer radical on a monomer molecule

$$R—CH_2^{\cdot} + CH_2{=}CHX \rightarrow RCH_3 + CH_2{=}CX^{\cdot}$$

by its attack on a solvent molecule, e.g. CCl_4

$$R—CH_2^{\cdot} + CCl_4 \rightarrow RCH_2Cl + CCl_3^{\cdot}$$

G

Walling and Pellon (1957a, c) have found indirect evidence that both
kinds of reactions are accelerated by raising the pressure, and in fact the
increase in rate is very nearly identical with that for the chain propagation reaction (21). They concluded that $\Delta V^{\ddagger} \approx -11$ cm³/mole for
transfer between a styrene radical and carbon tetrachloride, at pressures
between 1 000 and 3 700 atm.

4. Restricted Rotation about a Single Bond

This is an interesting class of reactions in which bonds are neither
formed nor broken.

The rate of hindered rotation about a single C—C bond can be measured
by ultrasonic relaxation methods (Lamb, 1960) or more simply by
observing the rate of racemization of an optical isomer whose initial
asymmetry corresponds to one of two stable rotational configurations.
If the rotation is entirely prevented the optical isomer will remain stable
indefinitely, but if it is only partly impeded the isomer will racemize at
a measurable rate (for a review, see Adams and Yuan, 1933) and the
transition state for racemization will be the configuration of highest
potential energy during the rotation.

In a theoretical treatment of biphenyl compounds of the type

A

A

Westheimer (1947) showed that the transition state is formed with very
little stretching (about 0·04 Å) of the interannular C—C bond, but with
some bending of the bonds which hold the interfering groups A to the
benzene rings. Energetically, it is much easier to bend these groups out
of each other's way than it is to stretch the central bond. On this basis
we might expect the volume change for activation to be small and
perhaps positive.

Experimentally, McKelvey and Brower (1960) found this to be the
case for the racemization of three compounds having the general
structure

$$\phi SO_2 - N - CH_2 CO_2 H,$$
$$\mid$$
$$Ar$$

where Ar denotes an aryl group with hindering ortho- substituents.
The rate constants changed by no more than 10 per cent between 1 and
1 360 atm, and the largest value of $\Delta V^{\ddagger}$ was $+2$ cm³/mole. At the same

time, McCune *et al.* (1960) independently reported that the racemization of the sodium salt of L-6-nitro-2-2'-carboxybiphenyl was retarded by an increase in pressure to an extent corresponding to $\Delta V^{\ddagger} = +2$ cm³/mole at 1 atm. They observed that $\Delta V^{\ddagger}$ decreased rapidly with increasing pressure to 12 000 atm and appeared to be approaching zero asymptotically at that pressure. This suggests that the expanded transition state is more compressible than the initial state and that ultimately their volumes will become the same.

B. *Reactions Involving Ions*

In this section we shall review the data on ionic reactions in the following order:

(1) reactions in which the slow step leads to the formation of ions from neutral molecules,

(2) those in which ions combine to form neutral molecules,

(3) those in which ions participate without either increasing or decreasing the net charge of the system.

Within these classifications it is convenient to group the reactions in the way that was done in Section III, A, namely into (a) dissociations, (b) associations, (c) exchanges.

1. *Reactions Producing Ions from Neutral Molecules*

(a) *Ionic (Heterolytic) Dissociations:* $AB \rightarrow A^+ + B^-$. It is well established (Ingold, 1953, pp. 308–418) that the unimolecular (S_N1) exchange reactions of a number of alkyl halides RX occur in two steps, the first being the slow ionization of the halide

$$RX \rightarrow R^+ + X^-,$$

and the second a fast combination of the alkyl carbonium ion with the substituting group. For instance the hydrolysis of *t*-butyl chloride follows the scheme:

$$(CH_3)_3CCl \quad \overset{slow}{\rightarrow} \quad (CH_3)_3C^+ + Cl^-,$$
$$(CH_3)_3C^+ + H_2O \quad \overset{fast}{\rightarrow} \quad (CH_3)_3COH + H^+,$$

so that the rate of formation of HCl is equal to the rate of the initial ionization step. The transition state is presumably

$$(CH_3)_3C^{+\delta} \ldots \ldots Cl^{-\delta},$$

where the C—Cl bond has been stretched and partial charges, δ, have appeared on the separating fragments. Some potential energy calculations (Evans, 1946) suggest that the C—Cl bond must be stretched by about 0.7 Å to form the transition state for this reaction, and the resulting increase in volume $\varDelta_1 V^{\ddagger}$ would be about 4 cm³/mole if the effective cross-sectional area of the bond were the same as that of a chlorine atom. Although this figure is little better than a guess, there is no reason to doubt that bond-stretching must cause some increase in volume during activation, and if this were the only term in $\varDelta V^{\ddagger}$ the reaction should be retarded by increasing the pressure. However, the development of charges on the separating fragments will undoubtedly lead to a contraction $\varDelta_2 V^{\ddagger}$ of the surrounding solvent (see Section II, B, 2) which could well result in a net decrease in volume of the system as a whole.

Experimentally it has been found that $\varDelta V^{\ddagger}$ is, in fact, negative. Measurements by Buchanan and Hamann (1953) and David and Hamann (1954) have shown that the rates of S_N1 hydrolyses of t-butyl chloride and benzotrichloride are very much greater at high pressures than at atmospheric pressure. Some of their results are given in Table VI.

TABLE VI. The Influence of Pressure on the Rate of the Unimolecular Reaction $(CH_3)_3CCl \rightarrow (CH_3)_3C^+ + Cl^-$ in 80/20 Ethanol/Water (Vol.) Solution at 25° C.

p (atm)	$10^6 k$ (sec^{-1})	$\varDelta V_p^{\ddagger}$ (cm³/mole)	p (atm)	$10^6 k$ (sec^{-1})	$\varDelta V_p^{\ddagger}$ (cm³/mole)
1	8·4	-17	9 000	134	$-3·0$
1 500	21	-12	12 000	170	$-2·5$
3 000	41	-7	15 000	240	$-2·0$
6 000	74	$-4·5$			

It will be seen that the volume change for activation $\varDelta V_p^{\ddagger}$, calculated by Eq. (6) from the slope of a plot of log k against p, decreases rapidly with increasing pressure. This behaviour is characteristic of reactions in which ions are formed and it is shown both by activation volumes and by over-all volume changes for complete ionization (cf. Table V of Chapter 7.ii). It probably reflects the fact that the free solvent is more compressible than solvent bound around the ionic charges, so that as the pressure is raised the difference in density between the two decreases.

If we accept the rough theoretical estimate that $\varDelta_1 V^{\ddagger} \approx +4$cm³/mole, it follows that $\varDelta_2 V^{\ddagger} \approx -21$ cm³/mole at 1 atm, suggesting that the ionic charges are quite highly developed in the transition state.

(b) *Association and Exchange Reactions Producing Ions.* The following reactions of this class have been studied at high pressures:

(i) Solvolyses of alkyl halides RX in neutral hydroxylic solvents R'OH. These follow the S_N2 mechanism (Ingold, 1953; p. 310);

$$RX + R'OH \rightarrow ROR' + H^+ + X^-. \tag{30}$$

(ii) Menshutkin reactions, in which an alkyl halide reacts with a tertiary amine to form a quarternary ammonium salt

$$RX + R_3'N \rightarrow R\overset{+}{N}R_3' + X^-. \tag{31}$$

(iii) The " dark " halogenation of olefins in polar solvents which proceeds through a slow step

$$\text{>C=C< } + X_2 \rightarrow \text{ >}\overset{+}{C}\text{—C< } + X^-, \tag{32}$$

followed by the fast addition of X^- to the positive complex.

(iv) Knoevenagel condensations, whose rate-determining step is apparently the ionization

$$R_3N + CN.CH_2.CO_2R \rightarrow CN.\overset{-}{C}H.CO_2R + R_3\overset{+}{N}H, \tag{33}$$

where R_3N is an amine base.

(v) The formation of oximes from ketones and hydroxylamine, catalysed by weak acids. Although the mechanism of this reaction is not certain, there is some evidence that the slow stage may be

$$HA + R_2C\overset{\diagup NH.OH}{\diagdown OH} \rightarrow R_2C=\overset{+}{N}H.OH + A^- + H_2O, \tag{34}$$

where HA denotes the weak unionized acid.

The results will be discussed in the order in which the reactions are listed above.

The transition state for the bimolecular neutral solvolyses (30) is presumably formed by stretching the R—X and O—H bonds; by partially forming the R—O bond; and by developing charges on the X and H atoms, thus

$$\overset{R'}{\underset{\underset{+\delta}{H}}{\diagup}}\text{>O---R---X}^{-\delta}$$

There is no sure way of deciding from theory whether $\Delta_1 V^{\ddagger}$ is positive or negative for this reaction, since two covalent bonds are broken and one is formed. But this cancellation of effects suggests that $\Delta_1 V^{\ddagger}$ will in any case be small. On the other hand it is reasonable to suppose that the magnitude of the electrical charges will be comparable with that for the S_N1 solvolyses (see Section III, B, 1, (a)) so that $\Delta_2 V^{\ddagger}$ may be large and negative.

In agreement with this it has been found that the S_N2 solvolyses are accelerated by pressure to very nearly the same extent as the S_N1 reactions (David and Hamann, 1954). The measurements have covered a wider pressure range than is usually employed in kinetic experiments, and in one instance it was observed that at 45 000 atm the rate of etherification of allyl bromide in methanol was 2 000 times greater than at 1 atm (David and Hamann, 1956). Some of the results are illustrated in Fig. 2, where the relative rate constants k_p/k_1 have been plotted on a

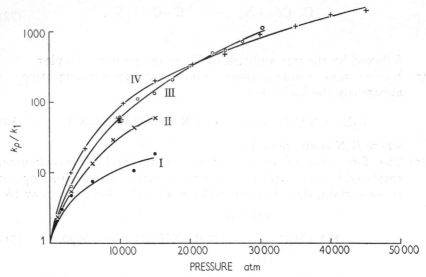

FIG. 2. The acceleration of some solvolyses in methanol under pressure. The reactions I–IV are defined in the text. k_p denotes the first-order rate constant at the pressure p atm. (Reproduced with permission from Hamann, 1957.)

logarithmic scale against the pressure. The curves in the diagram relate to the following reactions:

I. $C_2H_5I + CH_3OH \rightarrow C_2H_5OCH_3 + H^+ + I^-$, at $65°$ C

II. $C_2H_5Br + CH_3OH \rightarrow C_2H_5OCH_3 + H^+ + Br^-$, at $65°$ C

III. $C_2H_5Cl + CH_3OH \rightarrow C_2H_5OCH_3 + H^+ + Cl^-$, at $65°$ C

IV. $C_3H_5Br + CH_3OH \rightarrow C_3H_5OCH_3 + H^+ + Br^-$, at $23°$ C
(allyl bromide)

It will be seen that the slopes of the plots decrease steadily with increasing pressure, the value of $\Delta V^{\ddagger}$ for reaction IV being about -27 cm³/mole at 1 atm and $-1\cdot3$ cm³/mole at 40 000 atm. However, there is no indication of any tendency for $\Delta V^{\ddagger}$ to change sign. An interesting feature of the results is that the effect of pressure on the ethyl halide reactions I–III increases in the order $C_2H_5I < C_2H_5Br < C_2H_5Cl$, which is precisely the order of increasing electrostriction of solvent around the free halide ions (cf. Eq. (47) of Chapter 7.ii). This is further evidence that the ionic charges must be quite highly developed in the transition state, and that the solvation term $\Delta_2 V^{\ddagger}$ is the predominant one for these reactions.

Menshutkin condensations (31) have been more thoroughly examined at high pressures than any other simple reactions. The reason lies partly in the historical fact that the Menshutkin formation of cetyl pyridinium bromide from cetyl bromide and pyridine was one of the first reactions to be shown to depend strongly on the pressure (Fawcett and Gibson, 1934), and partly in a controversy which has recently arisen over the relative importance of the structural term $\Delta_1 V^{\ddagger}$ and the " solvation " term $\Delta_2 V^{\ddagger}$ in the total activation volume (Hamann, 1957, p. 173; Gonikberg, 1960, p. 142). A good deal of effort has been put into answering this question.

Formally, the Menshutkin reaction is an S_N2 exchange analogous to the solvolyses discussed above, and it is justifiable to suppose that the transition state consists of an arrangement like

$$R_3N^{+\delta}\text{---}R\text{---}X^{-\delta}, \tag{35}$$

where the initial R—X bond has been stretched; an N—R bond has been partially formed; and charges have appeared on the N and X atoms. Several theoretical attempts have been made to estimate $\Delta_1 V^{\ddagger}$ for the formation of such a transition state, but unfortunately they have all been based on arbitrarily assumed models, not on properly calculated potential energy surfaces. Stearn and Eyring (1941a, b) proposed a model in which they assumed the N—R bond to be fully formed in the transition state, without any concurrent stretching of the R—X bond. From this, and several other approximations, they estimated that $\Delta_1 V^{\ddagger}$ is typically about -13 cm³/mole. In more recent calculations Gonikberg and Kitaigorodsky (1958; see also Gonikberg, 1960, p. 144–148) have made the same assumption about the complete formation of the N—R bond and concluded that the bond-forming process contributes a volume change of -5 cm³/mole to $\Delta_1 V^{\ddagger}$ for all Menshutkin reactions. However, they suggested that in addition to this term there are others arising from the overlapping of interfering substituents of the amine and alkyl halide molecules. As an example, they cited the transition state for the reaction between trimethylamine and i-propyl iodide, which they considered to have the configuration shown in Fig. 3. Here, the i-propyl radical has become planar, the N, C(1) and I atoms are

collinear in a direction perpendicular to the plane of $(CH_3)_2HC(1)$, and
the amine has its original pyramidal structure with its apex facing $C(1)$

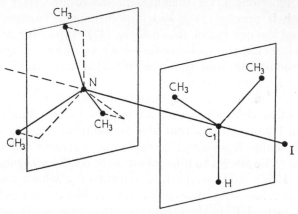

FIG. 3. A possible transition state for the Menshutkin reaction between
trimethylamine and i-propyl iodide.

and with its $N-CH_3$ bonds turned through 60° about the $N-C(1)$ axis
with respect to the bonds of the i-propyl radical (this minimizes the
steric interference between the groups on N and on $C(l)$. Imposing the
restrictions (1) that the $N-C(l)$ distance is equal to the final bond
length, 1·5 Å; (2) that the bond angles in the amine are 108°; (3) that
the bond angles in the planar i-propyl group are 120°; and (4) that the
$C-I$ distance is the same as in i-propyl iodide, Gonikberg and
Kitaigorodsky found that the centres of a number of pairs of non-
bonded groups are closer than the sums of their van der Waals radii.
The groups are:

	transition state separation (Å)	van der Waals separation (Å)
N. . .H (1 interaction)	1·85	2·8
N. . .CH_3 (2 interactions)	2·15	3·6
CH_3. . .H (2 interactions)	2·6	3·2
CH_3. . .CH_3 (4 interactions)	2·7	4·0

By taking account of the reduction in volume caused by this " inter-
penetration " of spherical groups, Gonikberg and Kitaigorodsky
arrived at the total value $\Delta_1 V^{\ddagger} = -24$ cm³/mole.

However, on energetic grounds it is extremely unlikely that such
high degrees of compression could occur. For example, there is
evidence from molecular scattering experiments (Amdur et al., 1961)
that the energy needed to compress a pair of methane molecules from
their equilibrium separation of 4·3 Å to a separation of 2·9 Å (corresponding to the 32% compression of non-bonded $CH_3...CH_3$ groups

listed above) is about 0·38 eV. Thus the four $CH_3...CH_3$ interactions *alone* would contribute 35 kcal/mole to the activation energy, whereas the experimental activation energy is only 13·5 kcal/mole for the reaction between trimethylamine and *i*-propyl iodide (Perrin and Williams, 1937). The main deficiency of the model lies in its rigidity, that is, in its failure to allow bonds to stretch and bend in order to relieve the steric strain. It corresponds in fact to Ingold's " stiff " model of the transition states of sterically hindered S_N2 reactions, rather than to a " plastic " model which properly minimizes the potential energy by allowing bond relaxations (Ingold, 1953, p. 403; de la Mare *et al.*, 1955). For this reason the model, although plausible, would need considerable modification before it could yield meaningful values of $\Delta_1 V^\ddagger$. At present the most that can be said is that $\Delta_1 V^\ddagger$ is probably negative and may be as large as -20 cm³/mole, by analogy with the non-ionic exchange reactions discussed in Section III, A, 3.

As to the solvation term $\Delta_2 V^\ddagger$, there is ample evidence that the transition state for Menshutkin reactions is quite highly ionic and that it interacts strongly with the surrounding liquid, so that $\Delta_2 V^\ddagger$ can certainly not be ignored, as it was in Stearn and Eyring's (1941a, b) treatment of pressure effects. The main evidence for solvent participation is (a), that Menshutkin reactions do not occur in the gaseous phase (Moelwyn-Hughes and Hinshelwood, 1932) but require a liquid or active surface to stabilize the transition state by " solvating " it; (b), that, as Menshutkin (1890) himself observed, the rate of reaction varies enormously with the nature of the solvent; (c), that the entropy of activation usually has a large negative value, reflecting the loss of translational and rotational freedom by solvent molecules which become electrically bound around the transition state. The following discussion of the results of rate measurements at high pressures will show that they are quite consistent with this picture of solvent participation and with the importance of the term $\Delta_2 V^\ddagger$ in $\Delta V^\ddagger$.

It would require a great deal of space to present all the available data on Menshutkin reactions at high pressures, and it is in any case unnecessary to do so, as there are already a number of detailed reviews of the results (Perrin, 1938; Gonikberg, 1960, pp. 142–150; Harris and Weale, 1961; Brower, 1959). Here it will be sufficient to summarize the general effects that have been found. They are:

(i) All the Menshutkin reactions studied so far are strongly accelerated by an increase in pressure, in extreme instances by factors as great as 500 between 1 and 15000 atm (Perrin, 1938; Hamann and Teplitzky, 1956). The activation volumes $\Delta V^\ddagger$ at 1 atm are usually in the range -20 to -40 cm³/mole, although in a few exceptional cases they have been found to be as large as -60 cm³/mole (Brower, 1958).

(ii) The value of $\Delta V^{\ddagger}$ for a particular reaction varies with the solvent.

(iii) $-\Delta V^{\ddagger}$ always decreases with increasing pressure, its value at 2 000 atm being about half that at 1 atm (Harris and Weale, 1961; Gonikberg and El'yanov, 1960).

(iv) The temperature dependence of $\Delta V^{\ddagger}$ shows that the entropy of activation $\Delta S^{\ddagger}$ becomes less negative with increasing pressure, the value of $T \Delta S^{\ddagger}$ increasing by about 2 kcal/mole between 1 and 3 000 atm. On the other hand the activation energy is only slightly altered (see, e.g., Hamann, 1957, Fig. 9.1), which means that the acceleration of the reaction under pressure must be attributed to a more favourable entropy change.

The large magnitudes of $\Delta V^{\ddagger}$ are scarcely consistent with an unsolvated transition state, since the "structural" term $\Delta_1 V^{\ddagger}$ is unlikely to be much greater than -20 cm³/mole. Even more significant is the fact that, for a particular reaction, $\Delta V^{\ddagger}$ may be considerably altered by a change of solvent. This effect is illustrated by the data in Table VII and by other results for reactions between piperidine and

TABLE VII. The Effect of Solvent on Volumes of Activation for Menshutkin Reactions at 1 atm

Reaction	Solvent	$\Delta V^{\ddagger}(cm^3/mole)$	Reference
ϕ-NMe$_2$ + EtI	MeOH	-34	Harris and Weale (1961)
	ϕ-NO$_2$	-20	Harris and Weale (1961)
o-Me-ϕ-NMe$_2$ + MeI	MeOH	-24	Harris and Weale (1961)
	Acetone	(-27)	Weale (1956)
Pyridine + EtI	Acetone	-30	Gonikberg and Zhulin (1958)
	c-Hexanone	-27	Gonikberg and El'yanov (1960)
	ϕ-NO$_2$	-24	Gonikberg and El'yanov (1960)
Pyridine + butyl Br	Toluene	$-42\cdot5$	Brower (1962)
	Ethanol	$-33\cdot4$	Brower (1962)
	Ethanol–water	$-25\cdot7$	Brower (1962)

aromatic halides (Brower, 1959). It can only be due to a variation of the solvation term $\Delta_2 V^{\ddagger}$ with a change of medium, and the evidence from the magnitude of the effect is that $\Delta_2 V^{\ddagger}$ is probably at least as great as $\Delta_1 V^{\ddagger}$.

Gonikberg (1960, p. 143) has pointed out that the large decrease of $\Delta V^{\ddagger}$ with increasing pressure is analogous to the behaviour of $\Delta V^{\ddagger}$ for the ionic solvolysis of t-butyl chloride (see Section III, B, 1, (a)) and is indicative of a solvated transition state. Also, it seems that the increase in activation entropy $\Delta S^{\ddagger}$ with increasing pressure is to be expected on theoretical grounds for a reaction which involves an increase in solvation in the activation step (Hamann 1957, p. 174) whereas the influence of pressure on a non-solvated association reaction should primarily be to reduce the activation *energy*. A further point of interest is that for a given attacking amine $R_3'N$ and a given alkyl radical R in formula (30), the value of $-\Delta V^{\ddagger}$ decreases with an increase in the size of the halogen atom X (Hamann and Teplitzky, 1956); an effect which is consistent with the fact that the electric field strength around a charged atom varies as the inverse of the atomic diameter (cf. formula (44) of Chapter 7.ii). These and a number of other arguments make it quite certain that electrostriction plays an important role in the behaviour of Menshutkin reactions under pressure.

Gonikberg and his colleagues have recently tried to estimate the actual amount of solvent that becomes bound into the transition state. Essentially, their method consists in comparing the activation volume for a reaction $\Delta V^{\ddagger}$ with the total volume change ΔV for complete formation of the quaternary salt under the same conditions. For example, Gonikberg and Zhulin (1958) found that $\Delta V^{\ddagger}$ for the reaction

$$\langle\text{hexagon}\rangle\text{N} + \text{EtI} \quad \rightarrow \quad \langle\text{hexagon}\rangle\overset{+}{\text{N}}\text{Et} + \text{I}^-$$

in acetone at 40° C is -30 cm³/mole, whereas the difference between the partial molar volumes of the final and initial species in solution is about -56 cm³/mole, showing clearly that the transition state is not as fully solvated as the final state. Gonikberg and El'yanov (1960) and Harris and Weale (1961) have observed similar differences between $\Delta V^{\ddagger}$ and ΔV for other Menshutkin reactions, but Brower (1959), on the other hand, found that for some aromatic Menshutkin reactions the two values are quite close, implying that the transition state must be almost as fully ionized and solvated as the final state. Although a great deal of work remains to be done in this field, it is now clear that the value of $\Delta V^{\ddagger}$ for a reaction can sometimes give useful information about the polarity of its transition state.

The addition of a halogen molecule X_2 to an olefin in the liquid phase and in the dark is, molecularly, rather similar to Menshutkin reactions in that its slow step involves the breaking of one bond and the formation of another, with the simultaneous development of two ionic charges (Roberts and Kimball, 1937):

$$X_2 + R_2C:CR_2 \quad \xrightarrow{\text{slow}} \quad \overset{+}{R_2C}.CR_2X + X^-,$$
$$\overset{+}{R_2C}.CR_2X + X^- \quad \xrightarrow{\text{fast}} \quad XR_2C.CR_2X.$$

Hamann and Teplitzky (1956) have found that several of these halogenations are accelerated by pressure to roughly the same extent as Menshutkin reactions, and it is possible that a corresponding effect may be responsible for the acceleration at high pressures of the cationic polymerization of i-amyl-vinyl ether, catalysed by molecular iodine (Hamann and Teplitzky, 1961).

Knoevenagel condensations are also remarkably analogous to Menshutkin reactions, since the rate-determining step is the attack of a tertiary amine on a neutral molecule, leading to the abstraction of proton and the formation of what is essentially a highly unstable quaternary ammonium salt (see Eq. 33). Their kinetics have not been studied in detail at high pressures, but some qualitative measurements by Newitt et al. (1937) have shown that the rate of condensation of cyanoacetic ester with cyclopentanone at 180° C, catalysed by piperidine, increases by a factor of 15 between 1 and 5 000 atm, which is again of the same order as the corresponding acceleration of Menshutkin reactions.

Although there is doubt about the exact mechanism of formation of oximes, there is some evidence that the slow step may be the ionization reaction (34). Jones et al. (1959) consider that this suggestion is supported by the results of high pressure measurements which they have carried out on the reactions between hydroxylamine and some sterically hindered ketones. They have found, for instance, that the rate of formation of cortisone-3:20-bis-dioxolane-11-oxime increases 140-fold between 1 and 9 400 atm, and that the value of $\Delta V^{\ddagger}$ at 1 atm is approximately $-20 \text{ cm}^3/\text{mole}$. Although these figures may be subject to quite large errors, there is no doubt about the general accelerating influence of pressure; in fact, Jones et al. discovered that whilst di-t-butyl ketone will not condense at all with hydroxylamine at atmospheric pressure, it does so rapidly at 9 130 atm.

Finally, in this class of reactions, Cairns et al. (1957) have reported that the formation of quinazolinediones from amines and carbon dioxide (in the homogeneous liquid phase) proceeds rapidly above a threshold pressure of 3 300 atm, and they were able to obtain high yields of the products at 8 500 atm and 200–250° C. It seems likely that the reason why pressure facilitates these condensations is that it accelerates the initial step

$$2\phi NH_2 + CO_2 \quad \rightarrow \quad \phi N\overset{-}{H}\overset{-}{CO_2} + H_3\overset{+}{N}\phi.$$

But further studies would be needed to confirm this mechanism.

2. Reactions Involving the Neutralization of Ionic Charges

(a) *Dissociations:* $A^-B^+ \rightarrow X + Y$. This class of reactions is to be understood to mean those in which associated ions decompose into free neutral molecules. The best-known example is the decomposition of quaternary ammonium salts in media of low dielectric constant

$$[R_3\overset{+}{N}R.X^-]_{\text{associated}} \quad \rightarrow \quad R_3'N + RX, \tag{36}$$

which is the reverse of the Menshutkin reaction (31). Although the kinetics are generally complex (Ross *et al.*, 1961) it is sometimes possible to find solvents in which they are accurately of the first order with respect to the concentration of quaternary salt, indicating that the salt exists in solution almost entirely as ion pairs.

Since the electrostatic binding between pairs of oppositely-charged ions is quite weak in comparison with covalent binding, we may expect the X---R distance to contract substantially during the formation of the transition state (35). There is probably a simultaneous stretching of the N—R bond, but from the arguments adduced in Section II, B, 1,(c), it is unlikely that this will wholly compensate for the X---R contraction. The total value of $\Delta_1 V^{\ddagger}$ will therefore be negative but small.

On the other hand any reduction in the electrical charges will tend to release bound solvent from around the ionic groups and contribute a positive term $\Delta_2 V^{\ddagger}$ to the activation volume.

Experiments show that reactions of the type (36) are retarded by increasing the pressure, proving that desolvation of the initial ions is the determining factor. Williams *et al.* (1936) found that the first-order rate constant for the decomposition of phenyl-methyl-allyl-benzyl ammonium bromide in chloroform at 25° C is decreased by a factor of 1·5 between 1 and 3 000 atm, which corresponds to an " average " value for $\Delta V^{\ddagger}$ of $+3$ cm³/mole over this pressure range. The rather small value of $\Delta V^{\ddagger}$ implies that the transition state has almost the same volume as the initial state, and the corollary is that the activation volume for the reverse (Menshutkin) reaction should be close to the total volume change for complete reaction. Stewart and Weale (1961) have pointed out that this is contrary to experimental findings on other Menshutkin reactions at atmospheric pressure (see Section III, B, 1,(b)), and they suggested that the cause of the discrepancy may be that $\Delta V^{\ddagger}$ decreases rapidly between 1 and 3 000 atm, so that its " average " value over this pressure range is considerably less than its true value at 1 atm. To test this hypothesis they made some new measurements on the system

$$\left[\underset{\underset{\text{associated}}{\overset{\displaystyle\text{Me}_2\overset{+}{\text{N}}\text{Et}}{\bigcirc}}}{} \text{I}^- \right] \overset{a}{\underset{b}{\rightleftharpoons}} \underset{\overset{\displaystyle\text{MeNEt}}{\bigcirc}}{} + \text{MeI}$$

in nitrobenzene solution at 50–65° C, taking smaller pressure intervals of only a few hundred atmospheres. They found that whilst the " average " value of $\Delta V^{\ddagger}$ for the decomposition (a) between 1 and 2 000 atm was $+11$ cm³/mole, its value at 1 atm (derived from the limiting slope of a plot of log k_a against pressure) was about $+45$ cm³/mole. For the reverse reaction (b), $\Delta V^{\ddagger}$ at 1 atm was found to be -20 cm³/mole, so that the evidence here suggests that the transition state resembles the final species rather than the initial species. However, it should be mentioned that the value $\Delta V^{\ddagger} \approx +45$ cm³/mole for the forward reaction at 1 atm is subject to a large uncertainty, perhaps as great as ± 15 cm³/mole.

(b) *Associations:* $A^+ + B^- \rightarrow C$. In 1954 David and Hamann (1954) observed that an applied pressure of 15 000 atm causes a five-fold decrease in the rate of transformation of ammonium cyanate into urea in aqueous solution at 60° C. They interpreted the effect in terms of the possible mechanism

$$\text{NH}_4^+ + \text{NCO}^- \overset{\text{slow}}{\longrightarrow} (\text{NH}_2)_2\text{CO},$$

and suggested that the partial cancellation of charges releases a volume of solvent $\Delta_2 V^{\ddagger}$ greater than the contraction $\Delta_1 V^{\ddagger}$ caused by the formation of covalent bonds between the ions. But more recent work makes it seem likely that the rate-determining step is actually the combination of neutral molecules of ammonia and cyanic acid, thus:

$$\text{NH}_4^+ + \text{NCO}^- \overset{\text{fast}}{\rightleftharpoons} \text{NH}_3 + \text{HNCO}$$
$$\text{NH}_3 + \text{HNCO} \overset{\text{slow}}{\longrightarrow} (\text{NH}_2)_2\text{CO},$$

which requires only a single, and not a double, hydrogen transference in the second step. The observed slowing-down of the reaction at high pressures is probably caused by a displacement of the preliminary equilibrium in favour of the ionized forms, with a consequent reduction in concentration of the true reactants (cf. reaction (54) of Chapter 7.ii).

Reactions which belong more properly to this class are the alkali-induced transformations of the coloured ions of crystal violet (CV) and malachite green (MG) into the colourless quinoid forms:

$$(\text{CV})^+ + \text{OH}^- \longrightarrow (\text{CV.OH}),$$

$$(MG)^+ + OH^- \rightarrow (MG.OH).$$

Chen and Laidler (1959) have found that the values of $\Delta V^{\ddagger}$ for these two reactions in water are 0 and -12 cm³/mole respectively, showing that there is no large amount of desolvation during the activation steps. In the case of malachite green, it is clear that the structural term $\Delta_2 V^{\ddagger}$ must predominate, but for crystal violet there appears to be a balance between $\Delta_2 V^{\ddagger}$ and $\Delta_1 V^{\ddagger}$.

(c) *Exchange Reactions: e.g.* $A^- + BC^+ \rightarrow AB + C$. Table VIII summarizes the results of high pressure measurements on this kind of reaction.

TABLE VIII. The Influence of Pressure on Ionic Exchange Reactions involving Cancellation of Charges

Reaction	Solvent	Temp. (°C)	p (atm)	k_p/k_1[†]	$\Delta V^{\ddagger}$ (cm³/mole)	Reference
$2H^+ + Br^- + BrO_3^- \rightarrow$ $HBrO + HBrO_2$	water	25	1 500	0·85	+4	Moesveld, 1922
p-NO_2-$C_6H_4NMe_3^+ + OH^- \rightarrow$ p-$NO_2C_6H_4OH + NMe_3$	water	51·4	1 360	0·96	+1	Brower, 1960
$\phi.\overset{+}{N}HCl.COMe + Cl^- \rightarrow$ $\phi.NH.COMe + Cl_2$	water	25 35	2 000 2 000	0·56 0·57	+8 +7	Harris and Weale, 1956

† This quantity is the ratio of the rate constant at the listed pressure p to that at 1 atm.

It will be seen that in each case the reaction rate decreases with increasing pressure and since it is almost certain that $\Delta_2 V^{\ddagger}$ is negative for these reactions (by analogy with the neutral exchanges discussed in Sections II, B, 1, (c); II, A, 3) it seems that the cause of the positive sign of $\Delta V^{\ddagger}$ must lie in the release of electrostricted solvent molecules from around the original ions. These reactions are, in fact, very similar to those discussed in Section II, B, 2, (a), the difference being that here the initial ions are free and not associated.

3. *Ionic Reactions Involving No Change in Total Charge*

(a) *Dissociations:* $(AB)^+ \rightarrow A^+ + B$. Brower (1962) has recently found that the homolytic S_N1 decomposition of the dimethyl-t-butyl sulphonium ion in water

$$Me_3C.\overset{+}{S}Me_2 \overset{slow}{\rightarrow} Me_3\overset{+}{C} + SMe_2$$

$$H_2O + Me_3C^+ \overset{fast}{\rightarrow} Me_3COH + H^+$$

is slowed down at high pressures, the value of $\Delta V^{\ddagger}$ being $+9$ cm^3/mole at 1 atm. In contrast to the heterolytic S_N1 decomposition of t-butyl chloride (Section III, B, 1, (a)) this reaction involves no great change in electrostriction during its activation step. If anything, the t-butyl ion will be more strongly solvated than the larger sulphonium ion, so that $\Delta_2 V^{\ddagger}$ should be negative. It follows that the positive sign of $\Delta V^{\ddagger}$ must be ascribed to the contribution of bond-stretching to $\Delta_1 V^{\ddagger}$ (Brower, 1962).

A similar argument applies to the S_N1 dissociations of aromatic diazonium salts:

$$\text{Ar.}\overset{+}{\text{N}}\equiv\text{N}\rightarrow\text{Ar}^+ + \text{N}_2,$$

which Brower (1960) has found to be uniformly retarded by pressure, to the extent of about 40 per cent between 1 and 1 360 atm at 30–70° C. The value of $\Delta V^{\ddagger}$ is close to $+10$ cm^3/mole for a wide variety of aromatic groups, and it is almost certainly associated with the stretching of the Ar—N bonds in forming the transition states. If we adopt Stearn and Eyring's (1941a, b) assumption that a breaking bond becomes stretched by 10 per cent of its initial length during the activation process, we find that the observed expansion of 10 cm^3/mole requires the effective molecular cross-section along the Ar—N bond to be 125 Å^2 (Brower, 1960), which is improbably large. But we have seen earlier that there are theoretical reasons for believing that the degree of stretching may be much greater than 10 per cent (See Table I) and the required cross-sectional area is correspondingly less.

Another reaction of this class is the acid-catalysed hydrolysis of acetals, whose slow step is generally accepted to be the unimolecular A-1 dissociation (Ingold, 1953):

$$\begin{array}{c}\overset{+}{}\\ \text{R}_2\text{C}-\overset{+}{\text{O}}\text{HR}' \\ | \\ \text{OR}\end{array} \quad \rightarrow \quad \text{R}_2\text{C}=\overset{+}{\text{O}}\text{R} + \text{R}'\text{OH}$$

Here, again, it has been found that an increase of pressure reduces the rate of reaction (Whalley, 1959, second reference), the value of $\Delta V^{\ddagger}$ varying from 0 to $+2$ cm^3/mole for several compounds in water at 0–26° C. By analogy, Hamann (1957, p. 186) and Whalley (1959) have pointed out that the retardation, under pressure, of the acid-catalysed inversion of sucrose ($\Delta V^{\ddagger} \approx +6$ cm^3/mole at 25° C) strongly suggests that the rate-determining step is the decomposition of a protonated sucrose molecule, involving the breaking of a C—O bond without any marked change in solvation.

(b) *Association Reactions*, e.g. $A^- + B \rightarrow (AB)^-$. Koskikallio and

Whalley (1959; also Whalley, 1959, third reference) have measured the influence of pressure on a number of acid- and base-catalysed reactions in which the slow step is the addition of an ion to a neutral molecule. In particular, they have made an extensive study of the hydrolysis of epoxides, catalysed by both acids and bases, at pressures up to 3 000 atm. The mechanisms of the two types of hydrolysis appear to be

acid:

$$\begin{array}{c} R_2C \\ | \\ R_2C \end{array}\!\!\!\searrow\!\! O + H_3O^+ \;\;\rightleftharpoons\;\; \begin{array}{c} R_2C \\ | \\ R_2C \end{array}\!\!\!\searrow\!\! \overset{+}{O}H + H_2O$$

$$\xrightarrow{\;slow\;} \begin{array}{c} R_2C-\overset{+}{O}H_2 \\ | \\ R_2C-OH \end{array} \xrightarrow[\;fast\;]{H_2O} \begin{array}{c} R_2C-OH \\ | \\ R_2C-OH \end{array} + OH_3{}^+$$

alkali:

$$\begin{array}{c} R_2C \\ | \\ R_2C \end{array}\!\!\!\searrow\!\! O + OH^- \;\xrightarrow{\;slow\;}\; \begin{array}{c} R_2C-OH \\ | \\ R_2C-O^- \end{array} \xrightarrow[\;fast\;]{H_2O} \begin{array}{c} R_2C-OH \\ | \\ R_2C-OH \end{array} + OH^-$$

In every instance Koskikallio and Whalley found that the reactions were accelerated by increasing the pressure, and that the value of $\Delta V^{\ddagger}$ at 1 atm was in the range -6 to -9 cm³/mole. As it is unlikely that there are any large changes in electrostriction in these reactions, it is reasonable to suppose that the volumes of activation represent the changes in structural volume of the reacting molecules ($\Delta_1 V^{\ddagger}$).

The fading of bromphenol blue (BPB) and phenolphthalein (PP) in alkaline solutions is evidently due to the transformation of their ions into quinoid forms by the reactions

$$(BPB)^{2-} + OH^- \;\rightarrow\; (BPB.OH)^{3-},$$
$$(PP)^{2-} \;\; + OH^- \;\rightarrow\; (PP.OH)^{3-}.$$

Chen and Laidler (1959) have measured the rates of these two reactions to a pressure of 1 000 atm in water and found that they are accelerated by amounts corresponding to activation volumes of -15 and -20 cm³/mole, respectively. It appears that the acceleration is mainly attributable to a negative "structural" term $\Delta_1 V^{\ddagger}$, although there may also be a contribution $\Delta_2 V^{\ddagger}$ arising from increased electrostriction of solvent around the trebly charged transition state. It is known that the electrostriction of solvent around simple inorganic ions is proportional to the *square* of their charges (Chapter 7.ii) so that the association of ions of the same charge sign should quite generally lead to an increase of the total electrostriction. But in large organic ions the charges can be widely separated and act independently on the solvent. In the present instance Chen and Laidler (1959) consider that the charges do not approach very closely in the transition state and that while there may be small increases in electrostriction, the dominant factor is the structural one.

(c) *Exchange Reactions: e.g.* $A^- + BC \rightarrow AB + C^-$. This section will be concerned with exchange reactions in which the initial and final species carry the same total number of electrical charges although, of course, the transition states may be either more or less polar than the initial states.

The simplest exchanges of this kind are bimolecular S_N2 or S_E2 substitutions (Ingold, 1953):

$$X^- + RY \quad \rightarrow \quad RX + Y^- \tag{37}$$

$$X^+ + RY \quad \rightarrow \quad RX + Y^+, \tag{38}$$

typified by the alkaline hydrolysis of methyl iodide

$$OH^- + CH_3I \quad \rightarrow \quad CH_3OH + I^- \tag{39}$$

and by the nitration of benzene by nitric acid

$$2HNO_3 \quad \overset{fast}{\rightleftharpoons} \quad H_2O + NO_3^- + NO_2^+ \tag{40}$$

$$NO_2^+ + \phi H \quad \overset{slow}{\rightarrow} \quad \phi NO_2 + H^+. \tag{41}$$

Some of the results of high pressure measurements on these reactions are summarized in Table IX, which has been taken from a paper by Koskikallio and Whalley (1959).

TABLE IX. Volumes of Activation calculated from the Influence of Pressure on Simple Ionic Exchange Reactions†

	Reaction	Solvent	Temp. (°C)	$\Delta V^\ddagger$ ($cm^3/$ mole)
1	$Et_2O + H_3O^+ \rightarrow EtOH_2^+ + EtOH$	water	161	-8
2††	$MeBr + RO^- \rightarrow MeOR + Br^-$	80/20 ethanol/water	0	-8
3	$EtBr + MeO^- \rightarrow EtOMe + Br^-$	methanol	30	-9
4	$EtI + EtO^- \rightarrow Et_2O + I^-$	ethanol	30	-5
5	$ClCH_2CO_2^- + OH^- \rightarrow HOCH_2CO_2^- + Cl^-$	water	60	-8
6	$PrBr + {}^{82}Br^- \rightarrow Pr^{82}Br + Br^-$	90/10 ethanol/water	19	-12
7	$PrI + {}^{131}I^- \rightarrow Pr^{131}I + I^-$	,,	19	-13

† The sources of the data are given in Koskikallio and Whalley's paper (1959).
†† R denotes either a hydrogen atom or an ethyl group.

It will be seen that the mean activation volume at 1 atm is -10 cm³/mole, which is quite close to a theoretical value (-7 cm³/mole) which Hamann (1957, p. 177) calculated for the isotopic exchange

$$^{131}I^- + CH_3I \rightarrow CH_3{}^{131}I + I^-,$$

assuming that there is no change in solvation during the activation step and that $\Delta V^{\ddagger}$ is determined simply by the "structural" volume change $\Delta_1 V^{\ddagger}$. This has been considered to be evidence that the electrostrictive term $\Delta_2 V^{\ddagger}$ is unimportant for these reactions.

However, more recent experiments show that the values of $\Delta V^{\ddagger}$ in Table IX are by no means representative of all reactions of this kind and there is now strong evidence that $\Delta_2 V^{\ddagger}$ can sometimes be as important as $\Delta_1 V^{\ddagger}$. This is very clearly demonstrated by the discovery of Gonikberg et al. (1956) that, although reaction 7 is accelerated by pressure in mixtures of alcohol and water, it is retarded in acetone solution. Careful measurements by Ershov et al. (1959, 1960) have established that the values of $\Delta V^{\ddagger}$ for this reaction vary with the solvent in the following way:

Solvent	$\Delta V^{\ddagger}$ at 1 atm and 20° C for reaction 7 of Table IX
ethanol	−7
cyclohexanone	−9
methyl ethyl ketone	+2
acetone	+10

The authors have suggested that the cause of the change in sign of $\Delta V^{\ddagger}$ may lie in the fact that the formation of the activated complex

$$^{131}I^{-\frac{1}{2}}\ldots Pr \ldots I^{-\frac{1}{2}} \qquad (42)$$

involves a dispersal of charge and some consequent desolvation of the system. There is good evidence that if such desolvation occurs its effect will be greater in ketones than in alcohol, since the partial molar volume of KI at infinite dilution is known to be more negative by 40 cm³ in acetone than in alcohol. In fact it appears that I^- ions form strong complexes with acetone (Kosower, 1958).

Clearly, the dispersal of charge must be greatest in a symmetrical isotopic substitution in which the attacking and departing halogen atoms share the negative charge equally in the transition state (42). If the halogen atoms are different it is to be expected that one will carry a greater amount of charge than the other:

$$X^{-\delta}\ldots R \ldots Y^{-(1-\delta)}, \quad (\delta > \tfrac{1}{2}), \qquad (43)$$

and in this case there will probably be less desolvation in forming the transition state. To test this theory, the writer has recently measured the effect of pressure, to 2 000 atm, on a number of unsymmetrical halogen exchange reactions in acetone. It has emerged that, in contrast to the symmetrical exchange, these reactions are accelerated by raising the pressure. Table X summarizes some results for reactions in which the attacking ion was I^-.

TABLE X. Effect of Pressure on Halogen Exchange Reactions in Acetone†

Reaction	Temp. (°C)	p (atm)	k_p/k_1	Reference
$^{131}I^- + n\text{-}PrI \rightarrow n\text{-}Pr^{131}I + I^-$	20	1 500	0·75	Gonikberg et al. (1956)
$I^- + n\text{-}PrCl \rightarrow n\text{-}PrI + Cl^-$	30	1 000	1·2	Hamann (1962)
$I^- + n\text{-}PrBr \rightarrow n\text{-}PrI + Br^-$	20	,,	1·3	,,
$I^- + i\text{-}PrBr \rightarrow i\text{-}PrI + Br^-$	30	,,	1·4	,,
$I^- + \text{allyl Cl} \rightarrow \text{allyl I} + Cl^-$	25	,,	1·2	,,
$I^- + \text{benzyl Cl} \rightarrow \text{benzyl I} + Cl^-$	25	,,	1·4	,,

† The k's are second-order rate constants based on the molality scale.

All but the first of the reactions in Table IX are *nucleophilic* substitutions (37) involving attack by negative ions. Until recently, almost no attention had been paid to the behaviour of *electrophilic* substitutions (38) under pressure, which is surprising because these reactions are extremely important in the chemistry of aromatic compounds. For instance, the nitration of benzene by nitric acid in some inert solvents follows the scheme (40)–(41), where the slow step is the attack of a nitronium ion NO_2^+ on the benzene nucleus, with the subsequent expulsion of a proton. Coillet and Hamann (1961) have found that the rates of this and some similar nitrations are accelerated about six times by increasing the pressure from 1 to 2 000 atm. The apparent volume of activation is -20 cm³/mole at 1 atm, but this is not the true value of $\Delta V^{\ddagger}$ because an increase in pressure shifts the pre-equilibrium (40) to the right and increases the stationary concentration of nitronium ions. If allowance is made for this, it appears that the actual value of $\Delta V^{\ddagger}$ may be about -15 cm³/mole. A similar acceleration has recently been observed in the Friedel-Crafts benzoylation of aromatic compounds by benzoyl chloride in the presence of aluminium chloride (Coillet et al., 1962).

Even more interesting than the increase in the total rate of nitration is the fact that, by altering the pressure, it is possible to change the relative yields of different isomers formed by nitrating substituted benzene compounds. For example, Coillet and Hamann (1962) have found that the mono-nitration of toluene by nitric acid in acetic acid solution yields appreciably more of the *meta-* and *para-* isomers at 2 000 atm than at 1 atm. Similarly the relative amount of the isomer

$$NO_2$$

$$H_3C \diagdown \diagup CH_3$$

produced by nitrating *meta*-xylene, by the same method, is increased by 60 per cent when the pressure is raised from 1 to 2 000 atm. The reasons for these changes are not yet entirely clear but they probably lie in a combination of electrostatic and steric factors. In the case of toluene it is possible that compression has the effect of smearing out the distribution of charge around the benzene nucleus and in the case of *meta*-xylene it may provide some of the steric energy needed to effect substitution at the obstructed 2- position, between the two methyl groups.

C. *Diffusion-controlled Reactions*

To conclude this chapter it is necessary to refer briefly to a few exceptional cases in which pressure affects the rate of a bimolecular reaction

$$A + B \quad \rightarrow \quad X^{\ddagger} \quad \rightarrow \quad products$$

not through its influence on the relative free energies of the transition state $X^{\ddagger}$ and the initial species A and B, but because it raises the viscosity of the medium and prevents the reactants A and B diffusing together as rapidly as they can react on collision. A few instances of this effect were cited in Section III, A, 2,(a), but the evidence there was indirect.

Direct evidence of the effect was obtained by Hamann (1958) in an examination of the alkaline (S_N2) etherification of ethyl bromide

$$C_2H_5Br + RO^- \quad \rightarrow \quad C_2H_5OR + Br^-$$

in three solvents at pressures up to 40 000 atm. From a rather crude theoretical argument it appeared that this reaction (which has an activation energy of about 20 kcal/mole) should become diffusion controlled if the viscosity of the medium were to reach 10^8 poise, that is, if the solvent could be compressed into a glassy state. It also appeared that viscosities of that order are not attained in methanol below 40 000 atm but are probably reached at less than 37 000 atm in iso-propanol and below 27 000 atm in a 50/50 mixture of eugenol and iso-propanol.

The experimental results, plotted in Fig. 4, show that the first reaction, in methanol, is continuously accelerated by pressure and it is likely that the acceleration arises both because the transition state for S_N2 substitutions is more compact than the initial state (see Section III,

B, 3,(c)) and because compression favours the ionization of the sodium methoxide which supplies the attacking ions. Compared with reaction

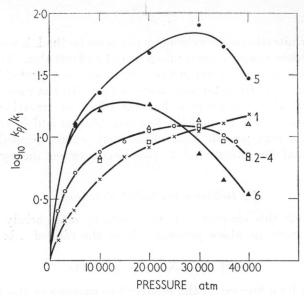

Fig. 4. The effect of pressure on rate constants for the bimolecular etherification of ethyl bromide. (Reproduced with permission from Hamann, 1958.)

			attacking ion	solvent
1.	×	;	methoxide	methanol
2.	○	;	iso-propoxide	iso-propanol
3.	△	;	phenoxide	,,
4.	□	;	α-naphthoxide	,,
5.	●	;	eugenoxide	,,
6.	▲	;	eugenoxide	50/50 eugenol/iso-propanol

1, reactions 2 to 5 in iso-propanol show larger accelerations over the first few thousand atmospheres, probably because of the greater tendency of the sodium aryl- and alkoxides to form ion pairs in the poorer ionizing solvent. But they are all retarded above 35 000 atm. Similarly the last reaction, in the most viscous solvent, is retarded above 20 000 atm. This reversal of behaviour can almost certainly be attributed to the hindrance of migration of the reacting species.

Ewald (1962) has recently measured the influence of pressure on the bimolecular quenching of fluorescence. This process has a negligible activation energy and, even at atmospheric pressure, its rate is determined by diffusion. Ewald found that the Volmer constant for the quenching of anthracene fluorescence by carbon tetrabromide decreases by a factor of 2·6 between 1 and 2 500 atm, at 30° C, in n-hexane, whose viscosity rises by a factor of 3·1 over that pressure range. In methylcyclohexane, whose viscosity increases 7·2 times over the same pressure interval, the decrease of rate constant was 3·4-fold. It will be seen from this that although there is a correlation between the rate constant and the fluidity, there is no exact proportionality.

REFERENCES

Adams, R., and Yuan, H. C. (1933). *Chem. Rev.* **12**, 261.
Amdur, I., Longmire, M. S., and Mason, E. A. (1961). *J. chem. Phys.* **35**, 895.
Bachmann, W. E., and Osborn, G. (1940). *J. org. Chem.* **5**, 29.
Bell, R. P. (1941). *Trans. Faraday Soc.* **37**, 493.
Bell, R. P., and Lidwell, O. M. (1940). *Proc. roy. Soc.* A**176**, 114.
Benson, S. W., and Berson, J. A. (1962). *J. Amer. chem. Soc.* **84**, 152.
Bernal, J. D., and Fowler, R. H. (1933). *J. chem. Phys.* **1**, 515.
Bridgman, P. W. (1938). *Proc. Amer. Acad. Arts. Sci.* **72**, 227.
Brook, A. G., Anderson, R. J., and Patot, T. V. (1958). *Canad. J. Chem.* **36**, 159.
Brower, K. R. (1958). *J. Amer. chem. Soc.* **80**, 2105.
Brower, K. R. (1959). *J. Amer. chem. Soc.* **81**, 3504.
Brower, K. R. (1960). *J. Amer. chem. Soc.* **82**, 4535.
Brower, K. R. (1961). *J. Amer. chem. Soc.* **83**, 4370.
Brower, K. R. (1962). Personal communication.
Buchanan, J. (1953). Thesis—Sydney University.
Buchanan, J., and Hamann, S. D. (1953). *Trans. Faraday Soc.* **49**, 1425.
Burnett, G. M. (1954). " Mechanism of Polymer Reactions ", p. 228, Interscience, New York.
Cairns, T. L., Coffman, D. D., and Gilbert, W. W. (1957). *J. Amer. chem. Soc.* **79**, 4405.
Chen, D. J. Y., and Laidler, K. J. (1959). *Canad. J. Chem.* **37**, 599.
Coillet, D. W., and Hamann, S. D. (1961). *Trans. Faraday Soc.* **57**, 2231.
Coillet, D. W., and Hamann, S. D. (1963). To be published. See: Coillet, D. W.—Thesis University of Sydney (1961).
Coillet, D. W., Hamann, S. D., and McCoy, E. F. (1963). To be published. See: McCoy, E. F.—Thesis University of Sydney (1961).
David, H. G., and Hamann, S. D. (1954). *Trans. Faraday Soc.* **50**, 1188.
David, H. G., and Hamann, S. D. (1956). *Disc. Faraday Soc.* **22**, 119.
de la Mare, P. D. B., Fowden, L., Hughes, E. D., Ingold, C. K., and Mackie, J. D. H. (1955). *J. chem. Soc.* 3200.
Ershov, Yu. A., Gonikberg, M. G., Neiman, M. B., and Opekunov, A. A. (1959). *C. R. Acad. Sci. U.R.S.S.* **128**, 759.
Ershov, Yu. A., Miller, V. B., Neiman, M. B., and Gonikberg, M. G. (1960). *Bull. Acad. Sci. U.R.S.S.* (*Chem. Series*), 2103.
Evans, A. G. (1946). *Trans. Faraday Soc.* **42**, 719.
Evans, M. G., and Polanyi, M. (1935). *Trans. Faraday Soc.* **31**, 875.
Evans, M. G., and Polanyi, M. (1937). *Trans. Faraday Soc.* **33**, 448.
Evans, M. G., Gergeley, J., and Seaman, E. C. (1948). *J. Polym. Sci.* **3**, 866.
Ewald, A. H. (1956a). *Disc. Faraday Soc.* **22**, 138.
Ewald, A. H. (1956b). *Disc. Faraday Soc.* **22**, 146.
Ewald, A. H. (1959). *Trans. Faraday Soc.* **55**, 792.
Ewald, A. H. (1962). Personal communication.

Ewald, A. H., Hamann, S. D., and Stutchbury, J. E. (1957). *Trans. Faraday Soc.* **53**, 991.

Eyring, H., Sherman, A., and Kimball, G. E. (1933). *J. chem. Phys.* **1**, 586.

Fawcett, E. W., and Gibson, R. O. (1934). *J. chem. Soc.* 386, 396.

Frost, A. A., and Pearson, R. G. (1961). " Kinetics and Mechanism ", p. 93, Wiley, New York.

Gerschinowitz, H., and Eyring, H. (1935). *J. Amer. chem. Soc.* **57**, 987.

Glasstone, S., Laidler, K. J., and Eyring, H. (1941). "Theory of Rate Processes ", McGraw-Hill, New York.

Godsay, M. P., Lohmann, D. H., and Russell, K. E. (1959). *Chem. & Ind.* 1603.

Gonikberg, M. G. (1960). " Chemical Equilibria and Reaction Rates at High Pressure ", Acad. Sci., U.S.S.R., Moscow.

Gonikberg, M. G., and El'yanov, B. S. (1960). *C. R. Acad. Sci. U.R.S.S.* **130**, 545

Gonikberg, M. G., and Kitaigorodsky, A. L. (1958). *C. R. Acad. Sci. U.R.S.S.* **122**, 231.

Gonikberg, M. G., Miller, V. B., Neiman, M. B., D'yachkovsky, F. S., Likhtenshtein, G. I., and Opekunov, A. A. (1956). *J. phys. Chem. Moscow* **30**, 784.

Gonikberg, M. G., and Vereshchagin, L. F. (1949). *J. phys. Chem., Moscow* **23**, 1447.

Gonikberg, M. G., and Zhulin, V. M. (1958). *Aust. J. Chem.* **11**, 285.

Gorin, E., Kauzmann, W., Walter, J., and Eyring, H. (1939). *J. chem. Phys.* **7**, 633.

Guggenheim, E. A. (1937). *Trans. Faraday Soc.* **33**, 607.

Hamann, S. D. (1957). " Physico-Chemical Effects of Pressure ", Butterworths, London.

Hamann, S. D. (1958). *Trans. Faraday Soc.* **54**, 507.

Hamann, S. D. (1962). To be published.

Hamann, S. D., and Teplitzky, D. R. (1956). *Disc. Faraday Soc.* **22**, 114.

Hamann, S. D., and Teplitzky, D. R. (1961). *J. phys. Chem.* **65**, 1654.

Harris, R. T., and Weale, K. E. (1956). *J. chem. Soc.* 953.

Harris, A. P., and Weale, K. E. (1961). *J. chem. Soc.* 146.

Hazell, J. E., and Russell, K. E. (1958). *Canad. J. Chem.* **36**, 1729.

Hinshelwood, C. N. (1937). *J. chem. Soc.* 629.

Hirschfelder, J. O., Curtiss, C. F., and Bird, R. B. (1954). " Molecular Theory of Gases and Liquids ", Wiley , New York.

Ingold, C. K. (1953). " Structure and Mechanism in Organic Chemistry ", Bell & Sons, London.

Johnston, H. S. (1961). Advances in Chem. Phys., Interscience, New York, **3**, 131.

Jones, W. H., Tristram, E. W., and Benning, W. F. (1959). *J. Amer. chem. Soc.* **81**, 2151.

Khambata, B. S., and Wassermann, A. (1939). *J. chem. Soc.* 375.

Koskikallio, J., and Whalley, E. (1959). *Canad. J. Chem.* **37**, 783.

Kosower, E. M. (1958). *J. Amer. chem. Soc.* **80**, 3261.

Laird, R. K. (1956). *Disc. Faraday Soc.* **22**, 147.

Laird, R. K., Morrell, A. G., and Seed, L. (1956). *Disc. Faraday Soc.* **22**, 126.

Lamb, J. (1960). *Z. Elektrochem.* **64**, 135.

McCune, C. C., Cagle, F. W., and Kistler, S. S. (1960). *J. phys. Chem.* **64**, 1173.

McKelvey, D. R., and Brower, K. R. (1960). *J. phys. Chem.* **64**, 1958.

Menshutkin, N. A. (1890). *Z. phys. Chem.* **6**, 41.

Mills, A. K., and Bennett, C. O. (1959). *A. I. Ch. E. Journal*, **5**, 539.

Moelwyn-Hughes, E. A., and Hinshelwood, C. N. (1932). *J. chem. Soc.* 230.

Moesveld, A. L. Th. (1922). *Z. phys. Chem.* **103**, 486.

Neiman, M. B., Gonikberg, M. G., Miller, V. B., Shapovalov, Yu. M., and Zvezdkin, V. S. (1953). *C. R. Acad. Sci. U.R.S.S.* **92**, 365.

Newitt, D. M., Linstead, R. P., Sapiro, R. H., and Boorman, E. J. (1937). *J. chem. Soc.* 876.

Nicholson, A. E., and Norrish, R. G. W. (1956a). *Disc. Faraday Soc.* **22**, 97.

Nicholson, A. E., and Norrish, R. G. W. (1956b). *Disc. Faraday Soc.* **22**, 104.

Pauling, L. (1960). " Nature of the Chemical Bond ", p. 261, Cornell University Press.

Peisach, J. (1958). Dissertation—Columbia University (quoted by Benson and Berson (1962)).

Perrin, M. W. (1938). *Trans. Faraday Soc.* **34**, 144.

Perrin, M. W., and Williams, E. G. (1937). *Proc. roy. Soc. A* **159**, 162.

Polanyi, M. (1937). *J. chem. Soc.* 629.

Raistrick, B., Sapiro, R. H., and Newitt, D. M. (1939). *J. chem. Soc.* 1761.

Reuben, B. G., and Linnett, J. W. (1959). *Trans. Faraday Soc.* **55**, 1543.

Ri, T., and Eyring, H. (1940). *J. chem. Phys.* **8**, 433.

Roberts, I., and Kimball, G. E. (1937). *J. Amer. chem. Soc.* **59**, 947.

Robinson, R. A., and Stokes, R. H. (1959). " Electrolyte Solutions ", p. 32, Butterworths, London.

Ross, S. D., Finkelstein, M., and Petersen, R. C. (1961). *J. Amer. chem. Soc.* **83**, 4853.

Rowlinson, J. S. (1959). " Liquids and Liquid Mixtures ", pp. 31–33, Butterworths, London.

Russell, K. E. (1954). *J. phys. Chem.* **58**, 437.

Slater, N. B. (1960). *J. phys. Chem.* **64**, 476.

Stearn, A. E., and Eyring, H. (1935). *J. chem. Phys.* **3**, 778.

Stearn, A. E., and Eyring, H. (1941a). *Chem. Rev.* **29**, 509.

Stearn, A. E., and Eyring, H. (1941b). Quoted in Glasstone, S., Laidler, K. J., and Eyring, H. (1941). " Theory of Rate Processes ", p. 471, McGraw-Hill, New York.

Stewart, J. M., and Weale, K. E. (1961). *Proc. chem. Soc., Lond.* 389.

van't Hoff, J. H. (1901). " Lectures in Theoretical and Physical Chemistry " (translated by R. A. Lehrfeldt), p. 241, Edward Arnold, London.

Walling, C. (1957). " Free Radicals in Solution ", p. 76, Wiley, New York.

Walling, C., and Metzger, G. (1959). *J. Amer. chem. Soc.* **81**, 5365.

Walling, C., and Peisach, J. (1958). *J. Amer. chem. Soc.* **80**, 5810.

Walling, C., and Pellon, J. (1957a). *J. Amer. chem. Soc.* **79**, 4776.

Walling, C., and Pellon, J. (1957b). *J. Amer. chem. Soc.* **79**, 4786.

Walling, C., and Pellon, J. (1957c). *J. Amer. chem. Soc.* **79**, 4782.

Waters, W. A. (1946). " Chemistry of Free Radicals ", p. 56, Oxford University Press, London.

Weale, K. E. (1956). *Disc. Faraday Soc.* **22**, 122.

Wheeler, A., Topley, B., and Eyring, H. (1936). *J. chem. Phys.* **4**, 178.

Westheimer, F. H. (1947). *J. chem. Phys.* **15**, 252.

Whalley, E. (1956). *Disc. Faraday Soc.* **22**, 146.

Whalley, E. (1959). *Trans. Faraday Soc.* **55**, 798; and subsequent papers in *Trans. Faraday Soc.* (1959) **55**, 809, 815; *Canad. J. Chem.* (1959) **37**, 788, 1360; (1961) **39**, 597, 1094, 1101.

Williams, E. G., Perrin, M. W., and Gibson, R. O. (1936). *Proc. roy. Soc. A* **154**, 684.

Chapter 9

SHOCK WAVES

G. E. DUVALL AND G. R. FOWLES

Poulter Laboratories, Stanford Research Institute,
Menlo Park, California, U.S.A.

I. INTRODUCTION

THE generation of high pressures by shock waves differs in essence from generation by conventional methods in that it relies on the inertial response of matter to rapid acceleration rather than on static constraints applied by fixed apparatus. Examination of data derived by shock methods reveals that there are sound physical reasons for its increasing importance. Some of these are:

1. Extremely high pressures can be reached in liquids and solids, e.g., pressures of nearly 10 000 kb have been produced and measured in copper, lead, and tungsten.

2. The precision with which high pressures and densities can be measured is very good; the error in pressure measurement is quite commonly less than 3% above 100 kb. Internal energy of the measured state is determined with comparable precision.

3. Where anisotropic features of the stress are important, as in plastic yield or brittle fracture, understanding of the material behaviour may be simplified by the condition of uniaxial strain produced by the shock wave.

4. The increment in stress associated with passage of the shock front is applied in much less than 10^{-8} seconds for many materials. The duration of the shock is also small, usually being between 10^{-7} and 10^{-5} seconds, and for certain studies—e.g. kinetics of reaction at high pressure—the short, well-controlled time of application of the shock is a definite aid to physical analysis of material behaviour.

In this chapter we have attempted to present primarily a summary of those aspects of research in which the shock wave is used essentially as a tool for the production of high pressures in condensed media. Discussions of the principles on which shock-wave equation of state measurements are based, the relation between such measurements and static measurements, means for producing shock waves and for measuring their effects, and a summary of current knowledge concerning shock effects and their applications are given. Some aspects of shock wave research have necessarily been omitted or treated only very briefly. These include: (1) phenomena associated with high speed flow, such as interactions of shock and rarefaction waves, jetting, and the like; (2) shocks in reacting media, notably detonation waves, (3) penetration and cratering due to impact.

Moreover, no attempt has been made to give a discussion of shock wave effects in gases, although this is an important and well developed area of research. The types of information sought and the experimental methods used for gases are sufficiently different from those for liquids and solids, that to accord them a fair treatment would require considerably more space than is available, and extensive review articles have recently appeared which deal with studies, by means of shock waves, of physical properties, chemical reactions, and non-equilibrium phenomena in gases (Soloukhin, 1959; Losev and Osipov, 1962). A comprehensive description of the use of shock tubes in gas research has been given by Wright (1961).

We note here only that because of the great compressibility of gases the major effect of shock waves is to produce extremely high temperatures in very short times. Pressures seldom exceed one kb; but temperatures in the range 20 000 to 30 000° C are readily achieved. The short rise times of shocks in gases and the high temperatures produced provide very suitable conditions for the study of non-equilibrium effects. The relaxation to statistical equilibrium of translational, vibrational, and rotational degrees of freedom, and the processes of dissociation and ionization can be studied nearly independently when the relaxation time for each of the processes is appreciably different from that of any of the others. The transparency and low density of gases permit many types of measurements to be made that are not feasible with condensed media. Particularly useful are interferometric methods for measuring density, and spectral methods (both absorption and emission) for studying dissociation and ionization. Various techniques are also available for measuring temperature, conductivity, pressure, and flow speed.

II. The Shock Equations

The shock wave concept can be illustrated by the idealized situation of Fig. 1. A uniform pressure, p_1, is suddenly applied to the entire face

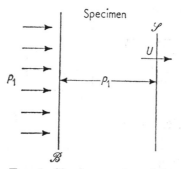

FIG. 1. Shock wave in a slab.

of a thick slab of compressible material. Information that this pressure has been applied is transmitted to the interior of the slab by means of a stress wave, and if the material behaves normally in compression, i.e. if the compressibility decreases with increasing pressure, the wave front $\mathscr{S}$—the harbinger of change—will be essentially a discontinuity in stress, density, material velocity, and internal energy which travels at supersonic velocity with respect to the material ahead. Only in the limit as $p_1 \to 0$ does its velocity become sonic. Except in the sonic limit, $\mathscr{S}$ is called a shock front.

If p_1 remains constant in time, the state variables are constant between the boundary, $\mathscr{B}$, and the shock front. The relations between these variables and their values in the undisturbed material ahead of $\mathscr{S}$ can be described by "jump conditions" supplemented by an equation of state for the specimen material. These jump conditions are expressions of the momentum equation and of the conservation of mass and energy which can be obtained directly from the equations of hydrodynamics. They can be shown to hold for any geometry, independent of the curvature of the shock front (Bleakney and Taub, 1949); here a derivation directly from first principles will be given for plane geometry. Conditions of thermodynamic equilibrium are assumed in both shocked and unshocked regions.

We focus attention on a tube of material with unit cross-sectional area normal to the direction of wave travel, indicated by ABCD of Fig. 2. The conservation of mass is expressed by observing that in a

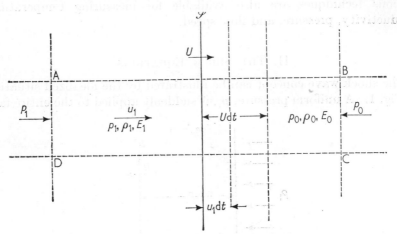

FIG. 2. Progress of a plane shock wave.

short time dt the shock front $\mathscr{S}$ advances a distance $U\,dt$, while the matter which was initially at the plane $\mathscr{S}$ has advanced only a distance $u_1\,dt$. Therefore, the material $\rho_0 U\,dt$ encompassed by the shock during dt has been compressed into the space $(U - u_1)\,dt$ at density ρ_1. If mass is to be conserved, we must have

$$\rho_0 U = \rho_1 (U - u_1). \tag{1}$$

The expression of Newton's second law is obtained by noting that the force acting on matter contained in the flow tube ABCD of unit area is, from the left, across the plane AD in the shocked state, p_1, and from the right, p_0. The net force is $p_1 - p_0$ to the right. In the time interval dt the mass of material encompassed by the shock is $\rho_0 U\,dt$, and this is all accelerated to the velocity u_1. The increase in momentum of the system is then $\rho_0 U u_1\,dt$, and the rate of change of momentum is found by dividing by the time interval dt; thus

$$p_0 - p_1 = \rho_0 U u_1. \tag{2}$$

The expression for conservation of energy in the shock transition is derived in a similar way. The surface AD moves a distance $u_1\,dt$ during the time dt, so the work done on mass contained in the unit area flow tube is $p_1 u_1\,\mathrm{d}t$. This must be equal to the sum of the increases of kinetic and internal energy of the system. The increase in kinetic energy is $\tfrac{1}{2}(\rho_0 U\,\mathrm{d}t)u_1^2$ and the increase in internal energy is $(E_1-E_0)\rho_0 U\,\mathrm{d}t$, where E_1 and E_0 are internal energies per unit mass of shocked and unshocked material, respectively. Equating the work done to the gain in energy produces the energy conservation equation:

$$p_1 u_1 = \tfrac{1}{2}\rho_0 U u_1^2 + \rho_0 U (E_1 - E_0). \tag{3}$$

FIG. 3. Receding shock wave.
(Reproduced with permission from Courant and Friedrichs, 1948.)

Combining Eq. (1) to (3) to eliminate U and u_1 yields the Rankine-Hugoniot relation,

$$E_1 - E_0 = \tfrac{1}{2}(V_0 - V_1)(p_1 + p_0), \tag{4}$$

where $V \equiv 1/\rho$. Equations (1), (2), and either (3) or (4) are the jump conditions which must be satisfied by material parameters on the two sides of the shock front.

An amusing illustration of the shock wave concept is provided in Fig. 3. This case is identical to the problem of Fig. 2, except that a " stopping shock " is shown, i.e. the problem is equivalent to that of Fig. 2 if co-ordinates are translated so the slab face is stationary and material flows into the shock front from the right with velocity $-u_1$. A similar phenomenon occurs when a lane of moving cars is stopped by collision.

When the shock transition, shock front, or simply shock connects a uniform, undisturbed state with a uniform shocked state, as in the case just described, it can be precisely defined. In co-ordinates fixed with respect to the transition, it is a steady region between two uniform, moving, thermodynamic states of the medium; material is flowing into the transition region at supersonic velocity and out at subsonic velocity. This second condition distinguishes the shock from a Joule-Thomson expansion, which is characterized by the same conservation equations (Oswatitsch, 1956).

While this definition is essential to understanding the basic physical nature of the shock transition, the experimental realization of two uniform states connected by a steady transition is difficult. For this reason it is convenient to extend the meaning of the word " shock " to include cases where stress and density change abruptly from one value to another, even though one or both of the connected states may be changing with time (Band and Duvall, 1961). Waves of this nature may be called " unsteady " or " nonuniform " shock waves, and the typical profile is illustrated in Fig. 4. In this case region I is steady,

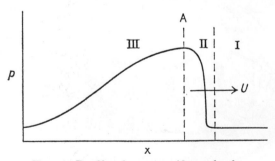

FIG. 4. Profile of a non-uniform shock.

but region III is not. The state of the boundary A between II and III is changing with time because region III consists of a relief or expansion wave which propagates at a higher speed than the shock in region II (Rice *et al.*, 1958). The state at A differs, in general, from that which would obtain if III were a uniform state, and while it is customary and very convenient to say that states A and I are connected by a shock transition, this is not precisely true. The accuracy of the approximation increases as the ratio of the magnitude of the pressure gradient in region II to that in region III increases, becoming exact when the transition is discontinuous. In most cases investigated, inaccuracies resulting from this approximation are believed to be negligible.

III. THERMODYNAMICS OF THE SHOCK TRANSITION

The shock transition imparts both kinetic and internal energy to the material through which it propagates; moreover, irreversible work is done on the material as it passes through the shock front. That this is true can be readily inferred from the Rankine-Hugoniot relation, Eq. (4). Suppose we consider two shock waves in separate specimens of the same material, one of pressure p_1, a second of pressure $p_1 + dp_1$; each is supposed to be running into material in the same state (p_0, V_0). Differentiation of Eq. (4) gives the difference in specific internal energies behind the two shock fronts:

$$dE_1 = \tfrac{1}{2}(V_0 - V_1)\,dp_1 - \tfrac{1}{2}(p_1 + p_0)\,dV_1. \tag{5}$$

Since both states are assumed to be in thermodynamic equilibrium, the change in entropy can be calculated from the combined first and second laws of thermodynamics:

$$T_1\,dS_1 = dE_1 + p_1\,dV_1$$

$$= \tfrac{1}{2}(V_0 - V_1)\,dp_1 + \tfrac{1}{2}(p_1 - p_0)\,dV_1$$

$$= \tfrac{1}{2}(V_0 - V_1)\left[1 - \left(\frac{U - u_1}{c_1}\right)^2\right]dp_1. \tag{6}$$

The last relation is obtained by use of the definition†

$$c_1{}^2 \equiv V_1{}^2\,dp_1/dV_1, \tag{7}$$

and by the relation

$$(U - u_1)^2 = V_1{}^2(p_1 - p_0)/(V_0 - V_1), \tag{8}$$

which is obtained by combining Eqs. (1) and (2).

The locus of all states (p_1, V_1) which can be obtained by a shock

† Note that c_1, as defined by Eq. (7), differs from the adiabatic sound velocity, though the two are nearly equal for compressions less than 10 or 15%.

transition from an initial state (p_0, V_0) is called the Rankine-Hugoniot curve, hereafter referred to as the R-H curve, centred about (p_0, V_0). If this curve is concave upward, as in Fig. 5, it is clear from Eqs. (6), (7), and (8) that $dS_1 > 0$, since $(U - u_1)^2/c_1^2$ is the ratio of the absolute values of the slope of the Rayleigh line, defined as the chord drawn between (p_0, V_0) and (p_1, V_1), to the tangent to the curve at (p_1, V_1). Since (p_1, V_1) is an arbitrary point on the R-H curve, the entropy, S_1, increases monotonically with pressure, p_1, and consequently, the R-H curve lies above the adiabat passing through the initial state, as shown in Fig. 5. The two curves agree in both slope and curvature at the

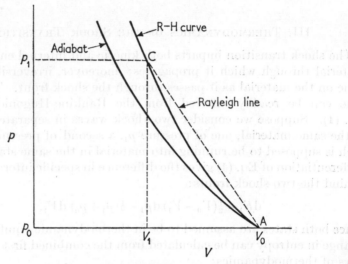

FIG. 5. Comparison of R-H curve and adiabat.

initial state, A; further, a straightforward thermodynamic calculation shows that the entropy change is third order in the compression (Courant and Friedrichs, Section 65, 1948):

$$S_1 - S_0 = -\frac{1}{12T_0}\left(\frac{\partial^2 p}{\partial V^2}\right)_{S_0, V_0}(V_1 - V_0)^3 + \cdots, \qquad (9)$$

where S_0 and T_0 are the entropy and temperature of the initial state. Given an equation of state, Eq. (9) can be replaced by an expression in closed form (Duvall and Zwolinski, 1955).

There are two problems associated with the R-H curve and its relation to the equation of state of a material. First is the derivation of the R-H curve, given an equation of state and specific heat. This offers no difficulties other than computational ones, since elimination of internal energy between the equation of state and Eq. (4) formally produces the required function (Duvall, 1958). Second is the derivation of information about the equation of state of a material, given an R-H curve obtained by experimental measurement of shock parameters. In order to accomplish this, it has been necessary to assume a form for the equation of state, or the equivalent in the form of the pressure or volume dependence of various thermodynamic quantities, and proceed to evaluate its parameters by combined use of Eq. (4), thermodynamic procedures, and some theory of the atomic lattice (Rice *et al.*, 1958).

One interpretation is based on the Mie-Grüneisen equation,

$$p(V) = p_k(V) + \frac{\Gamma(E - E_k)}{V}, \tag{10}$$

where the subscript k refers to some reference condition, such as an isotherm or adiabat, and Γ is the Grüneisen ratio, a function of density. Equation (10) follows from the assumption that the distortional and vibrational energy in a lattice solid are separable and from some simplifying assumptions about the lattice spectrum—e.g. that it follows the Debye or Einstein model (Born and Huang, 1954).

The form of Eq. (10) can be derived on entirely different grounds. Assume that the equation of state is an analytic function of volume and vibrational energy, $E_{\text{vib}} \equiv E - E_k$, and that the material will sustain a finite pressure at zero degrees Kelvin. Then a series expansion in V and E_{vib} leads directly to Eq. (10) if only the first-order term in E_{vib} is retained.

In order to extrapolate from the R-H curve, let $p = p_H(V)$, and $E = E_H(V)$, where the subscript H denotes known values on the R-H curve, then Eq. (10) provides an integral equation for p_k which can be evaluated, provided the function Γ is known and initial values for the problem can be determined. If $p_k(V)$ is an adiabat with constant entropy, S,

$$E_k(S, V) = E_k(S, \overline{V}_0) - \int_{V_0}^{V} p_k \, dV, \tag{11}$$

and Eq. (10) becomes

$$p_k(V) - \frac{\Gamma}{V} \left\{ E_k(S, V_0) - \int_{V_0}^{V} p_k \, dV \right\} = p_H(V) - \frac{\Gamma}{V} E_H(V). \tag{12}$$

Denoting the internal energy of the initial state before the shock transition by $E_0 = E_0(p_0, V_0)$, and substituting in Eq. (12) for E_H from Eq. (4), we get

$$p_k(V) - \frac{\Gamma}{V} \left\{ E_k(S, V_0) - \int_{V_0}^{V} p_k \, dV \right\}$$

$$= p_H(V) \left[1 - \frac{\Gamma(V_0 - V)}{2V} \right] - \frac{\Gamma E_0(p_0, V_0)}{V}. \tag{13}$$

TABLE I. Temperatures and Entropies of Typical Materials Shocked Explosively

Density Ratio (ρ/ρ_0) Material	1·1			1·3			1·5			1·7		
	p (kb)	$T\dagger$ (°C)	ΔS (cal/g deg)	p (kb)	T (°C)	ΔS cal/g deg)	p (kb)	T (°C)	ΔS (cal/g deg)	p (kb)	T (°C)	ΔS (cal/g deg)
Water††	4	32	0·004	18	86	0·051	55	277	0·247	120	710	0·543
Aluminium†††	90	75	0·008	374	545	0·157	861	2 367	0·386	1 650	6 520	0·588
Copper†††	167	87	0·005	755	877	0·089	1 858	4 080	0·197	3 880	12 0	0·292
Lead†††	53	91	0·001	250	770	0·025	655	3 280	0·062	1 330	8 200	0·095

† Initial temperature = 20° C.
†† Rice and Walsh (1957); above values obtained by interpolation between reported values.
††† Al'tshuler et al. (1960a); above values of ΔS computed by numerical integration using reported P, V, T values.

For the particular case $S = S_0$, $E_k(S, V_0) = E_0$, the equation integrates readily by numerical methods, given $p_H(V)$. A similar situation exists for the isotherm passing through p_0, V_0. The numerical procedure is considerably simplified if Γ/V is assumed to be constant (Doran, 1960).

Extensive theoretical and experimental studies of the variation of Γ with density have been made and their results incorporated in Eq. (13) [Rice et al., 1958; Al'tshuler et al., 1958a, 1960b; Doran, 1960]. Some typical values of S and T are given in Table I.

A useful relation between adiabatic sound velocity and the slope of the R-H curve can be obtained from Eq. (6). In differential form the Mie-Grüneisen equation of state can be written

$$dp = - (a^2/V^2)\, dV + \Gamma T\, dS/V,$$

where a is the adiabatic sound velocity at the state (V, S). Elimination of $T\, dS$ between this expression and Eq. (6) yields the result

$$a_1{}^2 = c_1{}^2(1 - \Delta)$$

where

$$\Delta = \frac{\Gamma(V_0 - V_1)}{2V_1} \left[1 - \frac{(U - u_1)^2}{c_1{}^2} \right].$$

IV. REFLECTION AT AN INTERFACE

Of fundamental importance in the generation and measurement of shock waves are the interactions which occur when waves overtake or collide with one another or with an interface between two media. Simple graphical representations and calculations are possible because of unique relations between stress and particle velocity in the waves for either one-dimensional, plane, time-dependent flow or for two-dimensional, plane, steady flow. Because of its more common experimental use, we shall develop the time-dependent case here.

The jump conditions for a shock transition, Eq. (1) to (3), can be

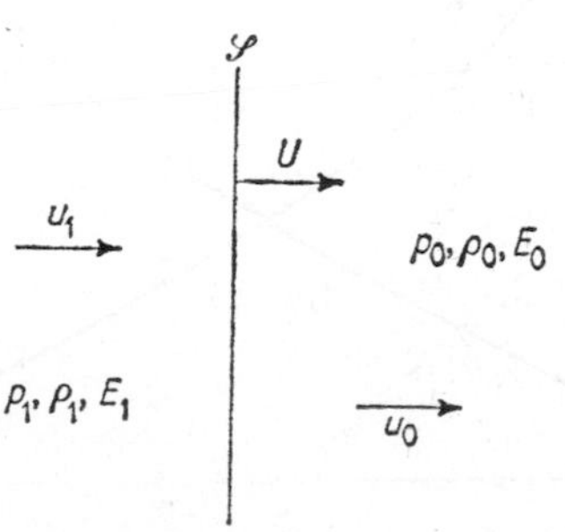

FIG. 6. Shock propagating into a moving medium.

generalized slightly by superposing on the system a uniform flow velocity, u_0, (Fig. 6). Then Eq. (1) and (2) become

$$\rho_0(U - u_0) = \rho_1(U - u_1) \tag{1A}$$

$$p_1 - p_0 = \rho_0(U - u_0)(u_1 - u_0). \tag{2A}$$

The Rankine-Hugoniot relation (Equation 4) remains the same and is equivalent to the third conservation equation.

The basic idea in dealing with wave interactions is that the jump conditions and the differential equations of flow restrict the dynamic states which can be joined in a single transition, and a convenient representation of these is afforded in the p-u plane. Consider, for example, the shock of Fig. 6 which is compressing material from its initial state, (p_0, ρ_0), to a higher pressure state, (p_1, ρ_1) and simultaneously accelerating it from velocity u_0 to u_1. The relation between $p_1 - p_0$ and $u_1 - u_0$ is found by eliminating $U - u_0$ from Eq. (1A) and (2A):

$$u_1 - u_0 = \pm \sqrt{[(p_1 - p_0)(V_0 - V_1)]}. \tag{14}$$

This equation is exhibited as curves AB and AC in Fig. 7. The branch AB represents the positive sign in Eq. (14), AC the negative sign, and any shock transition from (p_0, u_0) must lie on one or the other of these branches. Those lying on AB accelerate material from left to right and propagate towards the right, as in Fig. 6, and are denoted by $\mathscr{S} \rightarrow$; those on AC propagate and accelerate material to the left ($\mathscr{S} \leftarrow$). The velocity of a shock, relative to the material ahead, is given by Eq. (2A) and is represented by the chord drawn from (p_0, u_0) to (p_1, u_1) in Fig. 7:

$$\frac{p_1 - p_0}{u_1 - u_0} = \rho_0(U - u_0). \tag{15}$$

Transitions between dynamic states may also occur through rare-

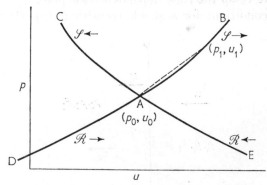

FIG. 7. Wave transitions in the p-u plane.

factions, which reduce the material to a lower pressure state and accelerate it in a direction opposite to that of propagation (Courant and Friedrichs, 1948, Section 43). Besides this, they differ from shocks in that the transition zone is not steady; the equation of motion analogous to Eq. (2A) is

$$u_1 - u_0 = \pm \int_{p_0}^{p_1} \frac{\mathrm{d}p}{\rho a} \qquad (16)$$

where a is adiabatic sound speed at density ρ, and p and ρ are joined by an adiabatic relation. Equation (16) is obtained by integration of the familiar acoustic impedance relation between $\mathrm{d}p$ and $\mathrm{d}u$ (Rayleigh, 1910); curves AD and AE of Fig. 7 represent the two branches of Eq. (16); the former is specified by the positive sign and the latter by the negative. A rarefaction propagating into the state (p_0, u_0) must produce a final state lying on AD if the wave is travelling to the right $(\mathcal{R}\rightarrow)$ and on AE if it is travelling to the left $(\mathcal{R}\leftarrow)$.

The two functions represented by Eqs. (14) and (16) have a second-order contact point at A, differing in third order, or, as seen by comparison with Eq. (9), with the entropy change. The compressions associated with explosively-produced shocks in condensed materials are frequently small enough that the entropy changes can be neglected in calculating pressures and velocities, and in this case the interaction

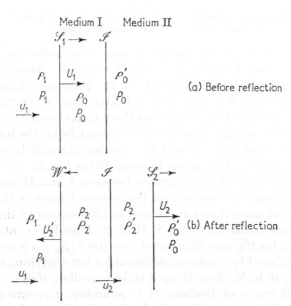

FIG. 8. Reflection of a plane, uniform shock wave from an interface between two media.

problem becomes very simple. The p-u plane is carpeted with a family of curves defined by Eq. (14) and an adiabatic p-V relation, and all transitions from a given state must lie on one of the two curves passing through that state.

For example, consider the reflection of a plane, uniform, right-travelling shock wave in one medium from the plane interface of a second medium, as in Fig. 8. We take the initial undisturbed state for both media to lie at the origin of the p-u plane, and consider the shocks to be weak so that entropy changes can be ignored. From the origin we draw the R-H curve for each medium, as in Fig. 9. The initial shock is

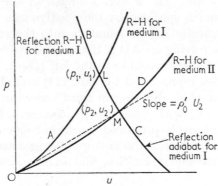

Fig. 9. Plane shock reflection in the pressure-particle velocity plane, characteristic or impedance method.

at L on the R-H curve for Medium I and, upon reflection, the shock induced in Medium II must lie on its R-H curve. Thus, when $\mathscr{S}_1 \rightarrow$ is incident on the interface, it produces the transmitted shock, $\mathscr{S}_2 \rightarrow$, and a reflected wave, $\mathscr{W}$. This reflected wave may, in general, be either a rarefaction or a shock depending on the relative positions of the R-H curves of the two media; in either case it must lie on the mirror image of curve A reflected in a vertical line passing through L, since it is a left-travelling wave. This image is curve BC in Fig. 9. Since pressure and particle velocity at the interface between I and II must be continuous, the dynamic state behind the reflected wave is the same for both media and must therefore lie at the intersection of the reflection R-H of Medium I and the direct R-H of Medium II, i.e. at point M in Fig. 9. Thus, for the case illustrated, the state (p_2, u_2) is reached from (p_1, u_1) in Medium I by a transition through a left-travelling rarefaction, and from $(p_0, 0)$ in Medium II by a right-travelling shock.

If the R-H curve of Medium II is unknown, measurement of the velocity, U_2, of the transmitted shock gives the slope of the straight line OM, from Eq. (2). State M is then determined as the intersection of the reflected R-H, BC, and the chord OM. This is the essence of the impedance-match method for measuring the R-H curve of an unknown material (Rice *et al.*, 1958).

If Medium II were a vacuum, its R-H curve would be the u-axis, and the velocity given to the free surface of Medium I by the reflection would be twice the particle velocity in the initial shock, $\mathscr{S}_1$, since BC is the mirror image of curve A. If Medium II were a rigid wall, the final state in Medium I would lie at the intersection of BC and the p-axis. The symmetry associated with the free-surface reflection does not exist in this case, and it is not possible to make a general statement about the magnitude of the pressure behind the reflected wave, except that it exceeds the initial pressure. The acoustic approximation that the reflected pressure is twice the incident pressure is valid only when the initial state, L, is so near the origin that curve A is well-approximated by a straight line. If Medium II is relatively incompressible compared to I, the reflected pressure may be several times the incident pressure.

V. PRODUCTION OF PLANE SHOCK WAVES

For the purpose of making precise experimental measurements which can be interpreted in terms of material properties, it is important to produce shock waves which correspond closely with the theoretical model on which interpretations are based. The most common practice has been to generate plane waves with explosive systems or by plane impact.

Some explosive plane-wave generators are illustrated in Fig. 10. The flying plate generator shown at (a) (sometimes called the " Mousetrap ") is a two-stage device which uses the ratio of driven plate velocity to detonation velocity to effect refraction. Its operation is illustrated in Fig. 11. A pad of high explosive (HE), in contact with an inert plate, is initiated at one end. The detonation propagates down the pad with velocity, D, and the high pressure of the detonation gases accelerates the plate to a velocity v. If the driving explosive and plate are inclined at an angle $\alpha = \sin^{-1}(v/D)$ to the explosive surface to be detonated, the flying plate will strike every point on this surface simultaneously and, if its velocity is great enough, will initiate a plane detonation wave. The device of Fig. 10(a) functions by successive application of this principle to the two driver plates.

Although it is simple in principle, the mousetrap suffers in practice from several defects. Near the edges of the plate, the driving pressure has shorter duration than in the centre; the plate edges consequently lag and the effective plane area may be substantially less than the plate area. Furthermore, the precision of manufacture required is very high for good results, so that, in practice, this generator is useful only where a rough approximation to planarity is required.

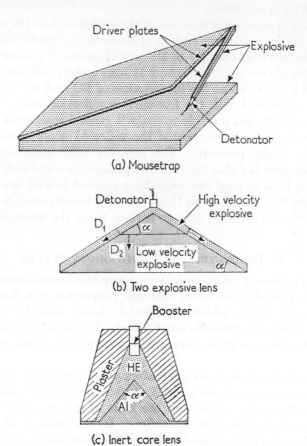

(a) Mousetrap

(b) Two explosive lens

(c) Inert core lens

FIG. 10. Explosive plane-wave generators.

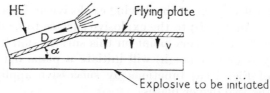

FIG. 11. Operation of mousetrap element.

The two-explosive lens of Fig. 10(b) consists of an explosive of high detonation velocity, D_1, surrounding an explosive of low velocity, D_2, as a core (Cook, 1948). A cross section normal to the vertical axis shows two concentric circles, the inner one being filled with the low explosive.

The geometry is chosen so that the high velocity detonation travelling down the outside initiates a detonation in the inner explosive which just keeps pace with the outer one; i.e. the angle α is chosen so that $D_2 = D_1 \sin \alpha$. The generator of Fig. 10(c) operates on the same principle as the two-explosive type, except that the inner element is inert.

Deviations from simultaneous arrival of the detonation at the face of the lens can be made less than 10^{-7} sec over a substantial area for either the two-explosive or the inert core lens. However, these designs produce non-uniform impulses across the lens face, and when they are used to propel a plate, this variation of impulse may cause it to deform as it travels.

The pressures induced in solids by explosives may be approximately calculated by supposing the detonation to be a shock wave incident on the surface of a different material, as in Fig. 12. Before the detonation

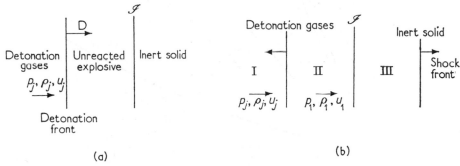

FIG. 12. Detonation wave incident on an inert solid.
(a) Before reflection   (b) After reflection

wave reaches the interface, the detonation front separates unreacted from reacted explosive. After reflection from the interface, the wave is travelling entirely through burned gases, and in order to determine the dynamic state at the interface, the transition curve for left-travelling waves advancing into region I must be constructed. To accomplish this the detonation process is simplified to the extent of being described by two parameters, p_j (the Chapman-Jouguet pressure), and u_j, the particle velocity, as if it were a uniform shock wave in an inert material. Experiments have shown that for a large range of pressures around p_j, the detonation gases from solid explosives have p-V relations closely approximated by the polytropic equation (Fickett and Wood, 1958),

$$p = p_j (\rho/\rho_j)^\gamma, \tag{17}$$

where ρ_j is density at the Chapman-Jouguet pressure and γ is a parameter characteristic of the explosive. The equation of the reflection

R-H curve passing through the Chapman-Jouguet state (p_j, u_j) is obtained by identifying p_0, u_0 of Eq. (14) with p_j, u_j. The pressure-density relation in region II of Fig. 12(b) is represented by Eq. (17); then, by eliminating density, ρ_1, between Eqs. (14) and (17), we obtain

$$(u_1 - u_j)^2 = [(p_1/p_j) - 1][1 - (p_j/p_1)^{1/\gamma}](p_j/\rho_j). \tag{18}$$

The equation of the reflection adiabat is obtained by a similar procedure, eliminating ρ_1 between Eq. (16) and (17) to obtain

$$u_1 - u_j = \frac{2}{\gamma - 1} \sqrt{\left(\frac{\gamma p_j}{\rho_j}\right)} \left[\left(\frac{p_1}{p_j}\right)^{(\gamma-1)/2\gamma} - 1 \right]. \tag{19}$$

Chapman-Jouguet data for several explosives are given in Table II and their reflection curves from Eq. (18) and (19) are plotted in Fig. 13.

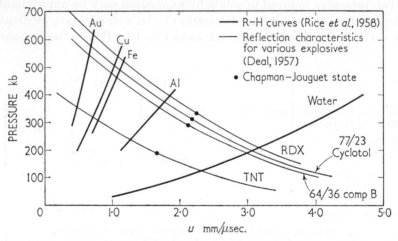

FIG. 13. Shock waves induced by high explosives. (Reproduced with permission from " Response of Metals to High Velocity Deformation," Interscience, New York.)

Plane shock wave generation by impact can be accomplished by use of explosively driven plates colliding with a target material or by driving a flat-ended projectile through a gun barrel and into the target. The former arrangement is especially useful for producing higher pressures than can be obtained with contact explosive; the latter enables one to more readily produce lower pressures.

An explosively driven plate arrangement is shown in Fig. 14. A plane wave generator produces a plane detonation in a slab of explosive which is several times wider than it is thick in order that rarefactions arising from the sides do not seriously limit the area of planarity (McQueen and Marsh, 1960). The detonation wave accelerates the flyer plate to a high velocity w during its flight across the void between flyer and target. The effective pressure accelerating the plate varies

TABLE II. Properties of Some Common Explosives (Deal, 1957)

	ρ_0 (g/cc)	ρ_j (g/cc)	p_j (kb)	u_j (mm/μsec)	D (mm/μsec)	γ
RDX	1·767 ± 0·011	2·375 ± 0·012	337·9 ± 3·1	2·213 ± 0·029	8·639 ± 0·041	2·904 ± 0·047
TNT	1·637 ± 0·003	2·153 ± 0·006	189·1 ± 1·0	1·664 ± 0·011	6·942 ± 0·016	3·172 ± 0·029
64/36 Comp B (64% RDX, 36% TNT)	1·713 ± 0·002	2·331 ± 0·008	292·2 ± 2·6	2·127 ± 0·019	8·018 ± 0·017	2·770 ± 0·034
77/23 Cyclotol (77% RDX, 23% TNT)	1·743 ± 0·001	2·366 ± 0·009	312·5 ± 2·9	2·173 ± 0·020	8·252 ± 0·017	2·798 ± 0·034

D is the detonation velocity. Subscripts j refer to values at the Chapman-Jouget plane. ρ_0 is initial density of the explosive.

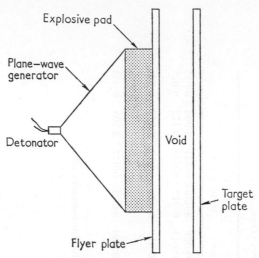

FIG. 14. Shock generation by impact of flying plate.

with time, $p = p(t)$, and the momentum per unit area delivered to the plate is $\int p(t)\, dt = p_a T$, where p_a is the initial pressure induced in the flyer plate and T is a time chosen to satisfy the equality. When the flyer strikes a target plate of the same material, it produces a pressure p_T and delivers its momentum in a time $\tau \simeq 2d/v$, where d is the flyer plate thickness and v is a mean velocity for wave propagation in the flyer plate; v is the order of the shock velocity at the induced pressure. This is the time required for the shock wave produced in the flyer plate on impact with the target to travel through the plate to the rear face and for the rarefaction thus generated to return to the front face—now an interface between flyer and target. The flyer plate is then substantially slowed or stopped, and the momentum delivered to the target is $p_T \tau = p_a T$. If the explosive is sufficiently thick, T is considerably greater than τ and p_T is correspondingly greater than p_a.

This discussion can be made quantitative with the use of Fig. 15, which gives the approximate speed of a flat plate accelerated by a plane slab of explosive, together with the R-H curves of flyer plate and target represented in the p-u plane (Fig. 16). Impact produces a right-travelling wave in the target, which is initially in the dynamic state $p = 0$, $u = 0$. The stopping shock produced in the flyer plate lies on the reflected R-H curve through $u = w$, and the direct shock induced in the target lies on the direct R-H curve of the target. The common state produced by impact is at the intersection, M, of the two curves. Pressures as great as 2 000 kb have been produced in iron by this technique (McQueen and Marsh, 1960).

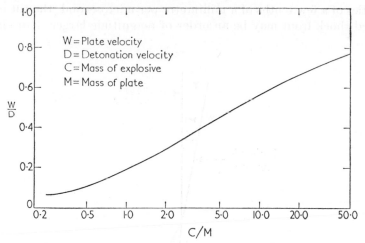

Fig. 15. Velocity of a plate accelerated by comp. B (Aziz et al., 1961).

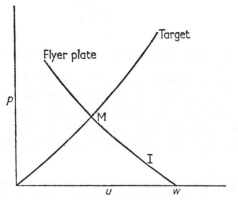

Fig. 16. Plane shock waves induced by impact.

Values of nearly 10 000 kb produced by impact have been reported (Kormer et al., 1962), but the experimental arrangement for plate acceleration was not described.

A flat-ended projectile in a precision-bored gun can be fired and well-controlled at quite low velocities, and it presently promises to be an extremely useful tool for investigations at pressures below 100 kb. There are, however, some new experimental problems at low projectile velocities. One of these arises from projectile tilt, illustrated in Fig. 17. If the projectile, travelling with velocity w, is tilted at an angle α with respect to the target, the shock induced in the target is tilted at the angle $\beta = \sin^{-1}(U \sin \alpha/w)$. Shock velocities at low pressures are the order of a few millimetres per microsecond, so that for projectile velocities of a few tenths of a millimetre per microsecond, the tilt of the induced shock front may be an order of magnitude larger than that of

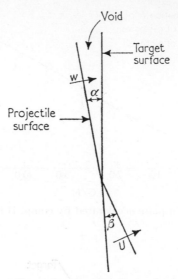

FIG. 17. Effect of projectile tilt on shock planarity.

the projectile. As a typical example, assume $U = 4$ mm/μsec and $w = 0 \cdot 1$ mm/μsec, then $\beta \simeq 40\ \alpha$, and a projectile tilt of several minutes of arc manifests itself as a shock tilt of several degrees. Although tilt can be measured and corrections made, the problem is nonetheless a serious one at low projectile velocities (Lundergan, 1960).

VI. Two-Dimensional Steady Flow

Two-dimensional, steady, plane flow is important both experimentally and analytically. The classical example of this is the supersonic flow of gas over a cylindrical wing in a tunnel, as in Fig. 18. The gas flowing with supersonic velocity from the left flows through shock waves AC and

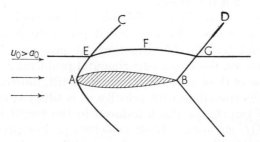

FIG. 18. Two-dimensional flow over a cylindrical foil.

BD created by the stationary foil. A streamline of the flow is EFG and all features of the flow field are independent of time.

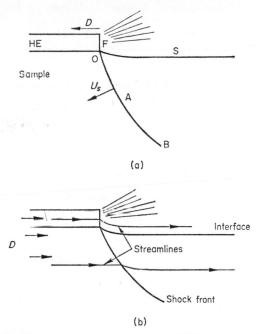

(a)

(b)

FIG. 19. Shock wave induced by an oblique detonation.
(a) Laboratory coordinates   (b) moving coordinates

A similar situation can be created in an explosive experiment, as shown in Fig. 19. A uniformly thick layer of explosive is placed in contact with the plane surface of an inert specimen [(Fig. 19a) and detonated so that a plane detonation front, F, normal to the sample surface and to the plane of the paper, propagates through the explosive with velocity, D. The surface, S, is depressed by the pressure of the explosive gases as the detonation front passes over it, and a shock with front OAB is driven into the specimen. Since D is constant, a constant velocity D can be superposed on the system to yield the equivalent steady flow field of Fig. 19b, provided flow in the sample is everywhere supersonic.

The analysis of two-dimensional supersonic problems follows the method developed above for the plane, time-dependent case, but the p-u plane is replaced by a plane in which x and y velocity components are co-ordinates—a hodograph plane (Courant-Friedrichs, 1948, Section 103). Detailed analyses of wave interactions in this geometry can be found in Shapiro, 1954; Drummond, 1958; Erkman, 1958. The results of some calculations are entered in Table III, which lists shock

TABLE III. Pressures Induced by Oblique Detonation in Comp. B†

Material:	Aluminium	Copper	Water	Lucite	Iron
Peak Pressure (kb):	189	205	121	105	196

† Drummond, 1958; Erkman, 1958.

strengths induced in several materials by Composition B explosive detonated in the geometry of Fig. 19. It is characteristic of oblique detonations that the induced shock wave in an adjacent material is always less than the Chapman-Jouguet pressure. This is in sharp contrast with the case of normal incidence, wherein the induced pressure may substantially exceed the Chapman-Jouguet pressure (Fig. 13).

A practical experimental arrangement for producing and using oblique shock waves is shown in Fig. 20. The detonation is started at

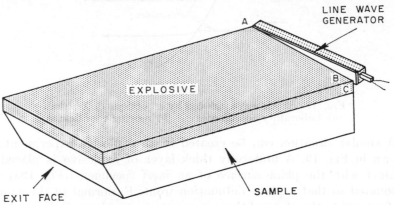

FIG. 20. Experimental arrangement for producing two-dimensional, steady plane flow.

ABC by a line wave generator, which may be the first stage of a mouse-trap, as shown, or of another type (Erkman, 1959). The detonation then progresses through the explosive with front parallel to the face ABC, driving a shock wave into the sample as it goes. The effect of the shock may be studied as it reflects from the bottom of the specimen or from the exit face. If the assembly is wide and long enough to prevent disturbances from the side and rear boundaries from influencing the flow in the central region, then the conditions of Fig. 19 for steady flow are satisfied, and a two-dimensional analysis can be used. To meet this requirement, the width of the specimen should be more than twice its depth, and the detonation should run a distance equal to a few sample thicknesses. In practice, the analysis of data obtained in this manner can be effected by a minor modification of the one-dimensional analysis described in Sections IV and V (Katz *et al.*, 1959; Fowles, 1961).

VII. TECHNIQUES OF MEASUREMENT

Principal efforts to use shock waves for the production of scientific and engineering data have been directed towards the determination of pressure-volume data on the R-H curve. If any two of the parameters, U, u_1, p_1, ρ_1, in Eq. (1) and (2) are determined, the other two can be calculated from the equations. Of these four parameters, shock velocity can be measured most easily, next in order of difficulty is particle velocity. The velocity u_{fs} imparted to a free surface by the shock can be measured with relative ease, and if entropy effects are negligible, this is just twice the particle velocity (cf. Section IV). Where this approximation is not valid, an iteration procedure is required to obtain the correct value of u_1 (Rice *et al.*, 1958); the approximation $u_{fs} = 2u_1$ is accurate within about 1% for compressions less than about 15% unless a phase transition occurs. The use of shock velocity and particle velocity, obtained in this way, to calculate p_1 and ρ_1 is called the " free surface method ". A valuable alternative procedure is the " impedance match method ", described in Section IV. In this procedure the shock is transmitted to the unknown specimen through a driver plate of material with well-known R-H curve. The shock strength in the driver material is determined by measuring its shock or free-surface velocity, and either of these velocities is also measured in the specimen. These two measurements provide enough information to obtain the state in the specimen, which must lie on the cross curve of the driver material (Fig. 9).

As for the other two parameters, significant efforts have been and are being made to measure density by optical or X-ray absorption methods, and there is increasing interest in the development of transducers for measuring shock pressures directly. As interest in the scientific applications of shock wave studies expands, methods are also developing for measuring other physical parameters, e.g. electrical conductivity.

A. *Free-Surface Motion*

When the shock wave is incident on a free surface, it is accelerated very rapidly to velocity u_{fs}. Since the rise time to peak pressure in the shock wave is normally very short, the time of first motion of the surface can be determined precisely, and the monitoring of first motion provides a means for measuring shock velocity. If the subsequent motion of the surface can be followed and its position traced as a function of time, free-surface velocity can be determined. Several methods have developed for accomplishing both of these objectives; some of these methods and their limitations are described here.

The short times normally available ($\sim 0\cdot 1$ to 1 microsecond) for shock and free-surface velocity measurements place some stringent requirements on the time and space resolution of any recording system. In order to obtain an accuracy of 1% in shock velocity in a travel distance of a few millimetres, for example, the time resolution must be of the order of $0\cdot 01$ microsecond and the space resolution of the order of 10 to 100 microns. Since the same system is also normally used to record free-surface motion, and since free-surface velocities may be smaller than shock velocities by factors of as much as 100, distance travelled in the available time is smaller and the space resolution must be increased to the order of microns in order to give comparable precision in the free-surface velocities.

Existing measurement techniques employ either optical or electronic methods; time resolutions of $0\cdot 01$ microsecond can be obtained with either method. The requisite space resolution of a complete recording system is more difficult to achieve and, consequently, several methods employ techniques for effectively magnifying free-surface displacements.

An ideal recording system would be capable of measuring the velocities of a large number of points of a free-surface continuously in time with the resolutions mentioned. Thus, it would be capable of continuous observations in two, or even three, space dimensions. In plane wave experiments, simultaneous observations of motion of the entire accelerated face of the specimen would allow monitoring of the tilt of the shock front and specimen surface. In oblique shock experiments, too, simultaneous monitoring of motion over the entire wedge or exit face of Fig. 20 enhances the value of an experiment because the wave amplitude is decaying with distance from the explosive, the line wave in the explosive may be tilted, and rarefactions from bottom and side faces of the specimen may be perturbing the otherwise steady flow.

In principle, a film is capable of recording four dimensions, if intensity of exposure and colour are considered in addition to the two space dimensions. No techniques currently in use, however, are capable of continuous measurements in all of these dimensions; usually they involve some compromise in that one or more space dimensions is recorded only at a number of discrete points. Nonetheless, good precision is obtained.

Little use has yet been made of combined optical and electronic instrumentation, e.g. photomultipliers. Other, more recent technological developments appear to hold promise for further improvements in shock-wave recording. Such devices as lasers for production of coherent, monochromatic light, and image-converter cameras, which have extremely high time resolution, will surely find important applications in this field.

In the following some of the more commonly used recording methods are described briefly.

1. *Optical Methods*

Nearly all optical methods which have been used employ a rotating-mirror streak camera as the recording instrument. In these cameras the field of view is stopped down by a narrow slit to admit only a thin line of the image. This line is swept along a stationary film by means of a rotating mirror driven by a turbine, and the linear sweep rate is determined by the angular frequency of the rotating mirror and the geometry of the camera. The resulting film record thus consists of a one-dimensional time plot of the light or dark events occurring within the field of view of the slit.

Modern streak cameras are capable of rotor frequencies up to about 10 000 per second, to give writing speeds of about 10 mm/μsec on the film. For slit widths of the order of 0·1 mm, the time resolution is thus approximately 0·01 μsec. The extremely short exposure times require that the observed event either be intensely self-luminous, or that it be illuminated by an intense auxiliary light source. Light sources utilizing

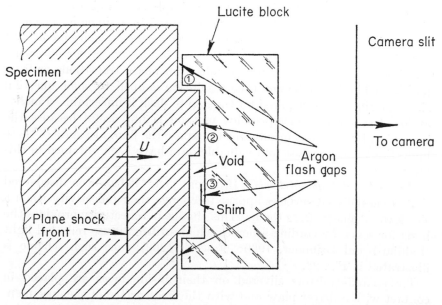

FIG. 21. Flash gap technique for recording shock and free-surface velocities.

explosively-induced strong shock waves in argon or xenon, or exploding wires, have proved to be satisfactory in most cases.

(a) *Flash Gaps.* The use of flash gaps is illustrated in Fig. 21. The gaps are typically a few thousandths of an inch thick and are filled with a noble gas, usually argon (Walsh and Christian, 1955). The incidence of the shock wave on the specimen surface first causes the gaps labelled (1) to close, compressing and heating the gas to brilliant luminosity. Similarly, gap (2) flashes when the shock has travelled through the additional, known thickness of specimen material. Finally, gap (3) closes when the free-surface accelerated by the shock strikes a thin metal shim positioned a known distance from the free surface.

These flashes are recorded with a streak camera of known writing speed and the time differences measured. These differences, together with the known distances, give the shock velocity and the associated average free-surface velocity over the free-surface gap. It is essential in measurements of this kind, where related events are measured at different positions on the sample surface, that the wave be plane and parallel to the sample surface. Further, care must be taken that rarefactions originating at the lateral boundaries of the sample do not disturb the shock front at the positions of measurement. For the latter reason the measurement positions should be removed from the lateral boundaries of the sample by a distance at least equal to the sample thickness.

This method is relatively direct and simple and is also inexpensive since a number of specimens can be measured in a single experiment. The method is limited to cases where the free-surface velocity is constant with time, however, and it is therefore of limited value for observing multiple shock systems such as result from phase transitions or from plastic yield. The inherent time resolution is open to some question since the time delay required for the gap to flash is uncertain. Finally, at low free-surface velocities this method is not useful because the intensity of the flash is insufficient to expose the film. In spite of these limitations many precise and valuable data have been obtained in this way.

(b) *Reflected Light Methods.* In recent years it has been discovered that some polished surfaces appear to change their reflectivity when a shock wave reflects from them. This change in reflectivity provides the basis for several recording schemes which utilize diffuse reflected light (Liddiard and Drimmer, 1960; Fowles, 1962); one such scheme is illustrated in Fig. 22.

Transparent mirrors silvered on their inside faces are placed in contact with a driver plate and with the free surface of the specimen. The mirrors on the driver plate are flat against the plate; the mirror on the specimen surface is inclined at a small angle, α. The assembly is illuminated by an intense light source and viewed through the slit of a

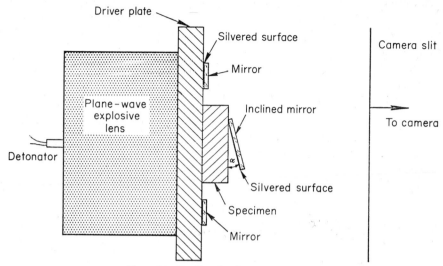

FIG. 22. Inclined mirror technique.

streak camera, as shown. The arrival of the plane shock at the free surface of the driver plate is indicated by an abrupt change in the intensity of the light reflected from the two outside mirrors. When the shock has propagated through the specimen, the free surface of the specimen is accelerated to the right and it begins to collide with the inclined mirror. The point of collision is indicated on the film by a change in the intensity of the light reflected from the mirror. The apparent velocity of the point of collision is evidently related to the free-surface velocity by

$$u_{fs} = U_a \sin \alpha, \qquad (20)$$

where α is the angle of inclination of the mirror to the free surface, and U_a is the velocity of the point of collision.

For this method to give reliable results U_a must exceed the velocity of the shock waves induced in both specimen and mirror by the collision or, more accurately, must be great enough that the flow in both media is everywhere supersonic. Otherwise, disturbances due to the collision could influence the apparent velocity of the point of collision, or even cause jetting. This requirement, then, restricts the usable mirror angles to values less than the critical angle for supersonic flow (Walsh *et al.*, 1953).

This technique allows the free-surface motion to be monitored continuously with time; hence, it is particularly useful where the wave in the sample consists of more than one shock front. The method is sensitive to tilt and to nonplanarity of the shock so that good plane wave generators are essential to its successful use.

A streak camera record obtained in such an arrangement is shown as Fig. 23. In this photograph t_0 represents the time of arrival of the

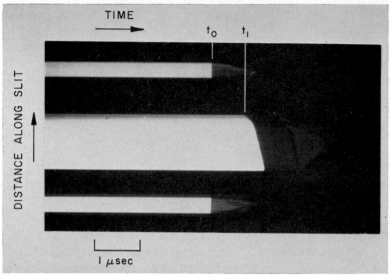

FIG. 23. Streak camera photograph of shock and free-surface velocities in $BaTiO_3$. Inclined mirror recording technique. (Reproduced with permission from ASME Publication No. 62-WA-252, 1962.)

shock front at the driver-specimen interface, indicated by the change in reflectivity of the outside mirrors; similarly, t_1 represents the time of first motion of the specimen free-surface. The slope of the free-surface trace is seen to abruptly increase shortly after the time of first motion, t_1. This acceleration is due to the arrival at the free surface of a second shock front. The existence of two shock fronts, in this case, is a characteristic of the specimen material ($BaTiO_3$). Multiple shock fronts are discussed more fully in Section VIII.

Other techniques utilizing diffuse reflected light have also been used. Thin sheets of Mylar, either clear or aluminized, have been found to abruptly lose reflectivity upon shock impact. They have been used successfully for gap measurements of average free-surface velocity in arrangements similar to that described for flash gaps (Doran et al., 1958). Because of their small thickness (0·0003 inch) they provide good time and space resolution. In some cases bare, polished metals have shown a change in reflectivity upon shock reflection, although this change appears to be less pronounced and reliable than it is for glass or lucite mirrors or for Mylar.

All of these methods require that the free-surface assembly be evacuated, since air shocks produced by the moving free-surface would interfere with the measurements.

(c) *Optical Image Methods.* Where the surface to be observed can be polished, and where it does not seriously lose reflectivity upon shock reflection, specular reflection methods can be used. Two such schemes have been reported. The first of these is based on the principle of the optical lever and is illustrated in Fig. 24.

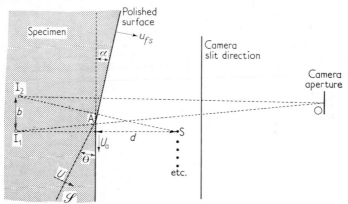

FIG. 24. Principle of optical lever recording technique.

In this method point light sources indicated by S are positioned a known (normal) distance, d, from the polished free surface. The shock wave, $\mathscr{S}$, is incident at a known angle, θ, on the free surface, and the point of intersection of the shock front with the free surface, indicated by A in the figure, travels along the surface with velocity, U_a, given by

$$U_a = U/\sin \theta. \tag{21}$$

Before the arrival of the shock the streak camera views the image, I_1, of the light source reflected in the polished surface. As the point of intersection, A, sweeps down, the surface is rotated through an angle α given by

$$\alpha = 2 \sin^{-1}(u_{fs}/2U_a). \tag{22}$$

In the rotated surface a new image, I_2, of light source, S, appears, displaced from I_1 by a distance, b.

For small angles, α, this displacement is given by

$$b = 2d\alpha; \tag{23}$$

hence, measurement of b and d determines α. This, in turn, determines u_{fs} once U_a is known. The method of obtaining velocity U_a is described with reference to Fig. 25.

This figure shows a portion of a record obtained with the optical lever method. Time is increasing from left to right and each bright line is the

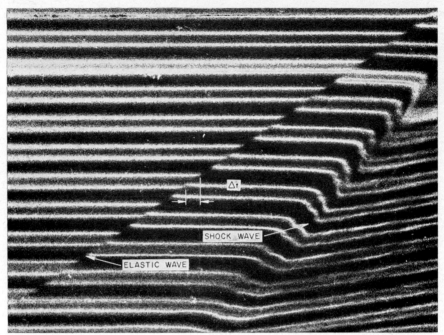

Fig. 25. Elastic and plastic wave arrivals in 2024 aluminium. Optical lever technique. (Reproduced with permission from Fowles, 1961.)

image of one of the sources S in Fig. 24. This record is obtained from the wedge face of a two-dimensional experiment like that shown in Fig. 20, and the amplitude of the shock wave is decaying from top to bottom of the record. The angle of the wedge is chosen so the wave is first observed at the bottom and the point A of Fig. 24 sweeps from bottom to top of the wedge face. Two waves are seen in this case. The first deflection at the left of the record is produced by an elastic wave that precedes the plastic shock, which exhibits a more continuous displacement. The apparent velocity can be obtained from such a record by measuring the slope of the line connecting the same wave break in successive traces, since writing speed and distance scale are known. For the elastic wave of Fig. 25, the ends of all the undeflected traces lie in a straight line. For the shock, a trace by trace measurement must be made to determine the instantaneous slope.

The elastic break in Fig. 25 illustrates a peculiarity of the optical lever method. Each trace is double for a short time, Δt, near the break. This can be understood by reference to Fig. 26. It is apparent that each flat portion of the mirror acts as an aperture so that I_1 can be seen only from a region below the line I_1AB, and I_2 can be seen only from a region

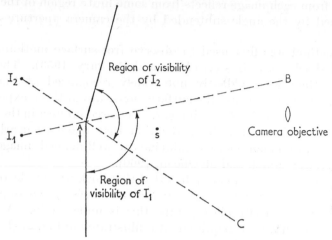

FIG. 26. Regions of visibility of two images of a single light source.

above the line, I_2AC. As point A sweeps down the surface, I_2 is invisible to the camera until I_2AC sweeps down past the camera objective, and I_1 is visible until I_1AB sweeps past. It follows that, for any source distance and free-surface rotation, there is a finite time in which both images are visible in the camera, as illustrated in Figs. 24 and 26. If the slope at A is not a mathematical discontinuity, the overlap of images is less apparent, and this, in turn, provides a means for estimating the finite rise time in a wave (cf. Fig. 25).

Summarizing, we can write for small turning angles,

$$u_{fs} = \frac{b}{2d} U_a \tag{24}$$

and

$$U = U_a \sin \theta. \tag{25}$$

All quantities on the right-hand sides of these expressions are measured.

It will be noted that where U_a is constant the displacement of the images is proportional to the free-surface velocity. Since velocity is the desired quantity, differentiation of experimental data is required only for the determination of U_a.

By using a number of light sources this technique provides a continuous mapping of the shape (curvature) of the free surface with time. Hence, it can be used to observe shock waves which are neither plane nor uniform. Further, it can be made extremely sensitive by increasing the distance, d. The main limitation in observing non-uniform shocks results from curvature of the surface caused by variations in free-surface velocity. Curvature tends to distort the images because the light from each image reflects from some finite region of the surface determined by the angle subtended by the camera aperture and the distance, d.

This method was first used to observe free-surface motions due to spherical shock waves in steel (Allen and McCrary, 1953). The utility of the method was evidently not widely recognized at that time, however, probably because the surface curvature in those experiments caused serious distortion of the images. Renewed interest in the method has recently arisen with the realization that plane or nearly plane geometries are much more conducive to well-defined image traces (Fowles, 1961; Marsh and McQueen, 1960).

The optical lever method requires that the shock wave to be observed be incident at some finite angle on the free surface. In some cases, particularly for anisotropic crystals, this is undesirable. A method which does not have this requirement is illustrated in Fig. 27 (Davis and

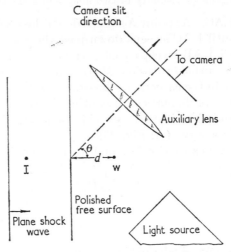

FIG. 27. Moving image technique.

Craig, 1961). A thin wire, W, is suspended a small distance, d, from the polished free surface, and the camera views both the wire and its image, I, reflected in the surface. Illumination is provided by a diffuse light source. When the shock reflects from the free surface, the image appears to move towards the wire with a velocity equal to twice the free-surface velocity. The camera records only a component of this motion because of the viewing angle, θ. Thus, the velocity, v, recorded by the camera is,

$$v = 2u_{fs} \sin \theta. \qquad (26)$$

In using this method the space resolution of the streak camera must be increased by the use of an auxiliary, expendable lens which effectively converts the camera into a microscope. Because the object distances of the wire and its reflection are different, the optical system must have a reasonably large depth of focus, and its f-number must be correspondingly large. The light requirements for adequate exposure become increasingly severe at higher magnifications; over-all magnifications of systems in current use are limited to factors of about 10.

One advantage of this method is that it is relatively insensitive to shock tilt. Because of the magnification limitation, however, it is probably not useful for very low free-surface velocities.

2. *Electrical Methods*

Electrical methods can readily be used where the material under study is a conductor, and with some difficulty otherwise. They have certain advantages and disadvantages in comparison to optical methods. They are generally less expensive since they do not require the substantial investment of a streak camera. Also, greater flexibility in amplification of signals, multi-channel recording, synchronization, etc., is available.

Disadvantages are the relatively less direct nature of the recording instrumentation and, in some cases, the necessity for completion of a circuit through the sample under investigation.

(a) *Pin Contactors.* " Pin " is the name commonly used to denote an electrical contactor connected to a simple pulse-forming circuit so that the circuit discharges when the contactor is closed (Minshall, 1955). A simple arrangement for measuring shock and free-surface velocity for a metal specimen is shown in Fig. 28. Pin No. 1 consists of a small

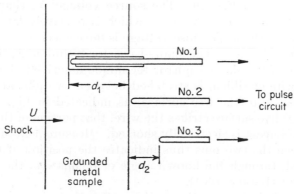

FIG. 28. Pin contactors.

diameter wire enclosed by an insulating sleeve and inserted in a narrow, flat-bottomed hole drilled to a depth, d_1, in the sample. The pin is pushed in until it contacts the bottom of the hole, and is then withdrawn slightly. The gap should be as small as will stand off the pin voltage, which may be from 50 to 300 volts. The delay between first motion of the surface and shorting of the pin is equal to the gap thickness divided by the free-surface velocity, and if the free surface is moving at 0·1 mm/μsec, the gap must be less than 0·01 mm to provide a closing time less than 0·1 μsec. Since these numbers are comparable to the times of interest in such experiments, it is clear that considerable precision is required for pin placement.

Pin No. 2 is a bare wire placed at the plane surface of the sample to record the arrival time of the shock there. Its closing time, with that of No. 1, provides the measure of propagation velocity for the oncoming shock. With pin No. 3, and the measured distance d_2, it provides the measure of mean free-surface velocity. There are many variations on pin design, method of support, determination of standoff, etc.; any

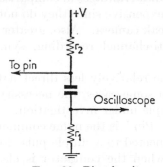

FIG. 29. Pin circuit.

procedure with the necessary precision is satisfactory. A typical pin circuit is shown in Fig. 29. The source voltage, V, charges a small capacitor through a resistance, r_2, which is relatively large compared with r_1, across which the pulse voltage is developed.

(b) *Slanted Resistor*. The slanted resistor technique is the electrical counterpart of the slanted mirror technique described above. A thin resistance wire or ribbon is stretched between two pins at a predetermined angle, α, to the free surface, as indicated in Fig. 30. As the (conducting) free surface strikes the wire, that portion of the wire up to the point of impact is electrically shorted. Measurement of the voltage drop between the two pins thus indicates the position of the point of impact, and, through the known angle of inclination, the free-surface displacement (Barker, 1961).

The same limitation on the angle, α, viz. that the point of impact

travel with supersonic velocity in either of the colliding surfaces, applies
to this technique as it does to the inclined mirror method.

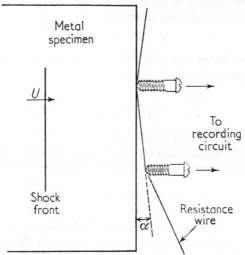

FIG. 30. Slanted resistor configuration.   (Reproduced with permission
from Barker, 1961.)

Some precautions are necessary to insure that the wire is straight,
that it has constant resistance per unit length, and that contact
resistance is negligible.   One advantage of the method is that several
wires can be used on a single specimen to record the motion over
different intervals, or to provide redundant measurements as a check
of consistency.

(c) *Condenser Microphone.*   If the sample to be measured has an
electrically-conducting plane surface, a portion of this surface can be
made one plate of a parallel-plate condenser, and any surface motion
results in a change in capacitance which can be measured by standard
electrical methods.   Several variants on this principle have been used

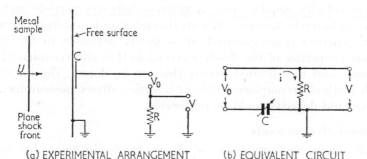

(a) EXPERIMENTAL ARRANGEMENT   (b) EQUIVALENT CIRCUIT
FIG. 31. Capacitor for free-surface velocity measurement.

for measuring the velocity imparted to a free surface by an incident shock wave; the one shown in Fig. 31 is essentially that of Rice (1961). The capacitance change is detected by the variations in voltage across the resistor, R; the relation between the two is

$$V = V_0 - Q/C = iR \tag{27}$$

where Q is the charge stored on the condenser at any time. Differentiating this equation leads to the expression,

$$\frac{dV}{dt} + V\left(\frac{1}{RC} + \frac{1}{C}\frac{dC}{dt}\right) = \frac{V_0}{C}\frac{dC}{dt}. \tag{28}$$

If $(1/C)\,dC/dt$ is sufficiently small compared to $1/RC$, the third term on the left-hand side of Eq. (28) can be neglected. Then if the right-hand side is treated as a constant we can readily integrate the equation to get

$$V = RV_0\frac{dC}{dt}\Big[\,1 - \exp(-t/RC)\,\Big]. \tag{29}$$

This shows that after a few time constants the voltage induced across the measuring resistor is nearly proportional to the rate of change of capacitance and thus quite directly related to the free-surface velocity.

If RC is very large, then

$$V - V_0 \propto 1/C \tag{30}$$

and the output voltage is more nearly related to the displacement; then the recorded signal must be differentiated to obtain free-surface velocity.

The capacitor technique is especially suited for measuring structure in the wave front because of the excellent time resolutions which can be obtained electrically.

B. *Internal Measurements*

The experimental methods described so far have been somewhat indirect in that the shock waves have been observed only by their interaction with a free surface. In particular, the determination of particle velocity requires that a relation between particle and free-surface velocity be known. Where this relation is uncertain or where shock structure is complicated, it is highly desirable to be able to measure properties of the shock wave while it is still contained in the specimen, and to a limited extent this can be done. The impedance match method accomplishes this in a sense; direct measurements of pressure and density would be preferable.

1. *Optical Measurements*

Aside from measurements of shock front thickness by optical reflection (Flook and Hornig, 1955), the only optical measurements made on shocks inside transparent materials have been of shock velocity. Two approaches have been used. One is to align the slit of a streak camera parallel to the direction of shock propagation and observe the progress along the slit of the shadow cast by the shock front (Cook *et al.*, 1960), as shown in Fig. 32. Differentiation of the trace yields the shock velocity as a function of position; a free-surface measurement is required if R-H data are to be obtained.

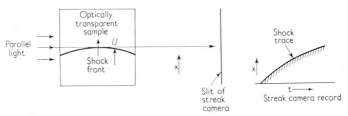

FIG. 32. Shock velocity by shadowgraph in a transparent material.

A related measurement can be made by flash photography to produce a shadowgraph of the shock in a two-dimensional steady experiment. An example of such a profile in water is shown in Fig. 33.

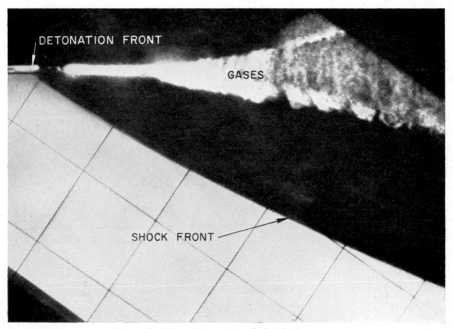

FIG. 33. Two-dimensional shock in water.

This shock is generated by a steady detonation running along the horizontal boundary of the figure. Since the detonation velocity is known, measurement of the inclination of the profile to the horizontal at any point gives the shock velocity at that point. If the R-H curve of the material is known, this in turn gives the pressure at each plane below the generating surface. The precision is poor at low pressures because of the relative insensitivity of shock velocity to pressure in that region. Again, this does not provide R-H data without supplementary measurements.

It would in principle be possible to make density measurements on transparent solids and liquids using interferometric techniques similar to those for gases (Bleakney *et al.*, 1949), but a basic difficulty is encountered. Such a measurement requires that transmission be measured in a direction normal to that of propagation, and if the source and detector are located outside the sample being studied, the properties of the shocked medium are inhomogeneous in the direction of transmission, as shown in Fig. 34. The rarefactions arising from the sample

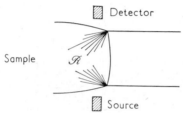

Fɪɢ. 34. Non-uniform density in a transverse section.

boundaries produce a region of varying density and velocity which must be taken into account if quantitative meaning is to be attached to the measurements.

2. *X-ray Measurements*

Several workers have measured density and shock velocity in thin specimens by a flash X-ray method and have published R-H data from their measurements (Schall, 1958). This method is based on the assumption that X-ray absorption is essentially an atomic phenomenon and hence independent of compression, i.e. it is assumed that there is no distortion of the inner electron shells primarily responsible for the absorption. That this is not strictly true is indicated by the observed pressure dependence of radioactive decay by K-capture (Bainbridge *et al.*, 1953), but the effect may not be large enough to significantly influence the results. The density measurement is quite straight-forward; a capacitor (Fig. 35) is charged to a voltage V_0, which may be several hundred kilovolts, by means of an external source through a high resistance, R. A breakdown discharge from field emission accompanied by melting of irregularities on the cathode, is initiated by a trigger electrode placed near the cathode, and as a result of the local

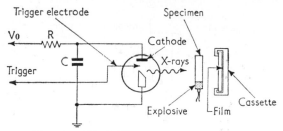

FIG. 35. Flash X-ray measurements.

ionization, a high current discharge is established between cathode and anode. This discharge produces an intense burst of X-radiation which may have a total duration considerably less than a microsecond and energy sufficient to blacken a photographic plate. If the specimen to be measured is interposed between cathode and film, density gradients in the film corresponding to density variations in the shocked specimen will be observed. The discharge of the X-ray tube must be synchronized with the passage of the shock wave through the specimen. Variations of this apparatus consist of replacing the breakdown tube by a field emission tube (Grundhauser *et al.*, 1961) operating at up to 600 kV, or using a linear accelerator to generate a burst of X-rays.

In reducing the photographic data to density behind the shock, corrections must be made for the rarefactions illustrated in Fig. 34. Since the experiments are normally done with thin specimens, corrections would be expected to be substantial. Agreement between R-H data obtained in this way and that inferred from velocity measurements on the same material has not been very good, nor do the differences between the two types of data lie within the asserted limits of experimental error (Schall, 1958). A more careful examination of comparable measurements is clearly required to resolve this apparent conflict.

3. Pressure Transducers

The ideal arrangement for making direct stress measurements would consist of a plane pressure sensing element embedded in the sample material and having the same impedance characteristics, as in Fig. 36. The pressure element would be small enough in diameter not to be influenced by rarefactions coming from the side of the sample; it would be thin enough to give the required time resolution ($\simeq$ thickness/shock velocity), and far enough removed from the right-hand boundary to be

uninfluenced by the reflected rarefaction until the event of interest was
past.

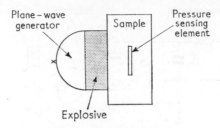

FIG. 36. Ideal pressure gauge.

An attempt has been made to essentially satisfy these requirements by
surrounding a thin wafer of sulphur with a Teflon insulator of matching

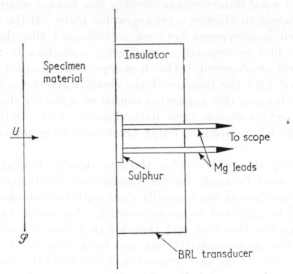

FIG. 37. Sulphur pressure transducer.

impedance and placing both wafer and insulator in intimate contact
with the plane face of the specimen, as shown in Fig. 37 (Hauver, 1960).
The electrical resistivity of sulphur is observed to change by many
orders of magnitude when shocked to pressures above about 90 kb, and
under the influence of a fixed potential, the observed current through the
sulphur is found to be a measure of the pressure existing in it.

The electrical signal is brought out on magnesium leads, which are an
approximate impedance match for the sulphur, and as a shock passes
over the wafer, changes in resistivity are recorded on a cathode ray
oscilloscope. In general there will be an impedance mismatch between

sample material and the gauge materials. If the transition curves OB
and OA for right-travelling shocks are drawn in the p-u plane for both

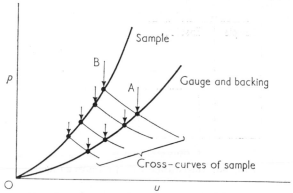

Fig. 38. Impedance interpretation of pressure gauge signal.

sample and gauge, the relation between gauge and sample pressures is
readily demonstrated (Fig. 38). The pressure in the gauge jumps to the
value A as the shock reaches it and then decays down the transition
curve to O. The state A was reached from the state B in the sample by
transition along the cross curve BA of the sample. Then as the wave
decays, each p-u state on OA is connected to a corresponding state on B
by one of the cross-curves of the sample. A conversion from gauge to
specimen pressures is in this way readily achieved.

The method appears to be particularly promising for relatively direct
measurements of pressure-time profiles of decaying shock-waves. With
the possible exception of the X-ray technique, no other method is
presently capable of such measurements over such a large pressure
range.

An important feature of this transducer is that the rise time can be
made very small, $<5 \times 10^{-8}$ seconds, so that good resolution of pulse
details can be obtained if development is successfully completed.
Some of the difficulties are:

1. The initial resistivity is very high so that stray leakage can seriously
   influence the results.
2. The useful pressure range is limited to between about 80 and 200 kb.
3. Calibration is by shock and is essentially destructive; it must
   therefore be carried out on models assumed to be identical to those
   used for measurements.
4. There are important basic questions about the mechanisms of
   conductivity and to what extent they are time-dependent.

Additional insight into these problems will be required before the conditions under which such a gauge will be reliable can be predicted.

A related approach to the resistance transducer is to substitute fine

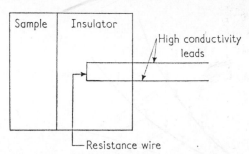

FIG. 39. Resistance wire pressure gauge.

resistance wires embedded in an insulating slab for Hauver's sulphur wafer (Bernstein, 1963), (Fig. 39). Measurements have shown that the rate of change of resistance with shock pressure is approximately uniform to 300 kb (Fuller and Price, 1962).

This approach avoids some of the difficulties with sulphur; the resistance is lower so that stray leakage is much less serious, and the useful pressure range is greater. Moreover, normalization of the gauge to be used is readily accomplished by measuring its initial resistance. Development problems are associated with possible resistivity changes due to stretching and bending, with the matching of wire and insulator impedances, and with possible effects of unknown temperature coefficients of resistance.

Still another instrument for making direct pressure measurements is the piezoelectric transducer. Tourmaline gauges have been used to measure pressures at the surface of an explosively-shocked iron specimen; measurements up to 330 kb were reported (Goranson et al., 1955). Difficulties arise in its use because electrical breakdown occurs internally as a result of contained impurities. Recently work has been directed towards the development of quartz for precision measurements at lower pressures.

The action of a quartz transducer can be illustrated with reference to Fig. 40 (Anderson, 1961). One face of an x-cut quartz disc is placed in contact with the metal specimen through which a plane shock is driven; the specimen itself serves as one electrode. The opposite face of the quartz is in contact with an aluminium disc which serves as the second electrode. The quartz-aluminium cylinder is surrounded by an insulator and the two electrodes are connected through a low resistance. The voltage developed across this resistance is recorded by an oscilloscope.

The integral of the current, I, gives the total charge released by passage of the shock.

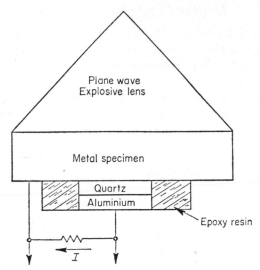

FIG. 40. Arrangement for pressure measurements using quartz transducer. (Reproduced with permission from Anderson, 1961.)

If the polarization, P, is supposed to be a function of the shock pressure, the electric displacement is

$$D = E + P(p), \tag{31}$$

and a shock front in the quartz divides it into two regions: one undisturbed and nonconducting, the other in a different polarization state and possibly conducting. The electric moment of a volume element $d\tau$ is $P\,d\tau$, and, if electrical conductivity is negligible, the integral of this is equal to the total charge, Q, on a face of the disc, times its thickness, L. Then the increment of charge on a face in time dt is

$$dQ = (A/L)\,dt\;\partial/\partial t \int_0^L P(p)\,dx, \tag{32}$$

where A is the area of the disc face. If the electrodes are shorted, dQ/dt is the external current flowing:

$$I = (A/L) \int_0^L \partial P/\partial t\,dx. \tag{33}$$

To a useful approximation, $P = kp$ and $p = p(x - vt)$ for waves propagating in the $+x$-direction. Here $v =$ constant is the propagation velocity of the elastic precursor within the quartz. Then

I

$$\partial P/\partial t = k \ \partial p(x - vt)/\partial t = - kvp'(x - vt) \qquad (34)$$

and

$$I = (Akv/L)[p(\ - vt) - p(L - vt)]. \qquad (35)$$

Before the wave front reaches the far side of the disc, current is proportional to pressure at the interface; the output of the device is used only during this interval. The pressure existing in the specimen is obtained by the procedure indicated in Fig. 38; time resolution of better than 0·1 microsecond is easily achieved. Preliminary measurements of elastic precursor waves in steel, using this principle, have been quite successful; records for Armco iron are shown in Fig. 41.

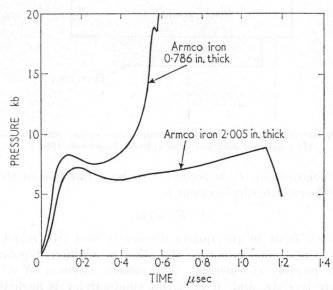

FIG. 41 Pressure-time profiles of elastic precursor in Armco iron. (Reproduced with permission from Anderson, 1961.)

In general, Eq. (35) is far too simple to describe the true shock effect on current; it applies fairly well in quartz at shock pressures up to about 21 kb when propagation is in the $+x$-direction; above that, the relation $P = kp$ is no longer an adequate approximation. Recent measurements reveal that even below 21 kb the proportionality between P and p does not hold completely (Graham, 1962). The piezoelectric coefficient $e_{11}c_{11}$ agrees with the zero-amplitude value up to a shock pressure of about 7 kb and is approximately equal to $2·04 \times 10^{-8}$ C/cm² kb. From 7 to 10 kb it increases to about $2·16 \times 10^{-8}$, where it remains to $p = 21$ kb. At 21 kb it jumps to approximately $3·3 \times 10^{-8}$ and maintains that value to at least 40 kb. Measurements at higher pressure have been less detailed; they show the total charge release to increase monotonically with pressure to 300 kb, except for an anomalous peak at 65 kb, and the slope, C/cm^2 kb, is less at 300 kb than at 40 kb (Anderson, 1961). The amplitude of an elastic precursor wave in x-cut quartz is about 60 kb; shear failure occurs there, and unusual behaviour of the polarization at higher pressures would be expected.

Two major questions to be answered before these direct stress or pressure-responding devices are understood concern their response to a directed stress compared with a hydrostatic pressure and whether or not their mechanisms of response are rate-dependent. These questions are discussed to some extent in the next section. Their ultimate resolution will rely on more advanced experimentation.

VIII. MATERIAL PROPERTIES AND SHOCK STRUCTURE

The preceding discussion has assumed that a shock wave consists of a single stress discontinuity travelling into an undisturbed medium, followed by a uniform or expanding state. Much useful information has been obtained on the basis of this assumption, but close observation reveals that shocks may be more complicated than this and that the compression phase of the shock wave often has important, time-dependent structure. This is suggested in the records of Figs. 25 and 41 used to illustrate experimental techniques. There is a connection between the properties of the material and the structure of the shock front, so study of this structure increases the amount of information that can be obtained from shock experiments. However, the connection between shock structure and material properties is not always unique, and possible alternative interpretations must be carefully weighed.

The first idea that must be abandoned in a more critical study of the shock wave is that shock pressure, so frequently mentioned in preceding sections, is a simple hydrostatic pressure, as would occur in an ideal fluid. The shock transition really takes place under precisely defined conditions of one-dimensional strain, or linear compression, and any material with finite strength ends up in the shocked state with anisotropic stress tensor. The shock compression allows no net macroscopic strain to occur immediately behind and parallel to the shock front, and a re-examination of the jump conditions, Eqs. (1) to (3), shows that measurements of propagation velocity and the normal component of particle velocity produce information only about the component of compressive stress normal to the shock front. We conclude, then, that the stress parallel to the wave front is essentially unknown, except by inference from other information we may combine with the velocity measurements.

To illustrate what may happen to a solid under shock conditions, consider an isotropic elastic material which fails in shear at a finite resolved shear stress. First, suppose a cylindrical specimen to be compressed by application of pressure p_x to its faces while all lateral expansion or contraction is prevented by the simultaneous application of supporting pressure $p_y = p_z$ to its cylindrical surface. Since the elastic properties of materials are conventionally summarized in terms of their response to hydrostatic pressure $\bar{p}$ and shear stress τ, it is convenient to write the linear compressive stress, p_x, in terms of these:

$$\bar{p} \equiv \tfrac{1}{3}(p_x + p_y + p_z) = p_x + \tfrac{1}{3}(p_y - p_x) + \tfrac{1}{3}(p_z - p_x) = p_x - \tfrac{2}{3}(p_x - p_y), \quad (36)$$

since $p_y = p_z$ from symmetry. Maximum resolved shear stress is defined as $\tau \equiv (p_x - p_y)/2$, so Eq. (36) is equivalent to

$$p_x \equiv \bar{p} + \tfrac{4}{3}\tau. \quad (37)$$

This is true whatever the stress-strain relations. While the compressed specimen behaves elastically, an explicit relation exists between p_x and τ. Since the only nonvanishing component of strain is in the x-direction, Hooke's law becomes

$$\left. \begin{aligned} p_x &= (\lambda + 2\mu)\epsilon_x \\ p_y &= p_z = \lambda\epsilon_x \end{aligned} \right\}, \quad (38)$$

where $\epsilon_x = 1 - \rho_0/\rho$, and λ, μ are the Lamé elastic constants. Equations (38) yield directly the resolved shear stress,

$$\tau = \mu\epsilon_x = \frac{\mu}{\lambda + 2\mu} \, p_x = \frac{1 - 2\nu}{2(1 - \nu)} \, p_x, \quad (39)$$

where ν is Poisson's ratio. Thus, for a solid which neither yields nor fractures, the maximum resolved shear stress increases monotonically with p_x.

Since every solid has only a finite shear strength, it must be presumed that the material will fail for some p_x. It may fail catastrophically, as in brittle fracture, or it may fail slowly with plastic yield. In any case there will result a deviation from simple elastic compression. In plastic failure the plastic deformation is microscopic and of the magnitude required by the yield properties. If the yield stress in simple tension is Y, then $2\tau = Y$, according to either Tresca's or von Mises' criterion. If Y is constant, then p_x and $\bar{p}$ increase together and above the yield point the former exceeds the latter by the constant stress $2Y/3$; the resulting compression curve is like that of Fig. 42(a) (Wood, 1952; Fowles, 1961).

The structure of a shock wave in such a material depends upon the final peak pressure, p_1, reached in the compression. If, in Fig. 42(a), p_1

lies above B, only a single shock is formed; if p_1 lies below A, a single elastic compression occurs. If p_1 is between A and B, the shock consists

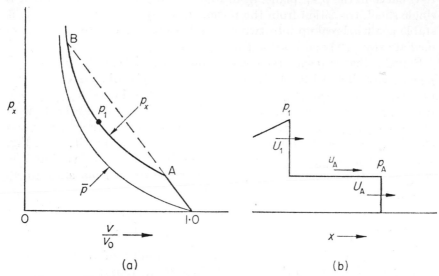

(a)   (b)

FIG. 42. Equation of state and shock structure in elastic-plastic solid
(a) Linear compression   (b) Shock wave structure

of an elastic precursor of amplitude p_A followed by a slower moving shock with peak pressure p_1. This case is illustrated in Fig. 42(b). Here the pressure between the elastic precursor and the shock is shown as constant in an ever-widening region; this holds for a sharp yield point and constant Y. More generally work-hardening and strain rate effects may alter the pressure distribution in this region.

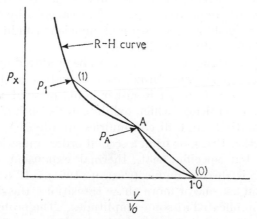

FIG. 43. Arbitrary R-H curve.

In order to establish a criterion for the existence of shock instabilities like that discussed in the preceding paragraph, consider an arbitrary R-H curve in the p_x-V plane, as in Fig. 43. We wish to determine if a single shock transition from the initial state (0) to the final state (1) is stable against breakup into two successive shocks: one to some intermediate state (A) and a second from (A) to (1).

Suppose that two successive shocks do exist. The first, of amplitude $p_A - p_0$, travelling with velocity U_A in laboratory coordinates, accelerates material to a velocity u_A. It then travels with velocity $U_A - u_A$ with respect to the material behind the shock front. The second shock, with amplitude $p_1 - p_A$, travels at velocity U_1 in laboratory coordinates and at velocity $U_1 - u_A$ with respect to the material ahead of it, as in Fig. 42(b). Then if $U_1 - u_A < U_A - u_A$, the assumption of instability is correct; if the inequality is reversed, a single shock from state (0) to state (1) must be stable. From Eq. (8),

$$U_A - u_A = V_A \sqrt{[(p_A - p_0)/(V_0 - V_A)]}, \tag{40}$$
$$U_1 - u_A = V_A \sqrt{[(p_1 - p_A)/(V_A - V_1)]}.$$

Using these relations, the condition for stability of a single shock against breakup at a state A is that (Rice *et al.*, 1958):

$$\frac{p_1 - p_A}{V_A - V_1} > \frac{p_A - p_0}{V_0 - V_A}. \tag{41}$$

We infer from this the following statement of the condition for shock stability: if state (1) on the R-H curve can be connected to the initial state (0) in the p_x-V plane by a straight line that lies above the R-H curve and intersects it in no other point, then (1) and (0) can be connected by a single shock transition, otherwise not. A stronger condition which is sufficient but not necessary for stability is that the curvature of the adiabat be everywhere positive; it can be weakened by hydrodynamic considerations to yield a necessary and sufficient condition equivalent to Eq. (41) (Weyl, 1949; Duvall, 1961).

A multiple shock structure in a solid can be produced by shear failure, which causes a cusp or region of negative curvature in the R-H curve. A similar structure may occur in either liquid or solid as a result of a first-order phase transition, which exhibits a discontinuity in V under isothermal conditions and discontinuities in $(\partial p/\partial V)_S$ at the phase boundaries (Bethe, 1942), or from a second-order transition, in which V is continuous but specific heat, thermal expansion coefficient, or compressibility is discontinuous (Curran, 1961). If a solid exhibits shear failure and has one or more phase transitions, the shock structure may be very complicated at some amplitudes. The problem of relating shock structure to material properties is clearly a complicated one, and clues must be sought in material properties determined by more conventional methods. This is particularly so when time and rate effects enter to influence the shock structure. One such effect is stress-relaxation, which is discussed below; another common one is viscosity, which serves to increase the thickness of the shock transition zone (Holtzmann and Cowan, 1961).

The influence of stress-relaxation effects on the structure and development of the shock wave can be understood qualitatively in terms of a simple model. Consider the yielding process in an elastic-plastic solid which has the following property: if a volume-element has a shear stress applied to it very slowly, it yields at some well-defined value, say, Y. If a shear stress greater than Y is applied to it very quickly, it will momentarily support this larger stress, but the value supported will decay towards Y, say exponentially. Now consider the history of such an element in a material through which a shock wave is passing. It is elastically stressed and accelerated to a velocity u, and if the rapid, nearly discontinuous, stress increase in the precursor has an amplitude greater than the static or equilibrium value, each material element will be found in just the situation described—supporting a greater-than-equilibrium shear stress and relaxing towards its equilibrium state. As this relaxation occurs, the elastic wave front continues on with the velocity $a_0 - u$ relative to the element, compressing new material and leaving the element under consideration behind. However, as this element relaxes, it produces infinitesimal rarefactions which propagate ahead at speed $a > a_0 - u$. These eventually overtake the elastic front and cause its amplitude to decrease. If the relaxation time of the isolated volume element is t_0, a simple calculation shows that the effective relaxation time with which the amplitude of the elastic precursor approaches its equilibrium value is approximately $t_1 = t_0 a_0/(a - a_0 + u)$. This relaxation also contributes to deviations from the uniform stress state between elastic precursor and following shock shown in Fig. 42b (McQueen, 1961).

If the material also exhibits strain rate effects, as from viscosity, the problem is further complicated by spreading of the wave front and relaxation during the initial compression. Experimental observations on these effects in solids are just now becoming available through the application of new experimental techniques with improved time resolution (Fig. 31) (Rice, 1961).

To summarize, the direct results of shock wave measurements, coupled with the jump conditions, are density internal energy, and a single component of stress; to infer more requires supplementary measurements or assumptions. Irregularities in the R-H curve may produce multiple wave fronts, and from these we hope to infer information about phase changes, material strength, etc. In using this information and in the taking of measurements, due caution must be exercised to ensure that time rate and relaxation effects are not confusing the interpretation of shock parameters in terms of equilibrium material properties. This latter point may be additionally complicated if shear strength depends on the mean pressure to which the material is subjected.

IX. Applications and Results

A. *Equations of State*

In spite of the difficulties pointed out in the preceding section, it has been customary among workers in this field, who well recognize the problems, to treat the shock wave data as equivalent to equilibrium pressure-volume information, except where definite experimental evidence of deviation exists. This practice is not entirely without basis, since R-H curves for most materials represent smooth extrapolations from hydrostatic p-V relations (Rice *et al.*, 1958), and shock parameters calculated from the static data extrapolated to high pressures by quasi-theoretical formulas are in reasonable accord with observations (Duvall and Zwolinski, 1955). Moreover, known yield strengths for most materials are negligible compared to moderate shock pressures, so, except for possible increases of yield-strength with pressure, it is plausible to suppose that stress anisotropy in the shock is negligible. A set of measurements on single crystal zinc is also encouraging in that it indicates no measurable anisotropy for R-H values in the vicinities of 200 and 400 kb, although this material is highly anisotropic in the elastic regime (Walsh *et al.*, 1957).

The extent of work on experimental determination of the R-H relation in solids and liquids is indicated in Table IV, where information on most materials, investigators, and pressure ranges reported to 1962 is listed. The article by Rice *et al.*, (1958) is an excellent summary of information on metals reported before 1958; it deals primarily with pressures obtained with contact explosive. A similar collection for liquids is published in the paper by Walsh and Rice (1957). The article by McQueen and Marsh (1960) for pressures up to 2000 kb, obtained with explosively-driven flyer plates is the most extensive single collection of data published since then. The articles by Al'tshuler and his co-workers contain flyer plate data at much higher pressures than are reported by other investigators.

The p-V data obtained from shock measurements have been used to derive parameters for various forms of the equation of state; one interesting and useful empirical relation which has been discovered is that shock and particle velocity, in regions where no phase transitions occur, are usually linearly related (Rice *et al.*, 1958):

$$U = e + gu_p. \tag{42}$$

Combining this relation with jump conditions for mass and momentum, Eq. (1) and (2), yields a three-parameter expression for the p-V relation on the R–H curve:

$$p = e^2(V_0 - V)/[g^2(V - V_0 + V_0/g)^2]. \tag{43}$$

No satisfactory theoretical basis for Eq. (42) has been proposed, though it has been shown to be commensurate with a first-order expansion of the Mie-Grüneisen equation (Berger and Joigneau, 1959). It must be assumed and used with some reservations, but it serves as a useful indicator of the possible existence of phase transitions or other anomalous effects, and Eq.(43) is useful for interpolating between measured points on the R-H curve. Schall (1959) has attempted to correlate observed values of e for close-packed elements with atomic number and density. He finds that when e is plotted as a function of the quantity $(Z - 10)/\rho_0$, where Z is the atomic number and ρ_0 is the initial density, a single curve fits all the points fairly well.

The trends of recent work have been towards increased emphasis on production and measurement of very high shock pressures, refinement of measurements in the region below 100 kb, study of shock-induced phase transitions, and determination of thermodynamic parameters for extrapolating shock wave data to points off the R-H curve.

Extrapolation of p-V data to points off the R-H curve has received considerable attention; particular efforts, based on the Mie-Grüneisen equation, have been made to calculate isotherms for $0°$ K in order that the data might be used for theoretical purposes (cf. Section III) (Walsh *et al.*, 1957; Doran, 1960). One of the most critical elements in this extrapolation is the calculation of Grüneisen's ratio, Γ, and its dependence on density. Formulas for treating this dependence have been proposed by Slater and by Dugdale and McDonald; and both have been used in reducing shock data. Although the theoretical basis for the Dugdale-McDonald relation has been questioned, available experimental data are inadequate to discriminate between the two (Rice *et al.*, 1958; Doran, 1960). In addition, three methods have been reported for making measurements off the R-H curve. The first of these requires that the initial state of the material be varied in order to produce changes in the final, shocked state. This has been accomplished by comparing the R-H curve of initially powdered material with that of the solid, assuming that, at a given volume, the distortional energy of the lattice is the same in each case, and attributing the differences in measured pressures to differences in vibrational energy (Al'tshuler *et al.*,

I*

TABLE IV. Summary of Available R-H Data for Solids and Liquids

Substance	Initial Density (gm/cm³)	Pressure Range (kb)	e† (cm/μs)	g†	Pressures of observed transitions (kb)	Remarks	References
Metals							
Elements							
Antimony	6·69	248–1175	0·20	1·60			37
Beryllium	1·85	142–311	0·798	1·09			41
Bismuth	9·79	17·6–3450	0·20	1·34	27·2 (Initial Temp. 19°C); 31·3 (−28°C); 17·6 (236°C)	linear relation valid above 350 kb	6, 22, 30, 37, 41
Cadmium	8·64	360–3490	0·244	1·67			6, 26, 37, 41
Chromium	7·13	233–1379	0·522	1·47			37, 41
Cobalt	8·82	244–1603	0·475	1·33			37, 41
Copper	8·90	216–9550	0·396	1·50		porosity varies	6, 8, 35, 37, 41
Gold	19·24	590–5130	0·308	1·56	Initial Temp.		6, 37, 41
Indium	7·27	214–405	0·237	1·61	125 to 140·5 (ambient)		41
Iron	7·84	38–4870	0·380	1·58	19 (885°C); 150 (−195°C)	linear relation valid above 300 kb	5, 8, 10, 30, 34, 36, 37, 41
Lead	11·34	390–7300	0·203	1·58			6, 8, 35, 36, 37, 41
Magnesium	1·725	50–260	0·449	1·27		porosity varies	36, 41, 42, 43, 45
Molybdenum	10·20	254–1633	0·516	1·24			37, 41
Nickel	8·86	235–9560	0·465	1·45		porosity varies	37, 41
Niobium	8·60	244–482	0·445	1·21			41
Palladium	11·95	263–372	0·379	1·92			41
Platinum	21·4	295–586	0·367	1·41			41
Rhodium	12·42	279–551	0·468	1·65			41
Silver	10·49	216–4010	0·324	1·59			6, 37, 41
Sodium	0·97	7–32					16
Tantalum	16·46	272–547	0·337	1·16			41
Thallium	11·84	213–1517	0·186	1·52			37, 41
Thorium	11·68	203–1405	0·213	1·28			37, 41
Tin	7·28	330–3100	0·264	1·48			6, 37, 41
Titanium	4·51	168–1063	0·478	1·09			37, 41
Tungsten	19·17	394–2074	0·400	1·27			37
Uranium	9·5	307–3900	?	1·869			45 }
	18·9	335–6450	0·255	1·504			
Vanadium	6·1	204–1244	0·511	1·21			37

Zinc	7.14	186–3260	0.305	1.56			6, 37, 41
Zirconium	6.49	208–407	0.377	0.93			41
Non-Metals							
Elements							
Carbon	1.7–2.2	3–850	0.135	1.7	~180 to 400; 600	two transitions	4, 21
Iodine	4.93	50–1100	0.36	0.7	~700	below transition	3
			0.22	1.0		above „	
Sulphur	2.1	60–200	0.32	0.8	~67 to 106	below „	11, 12
						above „	
Alkali Halides							
CsBr	4.43	143–328	0.31	0.3			14
CsCl	3.95	60–318	0.22	0.5			14
CsI	4.49	140–324					14
KBr	2.73	112–264					14
KCl	1.98	40–229	0.18	1.8			14
KF	2.49	117–266	0.24	1.6			14
KI	3.1	110–278	0.18	1.4			14
LiBr	3.30	136–300	0.26	1.4			14
LiCl	2.05	12?–263	0.41	1.5			14
LiF	2.62	155–331	0.50	1.6			14
LiI	4.01	205–320	0.28	0.9			14
NaBr	3.16	58–305	0.26	1.3			14
NaCl	2.15	52–791	0.34	1.37			9, 14
NaI	3.64	134–312	0.20	1.6			14
RbBr	3.30	112–286	0.14	1.6			14
RbCl	2.70	105–268	0.15	1.6			14
RbI	3.5	117–279	0.14	1.5			14
Other							
$BaTiO_3$	5.72	10–1000	0.351	1.69		Linear relation above 24 kb	40, 44
$BaTiO_3$ (5% $CaTiO_3$)	5.54	12–30	0.216	1.46	~8?	Initial phase—cubic	20
		5–300				Initial phase—tetragonal	20
CO_2	1.54	53–631					49
Dunite	3.25	190–720			~150–300		29
Gabbro	3.0	150–720					29
Sand	1.65	0.7–120	0.13	1.35			48
Methacrylate Polymers	1.18	17–2000	0.274	1.35			17, 31, 36, 45, 48
Marble	2.70	51–518	0.35	1.95	150		1
Pb (Zr 0.52–Ti 0.45)O_3	7.58	2–400	0.163	3.53		Linear relation above 19 kb	17,

Substance	Initial Density (gm/cm³)	Pressure Range (kb)	$e\dagger$ (cm/μs)	$g\dagger$	Pressure of observed transitions (kb)	Remarks	References
Pyrex	2·23	22– 100					16
Quartz (crystal)	2·66	40– 200			400	anomalous compressibility below 35 kb	25, 46
Quartz (fused)	2·204	0– 623			250		46
Liquids							
Acetone	0·80	46– 106	0·19	1·4			47
Argon	1·40	10– 72					16
Benzene	0·88	52– 121	0·18	1·6			47
Bromoethane	1·46	68– 157	0·15	1·5			47
Carbon Disulphide	1·26	59– 130	0·20	0·9			47
Carbon Tetrachloride	1·60	74– 171	0·15	1·5			47
Ethyl Alcohol	0·79	47– 110	0·16	1·6			47
Ethyl Ether	0·70	41– 860	0·17	1·5			46, 47
Glycerin	1·25	76– 170	0·24	1·6			47
Heptane	0·69	5– 22					16, 47
Hexane	0·68	41– 860	0·19	1·4			47
Mercury	13·5	226– 464	0·12	2·4			47
Methanol	0·80	47– 110	0·18	1·5			47
Mononitrotoluene	1·17	65– 152	0·22	1·3			47
n-Amyl Alcohol	0·81	50– 116	0·20	1·5			47
Toluene	0·88	52– 122	0·18	1·6			47
Water	1·0	2–1140	0·17	1·7	115		7, 16, 43, 45, 47
Nitrogen	0·808	29·6– 404	0·16	1·4			49
Alloys							
Aluminium (commercial)	2·79	20–4930	0·525	1·39		linear fit inadequate over entire pressure range	8, 19, 24, 26, 34, 35
Brass	8·41	167–1764	0·38	1·42			36, 38, 41, 42, 43, 45
Invar	8·08	35– 160			50?	Possible Curie transition	37, 41
Iron-Chromium		160– 270			See Fig. 48		15
Iron-Nickel		160– 270			See Fig. 48		23
Iron-Chromium-Nickel		390– 460					23
Mild Steel	7·84	100–3700			125 to 140·5		34, 39, 45

† Parameters in the linear relation between shock velocity and particle velocity:

$$U_s = e + gu_p$$

The associated pressure-volume curve is given by

$$p = \rho_0 e^2 \eta/(1 - g\eta)^2; \quad \eta = 1 - V/V_0.$$

1958a; Kormer *et al.*, 1962). In this way the Grüneisen ratio was obtained as a function of specific volume. An alternative procedure is to vary the initial temperature of the specimen before shocking it. This has been successfully accomplished in studying dp/dT for a phase transition in bismuth (Duff and Minshall, 1957), and the p-T line of a new phase in iron has been traced out in this manner (Johnson *et al.*, 1962). It is apparent that further work along these lines should be productive.

A second procedure for producing information off the R-H curve is to measure hydrodynamic sound velocity in shocked material; this gives the slope of the adiabat that crosses the R-H curve. Such measurements have been accomplished in aluminium, copper, lead, and iron using two different methods (Al'tshuler *et al.*, 1960). The first involves the production of disturbances in a plane shock front which travel laterally along the shock front, as in Fig. 44. A step in the shocked specimen produces a rarefaction that travels laterally into the specimen. By measuring the width l of the disturbed region of the shock front, the angle α can be determined. If the state behind the shock is uniform, with constant particle velocity, u, this and the shock velocity, U, can be substituted into the relation

---

REFERENCES TO TABLES IV–VII

1. Adadurov *et al.* (1961)
2. Alder and Christian (1956)
3. Alder and Christian (1960)
4. Alder and Christian (1961)
5. Al'tshuler *et al.* (1958a)
6. Al'tshuler *et al.* (1958b)
7. Al'tshuler *et al.* (1958c)
8. Al'tshuler *et al.* (1960a)
9. Al'tshuler *et al.* (1961)
10. Bancroft *et al.* (1956)
11. Berger *et al.* (1960)
12. Berger *et al.* (1961)
13. Brish *et al.* (1960)
14. Christian (1957)
15. Curran (1961)
16. Dapoigny *et al.* (1955)
17. Dapoigny *et al.* (1957)
18. David and Hamann (1959)
19. Doran *et al.* (1958)
20. Doran (1962)
21. Doran (1963)
22. Duff and Minshall (1957)
23. Fowler *et al.* (1961)
24. Fowles (1961)
25. Fowles (1962)
26. Goranson *et al.* (1955)
27. Gregson and Grine (1962)
28. Grover *et al.* (1958)
29. Hughes and McQueen (1958)
30. Hughes *et al.* (1961)
31. James *et al.* (1958)
32. Johnson *et al.* (1962)
33. Joigneau and Thouvenin (1958)
34. Katz *et al.* (1959)
35. Kormer *et al.* (1962)
36. Lawton and Skidmore (1956)
37. McQueen and Marsh (1960)
38. Mallory (1955)
39. Minshall (1961)
40. Reynolds and Seay (1962)
41. Rice *et al.* (1958)
42. Schall (1956)
43. Schall (1958)
44. Schall and Vollrath (1959)
45. Skidmore and Morris (1962)
46. Wackerle (1962)
47. Walsh and Rice (1957)
48. Zel'dovich *et al.* (1958)
49. Zubarev and Telegin (1962)

$$a = U \sqrt{[(\tan \alpha)^2 + \{(U - u)/U\}^2]} \tag{44}$$

to obtain the sound velocity in the shocked state. The measurements reported from this technique yield values which are some 20% higher

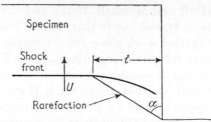

FIG. 44. Shock perturbed by a corner.

than computed hydrodynamic sound velocities. This discrepancy is due to an elastic rarefaction wave which travels with dilatational wave velocity and, consequently, affects the shock front to a greater distance, l, than the slower plastic rarefaction, travelling with hydrodynamic velocity. Assuming Poisson's ratio to be constant and equal to its zero pressure value, the hydrodynamic sound velocity can be estimated from the observed dilatational velocity. On this basis reasonable agreement is obtained with values predicted from R-H data.

In the second method for determining sound velocity, approximate corrections can be made for the effect of the elastic rarefaction. A uniform plane shock is produced in the specimen with a flyer plate and the distance at which the first rarefaction overtakes the shock front is determined by monitoring the free-surface velocity as a function of distance of travel of the shock front (Fig. 45). The results for Al, Pb, and Cu agree with calculated values within 2% at density ratios (ρ/ρ_0) up to 2·0.

A third method for getting data off the R-H curve is through a

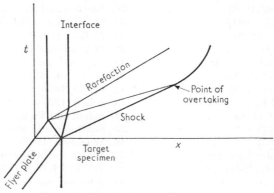

FIG. 45. Shock from a flyer plate.

reflection and impedance-match technique. A plane shock wave in material I (Fig. 46), with strength A, is reflected from an interface between materials I and II to produce a reflected shock of strength C. The points O, A′, B′, C′ in the state diagram of Fig. 46(b) are the images of the points OABC in the impedance diagram of Fig. 46(a);

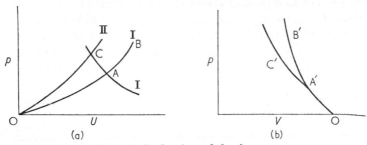

FIG. 46. Reflection of shock waves.

the point C′ lies off the Hugoniot OA′B′ because it represents a new shock transition from point A′. The R-H curve for the transition A′–C′ has a second order contact at A′ with the adiabat passing through A′. State C′ can be determined by measuring the shock pressure transmitted into material II. Internal energy is also known on both OA′B′ and A′C′, so $(\partial p/\partial v)_E$, $(\partial E/\partial p)_V$, $(\partial E/\partial V)_p$ and variants on these can be determined. Walsh and Rice (1957) have determined the rate of change of enthalpy, H, with volume in this way for water and find that $(\partial H/\partial V)_p \simeq 155e^{p/145}$ kb for $0 < p < 250$ kb. The estimated error is $\pm 15\%$ at a given pressure. The relative error should decrease as pressure, entropy, and the offset C′B′ increase.

This calculation of thermodynamic coefficients illustrates one use to be made of information off the R-H curve. Another is the use of p-V isotherms at zero degrees Kelvin, calculated from shock data, for the determination of cohesive energies of solids and atomic interaction within the lattice. The volume dependence of cohesive energy for several metals was calculated from R-H data by Benedek (1959); similar data have been used to determine the ion core repulsion in the noble metals (Koehler and Duvall, 1961). In the latter case the exponential term was relatively soft compared to previous estimates; it is not certain, however, how great is the influence of yield strength on this result.

For very strong shocks, the difficulties of extrapolation to p-V states neighbouring the R-H curve are complicated by the possibility that melting may occur (McQueen and Marsh, 1960) and by the excitation of electronic states, which influences the temperatures reached at the highest pressures (Al'tshuler *et al.*, 1960a). Both of the above-mentioned lattice calculations are based on isotherms which ignore these effects, and their results should accordingly not be considered conclusive.

Very high pressures have been produced and measured with flyer plates; values up to 2 000 kb were produced by plates driven by very large explosive assemblies (McQueen and Marsh, 1960). These pressures appear at present to represent about the upper limit of values which can be obtained in this way, using plane geometry. Skidmore and Morris (1962) have used spherical converging geometry to extend pressures to 6 megabars in solid uranium. Al'tshuler and his co-workers have reported pressures up to about 1 500 kb produced with contact explosive and to nearly 10 000 kb produced by flying plates driven in an unspecified manner (Al'tshuler et al., 1960a; Kormer et al., 1962). The experimental details provided in these papers from the U.S.S.R. are insufficient to allow independent verification, and until this unfortunate situation is remedied, some reservations must exist concerning the validity of their data.

A limiting shock compression is predicted by Eq. (43); pressure increases indefinitely as $V/V_0 \to (1 - 1/g)$. This is inherent in the nature of the shock transition because of the increasingly large amount of the internal energy that goes into heat as pressure increases. From the Mie-Grüneisen equation, for example, an R-H relation in the p-V plane is obtained by substituting Equation (4), into Equation (10). Thus

$$p_H = \left[1 \middle/ \left\{ 1 - \frac{\Gamma(V_0 - V)}{2V} \right\} \right] \left[p_k - \frac{\Gamma}{V}(E_k - E_0) \right].$$

The limiting compression in this case occurs as $V/V_0 \to \Gamma/(2 + \Gamma)$. When this limiting compression is approached, increases in shock pressure correspond to increased thermal excitation of lattice and electrons; therefore studies at higher pressures than those already achieved may yield little new information on the compressibility of materials. It is possible, however, that studies of temperatures produced under these conditions may yield important data on their own account (Zel'dovich et al., 1958).

B. Dynamic Failure in Solids

The investigation of elastic precursor waves in solids has been a substantial activity in the shock wave field; its interest for high pressure research is limited to the possibilities it presents for study of shear failure under pressure and to the necessity of correcting shock data for possible shear effects. The origin of the elastic precursor is discussed in Section VIII, and it is shown there that, if the solid behaves elastically up to failure, the shear stress and hydrostatic pressure at failure are

$$\tau = [(1 - 2\nu)/\{2(1 - \nu)\}]p_x{}^{(f)} \qquad \bar{p} = [(1 + \nu)/\{3(1 - \nu)\}]p_x{}^{(f)},$$

where $p_x^{(f)}$ is the wave amplitude at failure. The principal difficulty in measuring τ in this situation is the threat of relaxation effects which would overshadow the effect of $\bar{p}$. A preferred procedure, wherein $\bar{p}$ can be controlled, may be the measurement of relief wave effects behind the shock front. This has been suggested, but severe technical difficulties may prevent its accomplishment (Fowles, 1960).

It has been effectively demonstrated that corrections to shock pressures must be applied in aluminium (Fowles, 1961), and it is probably reasonable to assume that this is also true for other materials which fail by plastic yield. The situation may be different in brittle materials. The only evidence on this point indicates that in single crystal quartz the shock pressure behind the elastic precursor agrees

TABLE V. Elastic Precursor Amplitudes in Various Materials

(a) Plastic-Yielding Solids

Material	Condition†	Wave Amplitude (kb)	Dynamic Yield (kb)	Static Yield (kb)	References†††
Armco Iron	Ann	6·8	4·0	1·9	10, 39
SAE 1020	A.R.	11·3–12·6	6·7–7·4	4·8	39
SAE 1040	A.R.	5·8–(11·2)	3·4–(6·6)	5·9	39
Armco Iron	C.R. 75%	(13·1)–(14·8)	(7·7)–(8·7)	5·6	39
SAE 4340	C-35	25·1	14·8	12·7	39
SAE 4340	C-15	17·2	10·2	6·5	39
AISI 347	A.R.	1·9–(6·1)	1·1–(3·6)	2·4	39
2024 Al	Ann	0·7	0·4	0·7	24
	T4	5·2–5·5	2·7–2·8	2·4	24
Invar	Ann	12·5	7·5 (estim.)	2·7–4·1	15

† Condition: Ann = Annealed; A.R. = As Received; C.R. = Cold Rolled; C-35 = Rockwell hardness.

(b) Brittle Solids

Material	Orientation	Range of Precursor Amplitude kb	References†††
Quartz Crystal	X-cut	††35–50	25, 45
	Z-cut	††65–80	25, 45
Fused Quartz		93–102	45
Quartzite		40–15·5	27
Yule Marble		11–16	27
BaTiO₃		32–24	20, 40
Germanium		60–40	20
Silicon		76–66	20

†† Extrapolated to equilibrium from observed relaxation.
††† Numbers refer to list at bottom of p. 265.

with statically measured values and is presumably hydrostatic itself (Fowles 1962; Wackerle, 1962). In such case it is still necessary in experiments to determine the amplitude of the elastic precursor in order to correctly determine the amplitude of the following shock, but, having done this, no further correction for stress anisotropy is required.

The number of materials in which the amplitude of the elastic wave and its dependence on the initial state of the material have been measured is relatively few. Some results for both plastic and brittle solids are shown in Table V.

There is no particular evidence of stress-relaxation effects in the results quoted there for metals; the disparity between dynamic and static yield strengths demonstrates that some kind of strain rate effects do exist in iron and its alloys, and in fact the relaxation of the elastic precursor in Armco iron has been measured, but it has not been successfully related to any known property of the metal (Taylor and Rice, 1963). In those cases where a range of values is indicated for precursor

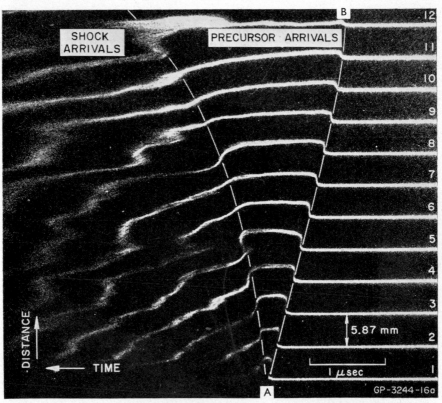

Fig. 47. Decay and speading of elastic precursor in quartzite. (Reproduced with permission from Duvall, 1961.)

amplitudes, these represent results on different samples or, where one or both of the values is in parentheses, the elastic precursor itself appeared to be a double wave.

In brittle solids the decay of the elastic wave is rapid and very apparent, even in a single record, as shown in Fig. 47. This record was produced in a wedge experiment of the kind described in Section VI, using an optical lever technique similar to that described in Section VII. The trace AB is the trace of the elastic precursor incident on the face of the wedge. The upper part of the record shows some curvature of this trace, which may result from a too-short run of the wave to establish steady state. The displacement of the source image by the elastic wave clearly diminishes with distance from the explosive, and the rise time of the wave increases. The amplitude near the bottom is approximately 40 kb, and near the top, 15 kb.

C. *Phase Transitions*

Materials in which multiple shock waves attributed to polymorphic phase transitions have been observed are listed in Table VI. In solid

TABLE VI. Shock-Induced Phase Transitions

Material	Shock Pressure of Transition (Amplitude of Plastic Wave)	References[††††]
Bismuth	17 to 31[†]	22, 30
Iron and Carbon Steel Alloys	125 to 140·5	39
Iron	19 to 150 kb[†††]	32
Fe/Ni and Fe/Cr Alloys	100 to 180	23
Water	115	7
Carbon (Graphite)	400, 600[††]	4
Phosphorous	25, 80 (see text)	28
Marble	150	1
Gabbro Rocks	~150–300	29
Quartz (fused)	250	45
Quartz (crystal)	400	45
Sulphur	~ 67–106	11, 12
Iodine	~700	3
BaTiO₃	8?	20, 40
Invar	~ 50?	15

[†] See Table IV.
[††] Initial temperature was varied from 78 to 1 158° K.
[†††] 2 transitions.
[††††] Numbers refer to list at bottom of p. 265.

materials with substantial yield stresses, e.g. iron and its alloys, the shock may consist of three distinct waves: the elastic precursor, the shock following this, which compresses material to the transition pressure—called by Minshall the Plastic I wave—and a second shock, which compresses the material to its final state—the Plastic II wave. The elastic and Plastic I waves have been intensively studied for iron alloys with the results shown in Tables V and VI.

For a given material there is considerable variation of the amplitude of the Plastic I wave, and some uncertainty is accordingly associated with the transition pressure. If the transition occurs at a particular hydrostatic pressure, $\bar{p}$, this is related to the quoted amplitude of the Plastic I wave, say, p_x^I, by Eq. (37),

$$\bar{p} = p_x^I - \tfrac{4}{3}\tau.$$

The resolved shear stress, τ, may vary from one experiment to the next because of changes in the specimen material, because of dynamic or relaxation effects, or both. This has been suggested by Minshall (1961), who notes that the density in the Plastic I wave in iron and carbon steels is constant to within $\tfrac{1}{4}\%$, even though the pressure varies about 8%; thus the fluctuations in p_x may result from changes in τ, not $\bar{p}$. On the other hand, it is entirely possible that the pressure of transition, $\bar{p}$, may itself be altered by the amount of plastic shear strain, in which case $\bar{p}$ and τ would vary together. No resolution of this point appears to be imminent. However, Minshall (1961) does demonstrate that the amplitude of the Plastic I wave diminishes with travel distance, indicating that stress relaxation is occurring.

Transitions in the Fe/Ni and Fe/Cr alloys show interesting dependence of transition pressure on alloy composition (Fig. 48). The results

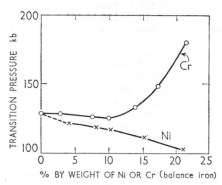

FIG. 48. Variations of transition pressures with Ni and Cr content in iron alloys. (Reproduced with permission from Fowler *et al.*, 1961.)

reported by these investigators indicate that a transition does not occur when the unshocked material is in the γ phase (fcc). If these transitions in iron alloys are generically related to the transition in iron, the work by Johnson *et al.* (1962) may explain this result. By varying the initial temperature of the iron from 78 to 1 158° K, using a metallurgical method to detect the point at which the Plastic II wave vanished, they traced out the p-T curve for the shock transition and compared it with the p-T curve for the α–γ transition determined statically and theoretically. Their results, shown in Fig. 49, clearly

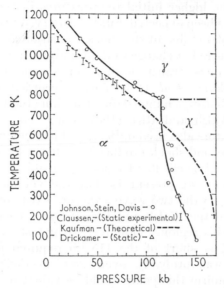

FIG. 49. Temperature-pressure diagram for iron. (Reproduced with permission from Johnson *et al.*, 1962.)

indicate the existence of a hitherto unsuspected phase lying between the alpha and gamma phases at temperatures below about 600° K. Jamieson and Lawson (1961) have suggested, on the basis of a high pressure X-ray diffraction line, that the phase may be hexagonal. Some additional substantiation of this has been supplied by Balchan and Drickamer (1961), who report a discontinuous change in resistance for iron at room temperature and 133 kb. This figure is so near the shock value that some coincidence may be involved, in view of the probability that the dynamic measurement is too high because of finite yield strength. Correction for this would reduce the shock-determined pressure to about 128 kb.

The multiple shock structure in bismuth has been studied as a function of initial temperature, and the authors conclude from the measured value of dp/dT that it is the bismuth I–bismuth II transition which is occurring. The shock transition pressure, however, is about 3 kb higher than the reported static pressure of the transition. They discount the possibility that this represents a dynamic yield strength and, if it is a relaxation effect, it is apparently slow since there was no evidence of attenuation of the 28 kb transition wave in their experiments. Their results are also interesting because of their bearing on the question of melting in a shock wave. It has been widely held that melting cannot occur in a shock wave because it is inherently a slow transition. The measurements on bismuth are in agreement with this hypothesis. At the higher initial temperatures in these experiments melting would have been expected, but the observed transition pressure lies on the extrapolated line of the shock transition at lower pressures. If melting had occurred, a change in dp/dT would have been observed.

The report of a phase transition in water is somewhat controversial inasmuch as Al'tshuler *et al.* (1958c) have recorded a shock-induced transition at 115 kb using an impedance-match method with aluminium driver, whereas Walsh and Rice (1957) found no transition. Both groups of investigators also used optical transparency measurements in searching for the second shock produced by such a transition, but only Al'tshuler *et al.* found an effect. The most plausible explanation of this apparent discrepancy at present is that the volume change in the transition is small, so the two-wave structure exists over only a small pressure range, and the Walsh and Rice pressure measurements were widely spaced in this region. Moreover, their tests for optical transparency stopped just short of the 115 kb required for the reported transition, so it was probably overlooked in their investigations. Experiments to confirm this point would be valuable.

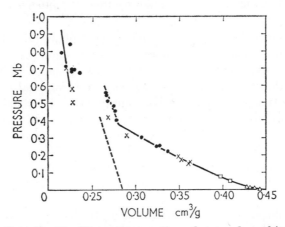

FIG. 50. The Hugoniot equation of state of graphite.
△ X-ray determination of crystal densities under pressure.
□ Static data.
× Results for sample of low initial density.
● Results for samples with initially higher density.
Dashed line, extrapolated static compressibility curve of diamond. (Reproduced with permission from Alder and Christian, 1961.)

The transformation of graphite by shock waves presents a new interpretation of shock data, since a phase transition is inferred from a sudden change in the slope of the R-H curve, though the curvature remains positive and a two wave structure does not develop (Alder and Christian, 1961). Their data are shown in Fig. 50. The slope of the R-H curve between 400 and 600 kb agrees approximately with the slope for diamond extrapolated from static measurements, so it is concluded that the material is in the diamond state in this pressure region. The plausibility of this assumption is confirmed by other experiments in which recovered samples of shocked graphite have been found to contain diamond (De Carli and Jamieson, 1961). The 600 kb discontinuity in Fig. 50 is attributed by the authors to collapse of the diamond to a metallic, close-packed liquid.

Evidence for a phase transition in iodine at a shock pressure of

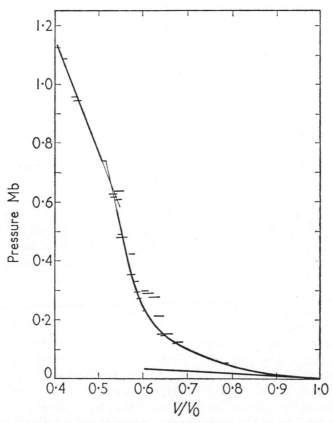

FIG. 51. The Hugoniot equation of state of iodine. (Reproduced with permission from Alder and Christian, 1960.)

approximately 700 kb is also reported by Alder and Christian (1960). The transition is inferred from a change in slope of the linear relation between shock and particle velocity, and a corresponding change in the sign of $\partial^2 p / \partial V^2$. The data are shown in Fig. 51. They attribute this transition to disruption of the diatomic bonds and formation of a body-centred cubic metal lattice. This interpretation is based on the assumption that the behaviour is analogous to that of the alkali metals, which are diatomic in the vapour phase and crystallize in the body-centred cubic lattice. Assuming the same change in interatomic spacing upon transformation for iodine as is observed for the alkali metals, the relative specific volume of the metallic iodine is computed to be $V/V_0 = 0.53$, in good agreement with the observed value at the transition.

Quartz, both single-crystal and fused, has been investigated by Wackerle (1962) and found to be quite complicated. Besides the high amplitude elastic precursors in both forms, there is a steepening of the R-H curve at about 400 kb in crystalline material and 250 kb (estimated) in glass. If the latter inference is correct, it is reasonable to suppose that the permanent transformation of crystalline to amorphous quartz by shock (De Carli and Jamieson, 1959) occurs because, for $p \sim 250$ to 400 kb, the amorphous form is denser than the crystalline material. Then the steeper region of the R-H curve for both materials may be a new phase of quartz; Wackerle suggests that it may be a recently discovered form called stishovite.

Considerable interest has developed in the response of rocks to shock waves, and hitherto unknown polymorphic phase transitions have been reported in marble (Adadurov et al., 1961) and in two gabbro rocks (Hughes and McQueen, 1958). The pressure value reported for the transition in marble appears to be fairly well determined; that for the gabbro rocks appears to be determined only to the extent indicated in Table VI, primarily because the recording method used in the experiment is sensitive only to mean free-surface velocity across a gap. It appears from the data that the transition might occur at less than 150 kb, but at not more than 300 kb.

Measurements of the electrical resistivity of sulphur under the influence of shock waves are discussed in the following section. They have been compared with measurements of shock and particle velocity and the suggestion has been made that the dramatic decrease in resistivity at about 100 kb shock pressure results from melting of the sulphur (Berger et al., 1960; 1961). This tends to be borne out by a calculation of the point of intersection of the shock line and the melting curve of sulphur in the pressure-temperature plane; the intersection occurs at about 90 kb. However, there remains the question whether or not melting will occur in a shock wave, and the shock measurements alone are inadequate for this to be answered.

The transition temperature for red to black phosphorous at 25 kb is estimated to be 200° C (Grover *et al.*, 1958). The static transition at room temperature, without shearing stresses was reported to be 85 kb, and with shear, 40 kb. The yellow to black transition occurs at 80 kb in shock, with $T > 200°$ C, and at 12 kb statically, with $T = 200°$ C (Grover *et al.*, 1958). These differences are so large and uncorrelated, that little can be done with them as they stand; a more thorough investigation with initial temperature as a shock variable is in order.

Besides these materials for which shock transition pressures have been determined, R-H data have also been reported for potassium and rubidium halides. These measurements at 100 kb and above lie on a p-V curve which, when compared to static pressure data, indicate that the well-known, low-pressure phase changes have occurred in the shock (Christian, 1957).

The phase transitions described above are presumably first-order transitions in which finite changes in latent heat and specific volume occur, though this is not firmly established. Curran (1961) has called attention to the possibility of detecting second-order transitions using shock waves. The isentropic incompressibility may be written

$$V\left(\frac{\partial p}{\partial V}\right)_S = -K(1 - \Gamma T \alpha c_v / c_p)^{-1},$$

where $\alpha = (1/V)(\partial V/\partial T)_p$, K is the bulk modulus, and c_p is specific heat at constant pressure. With the Ehrenfest relations, discontinuities in K, α, Γ imply discontinuities in $(\partial p/\partial V)_S$, and if these are large enough and of the right sign, they would result in a detectable double shock. Very few measurements of $p(T)$ for known second-order phase transitions have been made; one convenient one for shock experiments is the Curie transition in Invar. Unfortunately, the data indicate that $-(\partial p/\partial V)_S$ should increase at the transition point, which implies that the R-H curve steepens and no double shock will occur. The R-H data tend to confirm that this occurs at the statically predicted pressure, and the value of ΔV inferred from the measurements also agrees with static prediction. A similar phenomenon is observed in $BaTiO_3$ with a more definite discontinuity in K, and that effect is ascribed to the ferroelectric Curie transition (Doran, 1962). Further study of this subject is required and, in particular, shock-induced phase transitions already reported should be examined with the thought that some of them may be second order.

D. *Electrical Effects*

1. *Conductivity*

Changes in electrical conductivity of a material during the passage of a shock wave may result from thermal ionization, change in the electronic band structure produced by lattice compression, or change in the defect structure of the substance, if it is a solid. The measured electrical conductivity of gases has been compared with theoretical values based on statistical equilibrium at elevated temperatures reached in shock waves, and the agreement confirms that equilibrium ionization is the controlling mechanism (Thouvenin, 1961a, b). Measurements of the conductivity in detonating solid explosives have yielded values the order of 1 (ohm cm)$^{-1}$ (Schall and Vollrath, 1961), which is substantially greater than predicted by thermal equilibrium calculations. Birk *et al.* (1954) have suggested that the measured value more nearly confirms Saenger's hypothesis that all molecules with kinetic energy greater than their ionization energy are ionized. Each of these subjects—conductivity in gases and detonating explosives—has a literature of its own, and will not be further considered here.

Some results of electrical measurements on inert materials that are normally insulators are summarized in Table VII. The procedure for

TABLE VII. Shock-Induced Electrical Conductivity

Material	Approximate Pressure at Onset of Conduction (kb)	References[††]
LiAlH$_4$	50	2
Red Phosphorous	<100	2
I$_2$	80–130	2
KI	170	2
CsI, RbI	200	2
CsCl, CsBr	270	2
Teflon	>210	2
Water	30–125[†]	13, 18
Paraffin	700	13
Plexiglas	820	13
Sulphur	70–100	11, 12, 18, 83
NaCl	>210	2
	~200–800	9

[†] σ varies from 10^{-3} to $1(\Omega$ cm)$^{-1}$ in this pressure range.
[††] Numbers refer to list at bottom of p. 265.

making such measurements is to insert electrical probes in the sample, apply a potential difference between the probes and measure the resulting current before and during the passage of the shock. This gives resistance, and from the geometry, conductivity can be estimated. It is difficult to distinguish between a resistance greater than about 10^4 ohms and an open circuit, or between a few ohms and a short circuit with this method. In most cases the onset of conduction is quite sharp as pressure increases, and this may be partly due to these limitations in measuring techniques. This effect would also result from overlap of filled and conduction bands in insulators, and this mechanism is, in fact, supposed by Alder and Christian (1956) and by Brish *et al.* (1960) to be responsible for the conductivities they measure.

Alder and Christian base their assertion about metallic transitions on the fact that the separation between energy bands is generally expected to decrease with atomic spacing and that the energy gap between valence and conduction band for all the materials in which conduction is observed is less than 5 eV, whereas the gap for NaCl, which does not conduct in their experiments, is 9 eV. Furthermore, red phosphorus, which conducts under rather weak shock pressure, has a known metallic transition, determined statically, at about 40 kb. However, it must be recognized that the rate of change of energy gap with pressure is not known for most materials, so the observed pressures at which conduction occurs may not be the right magnitude for band overlap. Furthermore, a search for metallic conductivity in $LiAlH_4$ under the influence of static pressure shows no such effect at room temperature for pressure up to 200 kb or at 70 kb for temperatures up to 350° C (Griggs *et al.*, 1958). One possible explanation of this discrepancy is that the $LiAlH_4$ used in shock experiments may have contained a small amount of metallic aluminium powder (Alder and Christian, 1956).

A metallic transition is also supposed to occur in sulphur at shock pressures between 70 and 200 kb (David and Hamann, 1958), although Berger *et al.* (1960) suggest that this may also be associated with melting. Drickamer (1961) has measured the energy gap in sulphur at one bar and at 150 kb; he finds values of 2·9 eV and 1·7 eV, respectively, at these two pressures. If these data are extrapolated linearly, it follows that conduction and valence bands would overlap at 350 kb. If the shock-induced conductivity does result from a metallic transition, these numbers indicate that there are mechanisms other than pressure which influence the transition.

Al'tshuler *et al.* (1961) find that their measured conductivities in NaCl correlate well with $\exp(-A/kT)$, where $A \simeq 1·2$ eV, and they ascribe this to ionic conduction, independent of pressure effect. Since the energy band gap in NaCl is about 9 eV, this seems plausible. The shears produced in a shock of several hundred kilobar amplitude must certainly give rise to very large numbers of imperfections in the solid, and these would be expected to enhance ionic conductivity. Further, there appears to be inadequate reason to rule out ion motion on the basis of response time.

In water, as in NaCl, the conductivity can be measured in continuous variation over the entire range of pressure, and in this case both pressure and temperature may influence the results. David and Hamann (1959) consider the conductivity to result from an ionization constant which increases with density. Their data at the same time correlate well with $\exp(-A/kT)$, where $A \simeq 0.5$ eV.

It is clear from the nature of the questions raised by these experiments that the shock conditions may be providing new information about the electronic properties of solids, but that much more detailed investigations will be required before understanding and useful numbers can be reached.

2. *Polarization*

Measurements of electric currents generated as a consequence of the passage of shock waves have been reported in piezoelectric, ferroelectric, and polar materials. A typical experimental arrangement is illustrated in Fig. 40 of Section VII, where a theory for charge release in quartz is outlined. As pointed out there, the magnitudes of electrical signals measured in quartz correlate fairly well with compression effects up to the elastic limit. An interesting accompaniment to these electrical signals is the production of intense light as the shock traverses a quartz specimen. This is apparently a result of impurity-induced electrical breakdown occurring in the vicinity of the shock front or near fractures originating at crystal surfaces (Anderson, 1961).

The response of polarized ferroelectric materials to the passage of a shock is to lose its polarization in the shocked region (Neilson, 1957). The charge released as a function of time is then given by the rate at which the polarized volume is swept out by the shock wave. Total charge released in this way is reported as 46×10^{-6} C/cm^2 for lead–zirconate–titanate (PZT), with peak current of 300 amp/cm^2. When the external resistance is increased, high amplitude voltage pulses may be produced; 60 kV across 5×10^4 ohms was reported.

A related effect has been reported in polar solids and liquids (Eichelberger and Hauver, 1961). Substantial electric currents have been produced by the passage of shock waves through plexiglass, nylon, epoxy resin, polystyrene, water, and thallous nitrate. The mechanism proposed is that the permanent dipoles in these materials are aligned by material acceleration in the shock front to produce a dipole layer at the boundary between shocked and unshocked regions. The electrical currents produced are characterized by a sudden jump to a finite value when the shock enters the insulator, followed by a gradual rise and a sudden cut-off when the shock reaches the electrode on the far side of the specimen disc. The notion of dipole alignment is supported by the observation that the sign of the induced charge correlates with the sign of the heavy molecule in the polar material.

E. *Metallurgical Effects*

There is currently a keen interest in the use of shock waves in metallurgical studies, but this stems primarily from the unique shear and time relations in shocks rather than from the high pressures associated with them. Such stress and strain conditions provide interesting possibilities for the testing of theoretical ideas about plastic deformations, dislocation generation and movement, crystallographic changes under both shear and compressive stresses, and atomic motions associated with mechanical behaviour (Shewmon and Zackay, 1961). Besides these problems, there is an application to the work-hardening of materials, which is of interest here in view of previous observations of

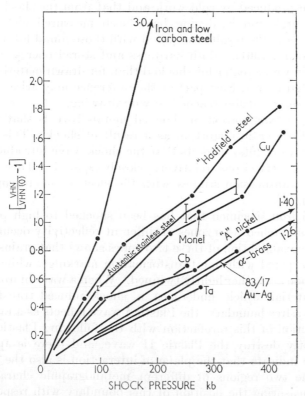

FIG. 52. Shock hardening of metals; VHN = Vickers hardness no. of shocked specimen VHN(0) = hardness of annealed specimen before shocking. (Reproduced with permission from Dieter, 1962.)

work-hardening under hydrostatic pressure (Swenson, 1960); some elegant metallographic methods have also been developed for studying properties of shock waves, and these will be described below.

Data on shock wave hardening are summarized in Fig. 52, where both bcc and fcc metals are represented (Dieter, 1962). Except for iron and 0·17% carbon steel, in which transformation hardening is believed to occur at pressures above that required for shock-induced transition, these data group remarkably well. This hardening is apparently similar to that produced by cold work, though the magnitude of change for a given plastic strain increment is greater than obtained in normal cold work.

The hardening in an 18–8 Cr/Ni stainless steel (type 304) is accompanied by a transformation from austenite to ferrite (Duvall *et al.*, 1960) and a change in electrical resistivity. The latter is interesting because its relation to ferrite content is different from that found from cold work experiments, indicating again a crystallographic difference between deformation produced by cold work and that from the shock wave.

Stored energy and hardening have been measured for a shocked Au–Ag alloy and the results compared with those found for drawn wire (Appleton *et al.*, 1961). Both hardness and stored energy at a given plastic strain were greater for shocked than for drawn material, though it is suggested that at least part of the difference may arise because of the greater temperatures reached in wire drawing.

Microscopic examination of shocked metals reveals that there has been very little grain distortion as a result of shock. This, together with the above results, suggests that the shock wave introduces a high density of imperfections relatively closely spaced. This has been verified by transmission studies with the electron microscope (Leslie *et al.*, 1961).

When an iron specimen that has been shocked to high pressure is sectioned and etched, two zones of different reflectivity occur, Fig. 53. Microscopic examination of these two zones shows that grains in one of them are carpeted with fine transformation markings, while grains in the other zone are rather lightly twinned. When a wave in iron or other ferritic material which undergoes a shock-induced transformation approaches a free boundary, the Plastic I wave reflects as a rarefaction. The interaction of this rarefaction with the following Plastic II wave may abruptly destroy the Plastic II wave, and there is appreciable evidence to indicate that the plane of interaction is also the boundary between the two regions of different metallographic characteristics. Then by measuring the position of this boundary with respect to the plane of origin of the shock and the parallel free-surface plane, the velocity of propagation of the Plastic II wave can be inferred. If the transition pressure is known and if a sample of calibrated material is a companion piece in the same experiment, a point on the R-H curve can

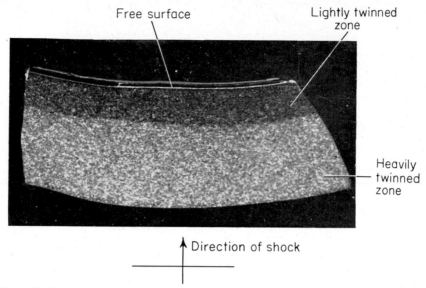

FIG. 53. Light and dark etching zones produced by shock wave in mild steel.

be obtained in this way. This technique has been successfully used to obtain R-H data on several iron alloys without external instrumentation (Fowler *et al.*, 1961).

The success of this procedure does not necessarily imply that the fine markings on grains are produced at the transformation pressure, but that, as a result of the interaction with the Plastic I rarefaction, the Plastic II wave is abruptly destroyed. It has been suggested that when the Plastic II wave decays without influence from a surface, the fine markings disappear when the Plastic II wave still exceeds the Plastic I amplitude by about 20 kb (Curran *et al.*, 1959).

It has also been pointed out that the light-dark zone boundary is useful for studying shock propagation in complicated geometry (Smith and Fowler, 1961). An interesting sidelight on this is supplied by the identification of crystallographic markings on etched meteorites as having been produced by shock, presumably on impact (Mariger, 1961).

F. *Geophysical Applications*

1. *Shock Propagation*

The explosion of a chemical or nuclear charge underground is manifested primarily by the propagation to large distances of small amplitude seismic waves, and by permanent changes in the near vicinity of the charge. Various aspects of these phenomena, such as the coupling of the energy of the explosive to that of seismic waves, the distance from the explosion and the wave amplitude beyond which the propagation is essentially elastic, and the frequency spectrum of the seismic waves generated, in addition to fracture and cratering, are of particular practical interest. Solutions to these problems require, in general, detailed knowledge of the propagation and decay of the high pressure shock wave in the near vicinity of the charge. This, in turn, requires knowledge of the behaviour of geologic materials under high pressures, specifically, under shock conditions.

For shock pressures greatly exceeding the strength of the medium it has been customary to utilize hydrodynamic theory for the description of shock propagation (Nuckolls, 1959). The necessary material properties of such calculations are the R-H curve and adiabats from various shocked states (Sections II and IX, A).

Departures from hydrodynamic behaviour are also indicated by the R-H curve. The Hugoniot elastic limit determines the maximum stress amplitude for which wave propagation can be considered elastic, and provides a basis for estimates of the pressures above which hydrodynamic theory is expected to be valid. Stress relaxation effects, where these occur, are also observable in shock wave experiments, as is discussed in Section VIII.

In some rocks, e.g. obsidian, it is to be expected that a stable shock front will not form over a certain pressure range. The observed anomalous compressibility of silica glass (Bridgman, 1938; Wackerle, 1962) violates the necessary condition for shock stability (Section VIII). Consequently, the rise time of the wave continually broadens as the wave propagates.

Phase transitions introduce additional complications into calculations of shock propagation, although these can presumably be handled by hydrodynamic methods. They can lead to multiple shock fronts (Section VIII), to rarefaction shocks (Drummond, 1957), and to permanent changes in the state of the material. Geologic materials in which phase transitions have been reported are marble, quartz, albite and gabbro (Table VI).

Permanent changes of state have been observed in shock-loaded quartz and albite (De Carli and Jamieson, 1959). Breakdown of the crystal structure in these minerals is evidenced by a complete lack of X-ray diffraction lines in recovered samples. No evidence of the high pressure polymorph of quartz, coesite, has been reported from explosively loaded samples, although the shock pressures are well above the known transition pressure. However, abundant coesite and a newly discovered higher pressure form, stishovite, have been found near Meteor Crater, Arizona, and are attributed to the shock produced upon impact of the meteorite (Chao *et al.*, 1960 and 1962). Coesite has also been found near underground nuclear explosions. Evidently, the conditions for formation of coesite are strongly time-dependent at high pressures and short times.

2. *Composition of the Earth's Interior*

Most of present knowledge concerning the earth's interior is based on measured seismic wave velocities, and on measurements of the moment of inertia and average density of the earth. The amount of information that can be deduced from these quantities is appreciable. The existence and the locations of the molten core, the solid outer mantle, and several layers within each of these major divisions is well-established. Moreover, the variation of pressure and density with depth are determined within narrow limits. The major uncertainties at the present time are the compositions of both core and mantle, and the crystal structure(s) obtaining in the lower part of the mantle (~ 900 to $2\,700$ km depth).

Direct comparisons of pressure-density relationships of known materials, with the known pressure-density variation of the earth would allow various assumed compositions to be rejected or accepted as reasonable possibilities. Until recently, comparisons of pressure-density relations could be made only at the moderate pressures obtainable with static apparatus ($< \sim 100$ kb), or with quantum mechanical calculations based on the Thomas-Fermi model, which are assumed valid at extremely high pressures. Interpolation between these extremes, based on semi-empirical equations of state, notably the Birch-Murnaghan theory of finite strain, is uncertain partly because the lower bound at which the Thomas-Fermi model is valid is not only very high but is also poorly defined.

The development in recent years of shock wave methods for determining equations of state allows direct comparisons of pressure-density relations to be made. The measurements of Al'tshuler *et al.*, (1958a) on iron and other metals at pressures up to 5 Mb allow such comparisons to be made at pressures as high as that at the centre of the earth (~ 3.5 Mb). These experimental data have recently been used by Knopoff and MacDonald (1960) in a new attack on the question of the composition of the core. Their results are in essential agreement with previous findings, viz. that the density of iron is somewhat larger (~ 10 to 20%) than the densities in the core and that a mean atomic number of about 23 is consistent with core conditions. These results can now be taken to be much more firmly established than previously, however. Jacobs

(1956) also calls attention to the correspondence of the transition pressure of iron (131 kb) to the observed 20° discontinuity in seismic velocity, at a calculated pressure of 141 kb.

Unfortunately, little high-pressure, shock-wave data are yet available for rocks or minerals of compositions reasonable for the mantle. Notable exceptions are the data for dunite and gabbro obtained by Hughes and McQueen (1958). Reasonable consistency of those results with Bullen's computed density variation (Model B) (Bullen, 1956), is obtained if it is assumed that the mantle consists of olivine to a depth of 400 km and of gabbro beyond 800 km.

TABLE VIII. Some Comparisons of Properties of the Earth's Core with Measured Values for Iron

Depth (km)	Sound Velocity (km/sec)		Pressure† (10^3 kb)		Density† (gm/cm³)	
	Jeffreys (1929)	Gutenberg (1951)	Model A	Model B	Model A	Model B
Earth						
Outer⎫ 2900	8·10	8·00	1·37	1·33	9·4	9·7
Core ⎬ 4980	10·44	10·04	3·17	3·22	11·5	12·0
Inner⎫ 5120	9·40	10·1		3·33		15·0
Core ⎬ 6370	11·31		3·64	3·94	17·3	17·9
Iron						
(After Al'tshuler	7·85		1·22		11·03	
et. al., 1960)	8·49		1·68		11·56	
	9·53		2·85		12·56	
	9·98		3·48		12·95	

† Bullen (1956).

It should be noted that the recently reported method for measuring hydrodynamic sound speeds under shock conditions mentioned in Section IX, A (Al'tshuler et al., 1960b) allows more direct and sensitive comparisons to be made between material properties and properties of the interior than are possible from p–V data alone. Data for iron, aluminium, copper, and lead at pressures up to 3·5 Mb have been obtained in this way. The results for iron are reproduced in Table VIII together with some of the reported values for the core (Jeffreys, 1929; Gutenberg, 1951; Bullen, 1956). The correspondence between sound velocities and pressures is seen to be fairly close for the outer core although the correspondence in densities is less close.

GENERAL REFERENCES

In addition to the special references given below, the following references of a general nature will be found useful for further study.

Cook, M. A. (1958). " The Science of High Explosives ", Reinhold Publishing Corp., New York.

Hopkins, H. G. (1961). *Appl. Mech. Rev.* **14**, 417–431.

Kolsky, H. (1953). " Stress Waves in Solids ", Oxford at the Clarendon Press, London.

Rinehart, J. S., and J. Pearson (1954). " Behavior of Metals under Impulsive Loads ", Amer. Society of Metals.

Cole, R. H. (1948). " Underwater Explosions ", Princeton University Press, N.J.

Bradley, J. N. (1962). " Shock Waves in Chemistry and Physics ", Wiley, New York.

Doran, D. G. (1962). " Measurement of Shock Pressure in Solids ", Paper No. 62-WA-252, *Am. Soc. Mech. Eng.*

Deal, W. E., Jr. (1962). "Modern Very High Pressure Techniques ", p. 200, R. H. Wentorf, Jr. (ed.), Butterworths, London.

Berger, J., and Viard, J. (1962). " Physique des Explosif Solides ", Dunod, Paris.

REFERENCES

Adadurov, G. A., Boloshov, D. B., and Dremin, A. N. (1961). AGU Translation of *Bull. Acad. Sci. USSR, Geophysics*, **5**, 463.

Alder, B. J., and Christian, R. H. (1956). *Disc. Faraday Soc.* **22**, 44.

Alder, B. J., and Christian, R. H. (1960). *Phys. Rev. Letters*, **4**, 450.

Alder, B. J., and Christian, R. H. (1961). *Phys. Rev. Letters* **7**, 367.

Allen, Wm. A., and McCrary, Clyde L. (1953). *Rev. sci. Instrum.* **24**, 165.

Al'tshuler, L. V., Krupnikov, K. K., Ledenev, B. N., Zhuchikhin, V. I., and Brazhnik, M. I. (1958a). *Soviet Phys. JETP*, **34**, 606.

Al'tshuler, L. V., Krupnikov, K. K., and Brazhnik, M. I. (1958b). *Soviet Phys. JETP*, **34**, 614.

Al'tshuler, L. V., Bakanova, A. A., and Trunin, R. F. (1958c). *Soviet Phys. Doklady*, **3**, 761.

Al'tshuler, L. V., Kormer, S. B., Bakanova, A. A., and Trunin, R. F. (1960a). *Soviet Phys. JETP* **11**, 573.

Al'tshuler, L. V., Kormer, S. B., Brazhnik, M. I., Vladimirov, L. A., Speranskaya, M. P., and Funtikov, A. I. (1960b). *Soviet Phys. JETP* **11**, 766.

Al'tshuler, L. V., Kuleshova, L. V., and Pavlovskii, M. N. (1961). *Soviet Phys. JETP* **12**, 10.

Anderson, G. W. (1961). " Les Ondes de Detonation ", Editions du CNRS, 15 Quai Anatole-France, Paris (VIIe).

Appleton, A. S., Dieter, G. E., and Bever, M. B. (1961). *Trans. Amer. Inst. min (metall.) Engrs.* **221**, 90.

Aziz, A. K., Hurwitz, H., and Sternberg, H. M. (1961). *Phys. Fluids* **4**, 380.

Bainbridge, K. T., Goldhaber, M., and Wilson, E. (1951). *Phys. Rev.* **84**. 1260 (L).

Balchan, A. S., and Drickamer, H. G. (1961). *Rev. sci. Instrum.* **32**, 308.

Bancroft, D., Peterson, E. L., and Minshall, S. (1956). *J. appl. Phys.* **27**, 291.

Band, Wm., and Duvall, G. E. (1961). *Amer. J. Phys.* **29**, 780.

Barker, L. M. (1961). " Measurement of Free-Surface Motion by the Slanted

Resistor Technique ", SCDR 78–61, Sandia Corporation. Available from Office of Technical Services, Dept. of Commerce, Washington 25, D.C.

Benedek, G. B. (1959). *Phys. Rev.* **114**, 467.

Berger, Jean, and Joigneau, Suzanne (1959). *C. R. Acad. Sci., Paris* **249**, 2506.

Berger, Jean, Joigneau, Suzanne, and Bottet, G. (1960). *C. R. Acad. Sci., Paris* **250**, 4331.

Berger, J., Joigneau, S., and Fauquignon, C. (1961). "Les Ondes de Detonation ", Editions du CNRS, 15 Quai Anatole-France, Paris (VIIe).

Bernstein, D. (1963). Technical Summary Report No. 2, Jan. 15, Contract No. DA-49-146-XZ-096; DASA, Wash., 25, D.C.

Birk, M., Erez, H., Manheimer, Y. (1954). *Bull. Research Council Israel*, Vol. 3, No. 4.

Bethe, H. (1942). " The Theory of Shock Waves for an Arbitrary Equation of State ", OSRD 545.

Bleakney, W., and Taub, A. H. (1949). *Rev. mod. Phys.* **21**, 584.

Born, Max and Kun Huang (1954). "Dynamical Theory of Crystal Lattices ", Section 4, Oxford University Press, London.

Bridgman, P. W. (1938). *Proc. Amer. Acad. Arts Sci.* **73**, 74.

Brish, A. A., Tarasov, M. S., and Tsukerman, V. A. (1960). *Soviet Phys. JETP* **11**, 15.

Bullen, K. E. (1956). " Physics and Chemistry of the Earth ", (L. H. Ahrens, *et al.*, eds.) Pergamon Press, New York.

Chao, E. C. T., Shoemaker, E. M., and Masden, B. M. (1960). *Science* **132**, 220.

Chao, E. C. T., Fahey, J. J., Littler, Janet, and Milton, D. J. (1962). *J. geophys. Res.* **67**, No. 1.

Christian, R. H. (1957). " The Equation of State of the Alkali Halides ", UCRL–4900, University of California Radiation Laboratory, Livermore, Calif.

Cook, M. A., Keyes, R. T., and Ursenbach, W. O. (1960). Third Symposium on Detonation, James Forrestal Research Center, Princeton University, ONR Symposium Report ACR-52, Vol. 2, 357–385.

Cook, J. H. (1948). *Research* **1**, 474.

Courant and Friedrichs (1948). " Supersonic Flow and Shock Waves ", Interscience, New York.

Curran, D. R. (1961). *J. appl. Phys.* **32**, No. 10, 1811.

Curran, D. R., Katz, S., Kelly, J. J., and Nicholson, M. E. (1959). *Trans. Amer. Inst. min. (metall.) Engrs.* **215**, 151.

Dapoigny, J., Kieffer, J., and Vodar, B. (1955). *J. Rech.* No. 31.

Dapoigny, J., Kieffer, J., and Vodar, B. (1957). *C. R. Acad. Sci., Paris* **247**, 269.

David, H. G., and Hamann, S. D. (1958). *J. chem. Phys.* **28**, 1006(L).

David, H. G., and Hamann, S. D. (1959). *Trans. Faraday Soc.* **55**, 72.

Davis, W. C., and Craig, B. G. (1961). *Rev. sci. Instrum.* **32**, 579.

Deal, W. E. (1957). *J. chem. Phys.* **27**, 796.

De Carli, P. S., and Jamieson, J. C. (1959). *J. chem. Phys.* **31**, 1675(L).

De Carli, P. S., and Jamieson, J. C. (1961). *Science* **133**, 1821.

Dieter, G. E. (1962). " Strengthening Mechanisms in Solids ", *Amer. Soc. Metals.*

Doran, D. G. (1960). " Shock Waves in Metals ", Doctoral Thesis, Washington State University, Dept. of Physics.

Doran, D. G. (1962). " Behavior of Ferroelectric Materials Under Explosively Induced Shock Waves ". Final Report, P.O. No. 13–1798, Sandia Corp., Albuquerque, N. Mex.

Doran, D. G. (1963). *J. appl. Phys.* **34**, 844.

Doran, D. G., Fowles, G. R., and Peterson, G. A. (1958). *Phys. Rev. Letters*, **1**. 1.

Drickamer, H. G. (1961). University of Illinois, U.S.A., Private Communication.

Drummond, W. E. (1957). *J. appl. Phys.* **28**, 998.

Drummond, W. E. (1958). *J. appl. Phys.* **29**, 167.

Duff, R. E., and Minshall, F. S. (1957). *Phys. Rev.* **108**, 1207.

Duvall, George E., and Zwolinski, Bruno J. (1955). *J. acoust. Soc. Amer.* **27**, 1054.

Duvall, George E. (1958). *Amer. J. Phys.* **26**, 235.

Duvall, George E., Davenport, D. E., and Kelly, J. J. (1960). " Metallurgical Effects of Explosive-Induced Shock Waves," Research Seminar on " High-Nickel Alloys for High Temperatures, Iron-Nickel Alloys, Stainless Steels," The International Nickel Co.

Duvall, George E. (1961). " Les Ondes de Detonation," Editions du CNRS, 15 Quai Anatole-France, Paris (VIIe).

Eichelberger, R. J., and Hauver, G. E. (1961). " Les Ondes de Detonation," Editions du CNRS, 15 Quai Anatole-France, Paris (VIIe).

Erkman, J. O. (1958). *Phys. Fluids*, **1**, 535.

Erkman, J. O. (1959). *Rev. sci. Instrum.* **30**, 818.

Fickett, W., and Wood, W. W. (1958). *Phys. Fluids* **1**, 528.

Flook, W. M. Jr., and Hornig, D. F. (1955). *J. chem. Phys.* **23**, 816.

Fowler, C. M., Minshall, F. S., and Zukas, E. G. (1961). " Response of Metals to High Velocity Deformation," pp. 275–300 (Shewmon and Zackay, eds.), Interscience, New York.

Fowles, G. R. (1960a). *J. appl. Phys.* **31**, 655.

Fowles, G. R. (1960b). *Bull. Amer. phys. Soc.* II, **5**, no. 7.

Fowles, G. R. (1961). *J. appl. Phys.* **32**, 1475.

Fowles, G. R. (1962). Doctoral Thesis, Dept. of Geophysics, Stanford University.

Fuller, P. J. A., and Price, J. H. (1962). *Nature, Lond.* **193**. 262.

Goranson, R. W., Bancroft, D., Burton, B. L., Blecher, T., Houston, E. E., Gittings, E. F., and Landeen, S. A. (1955). *J. appl. Phys.* **26**, 1472.

Graham, R. A. (1962). *Bull. Amer. phys. Soc.* II **7**, 123.

Griggs, D. T., McMillan, W. G., Michael, E. D., and Nash, C. P. (1958). *Phys. Rev.* **109**, 1858.

Gregson, V. G., and Grine, D. R. (1962). " Dynamic Properties of Rocks." Apr. 20; Contract No. AF 19 (604)–8419, Air Force Systems Command, Bedford, Mass.

Grover, R., Christian, R. H., and Alder, B. J. (1958). *Bull. Amer. phys. Soc.* II, **3**, 230.

Grundhauser, F. J., Dyke, W. P., and Bennett, S. D. (1961). " A 50 Millimicro-second Flash X-ray Photography System for Hypervelocity Research," Proc. of Fifth International Congress on High Speed Photography, SMPTE.

Gutenberg, B. (1951). *Trans. Amer. geophys. Un.* **32**, 373.

Hauver, G. E. (1960). Third Symposium on Detonation, ONR Symposium Report ACR-52, Vol. 2.

Holtzman, A. H., and Cowan, G. R. (1961). " Response of Metals to High Velocity Deformation," 447–481, (P. G. Shewmon and V. F. Zackay, eds.), Interscience, New York.

Hughes, D. S., and McQueen, R. G. (1958). *Trans. Amer. geophys. Un.* **39** 959.

Hughes, D. S., Gourley, L. E., and Gourley, M. F. (1961). *J. appl. Phys.* **32** 624.

Jacobs, J. A. (1956). " Advances in Geophysics," Vol. 3, (H. E. Landsberg, ed.) Academic Press, New York.

James, H. J., Buchanan, J. S., and Teague, G. W. (1958). *Phil. Mag.* **3**, 1432.

Jamieson, J. C., and Lawson, A. W. (1961). *J. appl. Phys.* **33**, 776.

Jeffreys, H. (1929). " The Earth," University Press, Cambridge, 122.

Johnson, P. C., Stein, B. A., and Davis, R. S. (1962). *J. appl. Phys.* **33**, 557.

Joigneau, S., and Thouvenin, J. (1958). *C. R. Acad. Sci., Paris* **246**, 3422.

Katz, S., Doran, D. G., and Curran, D. R. (1959). *J. appl. Phys.* **30**, 568.

Knopoff, L., and MacDonald, G. J. F. (1960). *Geophysical Journal* **3**, 68.

Koehler, J. S. and Duvall, G. E. (1961). *Bull. Amer. phys. Soc.* II, **6**, 132.

Kormer, S. B., Funtikov, A. I., Urlin, V. O., and Kolesnikova, A.N.(1962). *Soviet Phys. JETP*, **15**, 477.

Lawton, H., and Skidmore, I. C. (1956). *Disc. Faraday Soc.* **22**. 188.

Leslie, W. D., Hornbogen, E., and Dieter, G. E. (1962). *J. Iron St. Inst. G.B.* **200**, 622.

Liddiard, T. P. Jr., and Drimmer, B. E. (1960). NAVWEPS Report 7289, U.S. Naval Ordnance Lab., White Oak, Maryland.

Losev, S. A., and Osipov, A. I. (1962). *Soviet Physics, Uspekhi*, **4**, 525.

Lundergan, Don (1960).   " A Method of Measuring (1) The Parameters of Impact between Two Plane Surfaces and (2) The Properties of the Plane Shock Waves Produced," SC-4421(RR), Sandia Corporation, Albuquerque, N. Mex.

McQueen, R. G., and Marsh, S. P. (1960). *J. appl. Phys.* **31**, 1253.

McQueen, R. G. (1961).   Conference on " Pressure-Induced Phase Changes," A. D. Little, Cambridge, Mass., June 20–21, 1961.

Mallory, H. D. (1955). *J. appl. Phys.* **26**, 555.

Mariger, R. E. (1961). *In* " Response of Metals to High Velocity Deformation," p. 337. (Shewmon and Zackay, eds.), Interscience, New York.

Marsh, S. P., and McQueen, R. G. (1960). *Bull. Amer. phys. Soc.* II, **5**, 506.

Minshall, Stanley (1955). *J. appl. Phys.* **26**, 463.

Minshall, Stanley (1961). *In* " Response of Metals to High Velocity Deformation," p. 249, (Shewmon and Zackay, eds.), Interscience, New York.

Neilson, F. W. (1957). *Bull. Amer. phys. Soc.*, II, **2**, 302.

Nuckolls, John H. (1959). Proc. of the Second Plowshare Symposium, Part I, " Phenomenology of Underground Nuclear Explosions," 120–134, UCRL-5675 or TID-4500, UC-35, May 15, 1959.

Oswatitsch, Klaus (1956). " Gas Dynamics," Ch. II, Academic Press, New York.

Pack, D. C., Evans, W. M., and James, H. J. (1948). *Proc. phys. Soc.* LX, 1.

Rayleigh (1910). *Proc. roy. Soc. A***84**, 247.

Reynolds, C. E. and Seay, G. E. (1962). *J. appl. Phys.* **33**, 2234.

Rice, M. H. (1961). *Rev. sci. Instrum.* **32**, 449.

Rice, M. H., and Walsh, J. M. (1957). *J. chem. Phys.* **26**, 824.

Rice, M. H., McQueen, R. G., and Walsh, J. M. (1958). *In* " Solid State Physics," Vol. 6, (Seitz and Turnbull, eds.), Academic Press, New York.

Schall, R. (1956). " High Speed Photography," pp. 228–37, (ed. R. B. Collins), (Proc. 3rd Int. Congr. High Speed Photography, London, Sept. 10–15, 1956), Butterworths Scientific Publications, London.

Schall, R. (1958). *Explosivestoffe*, No. 6.

Schall, R., and Vollrath, K. (1959).   " Kurzzeitphotographie," pp. 329–334, (Schardin and Helwich, ed.), Verlag Dr. Othmar Helwich, Darmstadt.

Schall, R., and Vollrath, K. (1961). " Les Ondes de Detonation," Editions du CNRS, 15 Quai Anatole-France, Paris (VIIe).

Shapiro, Ascher, H. (1954). " The Dynamics and Thermodynamics of Compressible Flow," Vols. I and II, Ronald Press, New York.

Shewmon, P. G., and Zackay, V. F., Ed. (1961). " Response of Metals to High Velocity Deformation," Interscience, New York.

Skidmore, I. C., and Morris, E. (1962). " Thermodynamics of Nuclear Materials," International Atomic Energy Agency, Vienna; p. 173.

Smith, C. S., and Fowler, C. M. (1961). " Response of Metals to High Velocity Deformation," p. 309, (Shewmon and Zackay, ed.), Interscience, New York.

Soloukhin, R. I. (1959). *Soviet Phys. Uspekhi*, **2**, 547.

Swenson, C. A. (1960). *In* " Solid State Physics," Vol. 11, p. 141, (Seitz and Turnbull, ed.), Academic Press, New York.

Taylor, John W., and Rice, Melvin H. (1963). *J. appl. Phys.* **34**. 364.

Thouvenin, Jacques (1961a). " Les Ondes de Detonation," p. 295, Editions du CNRS, 15 Quai Anatole-France, Paris (VIIe).

Thouvenin, Jacques (1961b). *Ibid.*, p. 305.

Wackerle, Jerry (1962). *J. appl. Phys.* **33**, 922.

Walsh, J. M., and Christian, R. H. (1955). *Phys. Rev.* **97**, 1544.

Walsh, J. M., and Rice, M. H. (1957). *J. chem. Phys.* **26**, 815.

Walsh, J. M., Shreffler, R. G., and Willig, F. J. (1953). *J. appl. Phys.* **24**, 349.

Walsh, J. M., Rice, M. H., McQueen, R. G., and Yarger, F. L. (1957). *Phys. Rev.* **108**, 196.

Weyl, H. (1949). *Comm. on Pure and Applied Math.* II, 103.

Wood, D. S. (1952). *J. appl. Mech.* **19**, 521.

Wright, J. K. (1961). " Shock Tubes," John Wiley, New York.

Zel'dovich, Ia. B., Kormer, S. B., Sinitsyn, M. V., and Kuriapin, A. I. (1958). *Soviet Phys. Doklady*, **3**, 938.

Zubarev, V. N., and Telegin, G. S. (1962). *Soviet Phys. Doklady* **7**, 34.

Chapter 10.i

RADIOFREQUENCY SPECTROSCOPY AT
HIGH PRESSURES

J. A. S. Smith

School of Chemistry, University of Leeds, England

I. Introduction

The first experiments on radiofrequency spectroscopy in condensed states of matter were reported in 1945, the first high pressure work in 1953. Since then, such studies have rapidly diversified and the established methods of radiofrequency spectroscopy—nuclear magnetic resonance, nuclear quadrupole resonance, electron spin resonance, ferromagnetic and antiferromagnetic resonance—have been studied at high pressures, and some work has been done on crystals under strong uniaxial stress (Watkins and Pound, 1953; Shulman *et al.*, 1957; Walsh, 1959a; Lemanov, 1961).

II. Nuclear Magnetic Resonance Spectroscopy

A. *Introduction and Experimental Methods*

The energy levels in nuclear magnetic resonance spectroscopy (NMR) are provided by the magnetic interaction of the nuclear moments with fields varying from a few thousand to 25 000 gauss (Andrew, 1955; Abragam, 1961). The levels are specified by the component of nuclear angular momentum $(Ih/2\pi)$ in the direction of the applied magnetic field, conventionally the z-axis of a system of Cartesian axes; we write these $2I + 1$ components as $I_z h/2\pi$. Each has an energy in a magnetic field H of

$$E = -\gamma\hbar H I_z, \tag{1}$$

in which $\hbar$ is $h/2\pi$; γ, the gyromagnetic ratio, is a constant (either positive or negative) for each nuclear moment and depends on its magnitude and on the nuclear spin quantum number. Magnetic dipole transitions may occur between these levels at a frequency ν_L given by

$$h\nu_L = E_1 - E_2 = -\gamma\hbar H[(I_z - 1) - I_z] = \gamma\hbar H$$

or

$$2\pi\nu_L = \gamma H, \tag{2}$$

appropriate to a selection rule $\Delta I_z = \pm 1$ (the sign of γ is disregarded). Typical values of γ range from $2 \cdot 675 \times 10^4$ e.m.u. for ^{1}H to $0 \cdot 043 \times 10^4$ for ^{197}Au, so that in a field of 10^4 gauss, there is a range of frequencies from 43 to $0 \cdot 7$ Mc/s and overlap of one NMR frequency with another is extremely rare.

Such transitions may be studied by placing the sample in a magnetic field H and irradiating it at a frequency ν_L, either continuous wave (cw) or pulsed; in many experiments (Andrew, 1955), the rf power is coupled to a small coil placed round the sample, and losses in the coil which occur when the nuclei absorb radiation are measured by an amplifying system. In high pressure studies, this coil (or microwave cavity in the case of electron spin resonance) is placed in a bomb made of non-magnetic material and the oscillators and amplifiers are connected by methods dependent on the frequency range. In the apparatus shown in Fig. 1, which has been used for nuclear quadrupole resonance studies near 30 Mc/s (Kushida *et al.*, 1956), a direct connection (B) to the coil (L) is required and this is led into the bomb *via* a beryllium-copper plug (C) sealed against leakage by lead and copper washers (D), a coned sealing stem (H), and a conical pipestone washer (I) ("Micalex" is to be preferred at frequencies above 200 Mc/s (Fuke, 1961)). The bomb itself (A) is made of a non-magnetic beryllium-copper alloy, and despite its narrow width ($1\frac{3}{4}$ in.) will withstand pressures of up to 10^4 kg/cm^2; it will also fit into 2 in. pole gaps even when surrounded by a slush-bath. The pressures are generated by a high-pressure ram and are transmitted through hardened stainless steel tubing (E) to the sample, which is suspended in a pressure-transmitting fluid (K) in order to ensure uniformity of compression; leakage through the thread (G) is considerably reduced by soldering a small piece of copper sheet (F) with a pinhole over the end of the tubing. Various types of pressure-transmitting media have been used, for example petroleum ether previously saturated with the sample to be studied, but explosions have been reported with $NaClO_3$ at 2 000 atm (Kushida *et al.*, 1960). Other

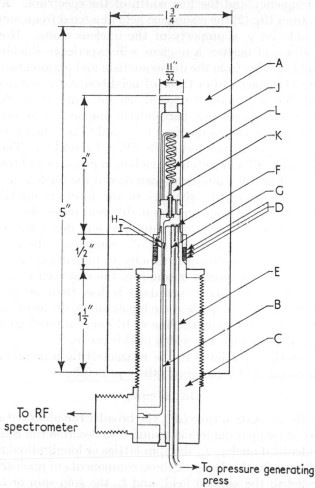

To RF spectrometer

To pressure generating press

FIG. 1. High pressure bomb for nuclear quadrupole resonance studies. (Reproduced with permission from Kushida *et al.*, 1956.)

workers have used " Kel-F " No. 10 liquid (Nolle and Mahendroo, 1960), or helium gas (Benedek and Kushida, 1960). At microwave frequencies, the cavity must be placed in the bomb and connected *via* a coupling loop to the spectrometer. One difficulty in this frequency range is the choice of a suitable dielectric filler; polystyrene is recommended (Walsh, 1961) rather than polytetrafluoroethylene which has discontinuities in dielectric constant at 250 and 5 400 kg/cm², but alumina is possibly even better because of its low compressibility (Kaminov and Jones, 1961).

Two quantities of importance in experimental work are the precise resonance frequency and the line width of the spectrum. As regards the former, from Eq. (2) the resonance field at a fixed frequency appears to depend only on γ, a property of the nucleus alone. However, in condensed states of matter, a nucleus will experience shielding or de-shielding fields arising from the diamagnetism and paramagnetism of its extranuclear electrons and of those of neighbouring atoms, so that the precise field that it " senses " depends on the state of combination of the atom. Such effects are particularly important in metals; for example, the field strengths required to record ^{63}Cu resonance at a fixed frequency in copper metal and CuBr differ by 0·24%. These shifts, known as Knight shifts in metals, have both a pressure and temperature dependence and in this example we can regard the nucleus as a " built-in-probe " which senses the changes in the internal shielding fields. Frequency shifts of the same nucleus in different molecules (" chemical shifts ") are also well-known and some pressure dependence has been reported, e.g. in ^{59}Co resonance in Co^{III} complexes (Benedek, 1961). Chemical shifts tend to diminish rapidly in magnitude as the atomic number decreases; for proton resonance, the observed range of shifts with respect to some proton standard is less than 50 ppm of the measuring frequency. At present such measurements are usually made on liquids; in the solid state, the line widths encountered are usually at least 10 times larger than the width of this range.

The line widths are related to the characteristic relaxation times of the nuclear moments by the uncertainty principle,

$$\Delta E . \Delta t \simeq \hbar; \tag{3}$$

the shorter the relaxation time (Δt), the broader the observed spectrum. A minimum of two parameters is required to describe the relaxation of any set of identical nuclei; t_1, the spin-lattice or longitudinal relaxation time, which governs the decay of those components of nuclear magnetization parallel to the applied field, and t_2, the spin-spin or transverse relaxation time, which governs the decay of the perpendicular components. One important distinction between t_1 and t_2 is that they are governed by different regions of the internal frequency spectrum of oscillating magnetic fields, generated, for example, by molecular motion. t_1 depends on those components at the resonance frequency or its first harmonic, $\gamma H/2\pi$ and $\gamma H/\pi$, i.e. in the range 10^6–10^8 c/s: t_2 on those components equal to or less than the frequency width of the line, i.e. less than 10^5 c/s. In liquids, the random nature of the molecular motions ensures that this distinction between frequencies is usually not important and $t_1 \simeq t_2$, but in solids the frequency spectrum may be very different from that in liquids, t_2 is very much less than t_1, and so governs the width of the line.

B. *Measurements in Gases*

The pressure variation of t_1 in gases has thrown some light on the mechanism of spin-lattice relaxation. In hydrogen gas, only the ortho molecules ($I = 1$) can give rise to an NMR signal and below 300° K these are nearly all in the $J = 1$ state. t_1 has been measured under these conditions by both cw and pulse techniques, by the latter up to pressures (p) of 750 Amagats, within the range 5–100 msec (Bloembergen *et al.*, 1948; Bloom, 1957; Lipsicas and Bloom, 1961). t_1 increases linearly with p at low pressures, the slope being largely independent of temperature down to 80° K, below which it increases sharply; at higher pressures ($p > 500$ Amagats) the slope also increases.

Two distinct local magnetic fields act at any one nucleus in the H_2 molecule (Bloembergen *et al.*, 1948): one due (a) to the rotational magnetic moment of the molecule (H') and the other (b) to the magnetic field produced by the other proton (H''). They are known to be of comparable magnitude when $J = 1$. Intermolecular magnetic fields can be neglected except at high pressures. In H_2 gas at sufficiently low temperatures, the lifetime (τ_c) of an H_2 molecule in any of the three magnetic sub-states of the $J = 1$ rotational state depends on the rate at which their condition is changed by intermolecular collisions. t_1 will be directly proportional to p at low densities, since $t_1 \propto \tau_c^{-1}$ when $2\pi\nu_L\tau_c \ll 1$ and τ_c is expected to be inversely proportional to p. The constant of proportionality between τ_c and p^{-1} contains the square of the effective collision diameter d; for hard spheres which collide elastically, d should be at least 2·75Å in H_2, whereas the t_1/p dependence, together with the known values of H' and H'', requires values of 1·24Å for ortho-ortho collisions and 0·72Å for ortho-para collisions (Bloom, 1957). Clearly the collision processes which tend to reorient the ortho-H_2 molecules are different from those which determine the transport properties of the gas, so that NMR studies at high pressure provide a method of studying these weak, anisotropic, intermolecular interactions. For example, the increase in the initial slope of the t_1/p curve below 80° K has been related to an increase in the contribution of the longer-range quadrupole term to the molecular interactions (Lipsicas and Bloom, 1961).

In polyatomic gases, the rotational magnetic moment term may still be important (Johnson and Waugh, 1961) but smaller, so that t_1 is longer than in H_2, e.g. about 0·2 to 2·4 sec in CH_4 according to the pressure. When a little oxygen is introduced into the gas, no effect

K*

occurs at low values of p, but eventually t_1 goes through a maximum as p is increased, e.g. at 35 Amagats in CH_4 with $1\cdot6\%$ O_2 at $194°$ K when $t_1 = 0\cdot6$ sec. To describe these effects, a third local field is required, namely the transient magnetic interaction between the CH_4 protons and the paramagnetic O_2 molecules which occurs on collision; this is therefore another collision process which can be studied at high pressures (Johnson and Waugh, 1961).

C. Measurements in Liquids

In liquids, the local magnetic fields can be both intramolecular and intermolecular in origin, because of the greater proximity of the molecules, so that the equation for t_1 contains at least two terms, the first an intramolecular term due to collision-modulated rotation and the second an intermolecular term due to diffusion (Bloembergen et al., 1948);

$$\frac{1}{t_1} = \frac{9}{10} \cdot \frac{\gamma^4 \hbar^2 \tau_c}{b^6} + \frac{3\pi}{10} \cdot \frac{\gamma^4 \hbar^2 N}{aD}. \tag{4}$$

In this equation, b is the interproton distance within the molecule, a the effective radius, N the number of molecules per cm^3, and D the diffusion coefficient; τ_c is now the time taken for a molecule to rotate through a sufficiently large angle to change the local field appreciably. Both terms are proportional to the viscosity, η; τ_c through the equation for spherical molecules moving in a viscous medium

$$\tau_c = 4\pi\eta a^3/3kT, \tag{5}$$

and D through the Stokes-Einstein equation

$$D = kT/6\pi\eta a. \tag{6}$$

We can therefore write Eq. (4) as

$$\frac{1}{t_1} = \left\{ \frac{\gamma^4 \hbar^2}{5} \left(\frac{6\pi a^3}{b^6} + 9\pi^2 N \right) \frac{\eta}{kT} \right\} = (\alpha + \beta N)\frac{\eta}{T}. \tag{7}$$

η is known for many liquids as a function of pressure; from Eq. (7), the product $t_1\eta$ should then be independent of pressure at constant temperature. This product has been studied by pulse techniques up to pressures of 10^4 atm in CH_3I and n-heptane, with dissolved air (Benedek and Purcell, 1954) or degassed (Nolle and Mahendroo, 1960). $t_1\eta$ is found to increase as the pressure increases, even when allowance is made for the variation of N; one explanation is that t_1 decreases relatively less rapidly than η increases because the molecular rotation term is affected much less by increasing pressure than are the translational jump processes which are governed by D. With pulse techniques, it is possible in certain cases to measure D separately, and to confirm, for example, that the pressure change in D is much greater than that in t_1 for CH_3I. With some liquids, e.g. benzene, the pressure behaviour is found to depend on the oxygen concentration (Nolle and Mahendroo, 1960) and the pressure dependence of the oxygen diffusion rate can then be studied. Other diffusion studies on liquids have been reported by McCall *et al.* (1959).

D. *Measurements in Solids*

In solids, $t_2 \ll t_1$ in many cases and the line width and mean square width (or second moment) depend almost entirely on t_2. In diamagnetic hydrogen-containing materials, the main reason for a low t_2 for any one proton is the presence of static and oscillatory local magnetic fields generated by adjacent protons. In solid H_2, for example, every proton has a nearest neighbour 0·75Å away which generates a local field whose component in the direction of the applied field H is equal to $(3 \cos^2 \theta - 1)\mu/r^3$, in which μ is the proton magnetic moment, r the proton-proton distance, and θ the angle that this vector makes with H. This local field, about 39 gauss in H_2, can either add to or subtract from H, so providing a mechanism for line broadening and therefore a low t_2. The precessional motion of the nuclear spins in the applied field also makes a comparable contribution to t_2 *via* spin-exchange processes which shorten the life-time of any spin state. Both these processes are susceptible to any form of motion which can change $[(3 \cos^2 \theta - 1)/r^3]$ provided that its frequency is greater than the frequency width of the line; the most important are hindered rotation and diffusion. For example, solid H_2 gives a strong signal from the ortho molecules and in the temperature range 1·2 to 14° K two changes in the line width occur as a result of changes in $\langle (3 \cos^2 \theta - 1)r^3 \rangle$. The higher near 10° ($p = 1$ atm) changes the line width from 1 to 7 gauss, and is attributed to a reduction in the frequency of self-diffusion to below the limit at which it can affect the line width; the second near 1·5° is attributed to the dropping of the ortho molecules into their ground rotational state, in which the local intramolecular fields are no longer averaged to zero. The first is pressure sensitive (at $p = 230$ atm it occurs at 13·2°), the second is not (Smith and Squire, 1958). The energy barrier to diffusion (E_d) is increased at high pressures and from a study of the rate of change of line width $\Delta H_{\frac{1}{2}}$ in the temperature range of the NMR transition, the values of E_d shown in Table I are derived.

A similar pressure shift to higher temperatures has been observed in the line width transition in 2,2-dinitropropane near 268° K (Billings and Nolle, 1958) and in polyisobutylene near 200° K (Nolle and Billings, 1959).

TABLE I. Pressure Variation of the Energy Barrier to
Diffusion in Solid Hydrogen

p (atm)	1	74	130	230
E_d (cal/mole) from $\Delta H_{\frac{1}{2}}$ (line width at half-height)	230	260	295	370

In metals, both the line width and the relative position of the resonance frequency can be studied as a function of pressure. Finely-powdered samples must be used, with particle sizes typically 10–30 microns, in order to provide sufficient rf penetration. Again, the pressure variation of the line width gives information on diffusion. In lithium metal at room temperature, the ^{7}Li line width of about 330 c/s is governed almost entirely by t_2 and this in turn is controlled largely by D (since the number of translational jumps per second $\gg$ the frequency width of the line) through the equation

$$t_2 = 5cD/4\gamma^4\hbar^2 I(I+1)N, \tag{8}$$

in which c is the nearest neighbour distance. The pressure variation of $\ln t_2$ gives us $(\partial \ln D/\partial \ln p)_T$, which is related to the activation volume for diffusion per g atom ($V_{\rm act}$) by the expression (G is a Gibbs free energy)

$$V_{\rm act} = \left(\frac{\partial \Delta G}{\partial p}\right)_T = -RT\left(\frac{\partial \ln D}{\partial p} - \frac{\partial \ln \nu_0}{\partial p} - 2\frac{\partial \ln d}{\partial p}\right)_T, \tag{9}$$

in which d is the lattice spacing and ν_0 the characteristic jump frequency. The ^{7}Li line width increases linearly with increasing pressure and by 3 000 atm has practically doubled (Barnes et al., 1959). If $(\partial \ln \nu_0/\partial p)_T$ is neglected and $(\partial \ln d/\partial p)_T$ calculated from compressibility data, values for $V_{\rm act}$ of $5 \cdot 10 \pm 0 \cdot 25$ cm^3 at 276° K and $5 \cdot 18 \pm 0 \cdot 25$ at 300° can be derived.

Not only is the line width increased by pressure, its position is also changed; at room temperature, the ^{7}Li resonance frequency at 10 Mc/s and atmospheric pressure diminishes by 27 c/s at 10^4 atm (Kushida and Benedek, 1958). These pressure shifts in Li, Na, Rb, Cs, Cu, and Al have been studied up to 10^4 atm or as far as the pressure broadening of the line permitted. The main contribution to the Knight shift (K) comes from the paramagnetism of the conduction electrons and ranges in magnitude from $\Delta H/H = 10^{-2}$ to 10^{-4}. K then depends on the product of χ_p, the paramagnetic volume susceptibility of the conduction electrons, Ω the atomic volume, and p_F, the probability density that a conduction electron with an energy equal to the Fermi energy can be found at the nucleus, i.e.

$$K = \frac{\Delta H}{H} = \frac{8\pi}{3}\chi_p \Omega p_F. \tag{10}$$

From measurement of K as a function of pressure and the p-V isotherms, K can be derived as a function of V, hence $\partial(\chi_p \Omega p_F)/\partial V$ and $(\partial \ln K/\partial \ln V)_T$ may be derived. From the first term and by means of a theoretical expression for $\chi_p \Omega$ derived by Pines (1955), values of p_F as a function of volume can be derived and compared with theoretical predictions. From the second term, K can be derived as an explicit function of temperature by means of the expression

$$\left(\frac{\partial \ln K}{\partial T}\right)_p = \left(\frac{\partial \ln K}{\partial \ln V}\right)_T \left(\frac{\partial \ln V}{\partial T}\right)_p + \left(\frac{\partial \ln K}{\partial T}\right)_V, \tag{11}$$

in which the first term on the right-hand side allows for the effects of thermal expansion of the lattice and the second gives the explicit temperature dependence of K, i.e. at constant volume. $(\partial \ln K/\partial T)_p$ has already been measured for Na, Rb, and Cs (McGarvey and Gutowsky, 1953); the high-pressure measurements and thermal expansion data give the thermal expansion term and the following values of $(\partial \ln K/\partial T)_V$ are then derived;

TABLE II. Temperature Variation of the Knight Shift

	$\left(\dfrac{\partial \ln K}{\partial T}\right)_p$	$\left(\dfrac{\partial \ln K}{\partial \ln V}\right)_T \left(\dfrac{\partial \ln V}{\partial T}\right)_p$	$\left(\dfrac{\partial \ln K}{\partial T}\right)_V$	(all $10^4 \times {}^\circ K^{-1}$)
Na	1·5	0·8	0·7	
Rb	1·7	−0·4	2·1	
Cs	−1·9	−3·1	1·2	

The non-zero values in the last column are attributed to the effect of lattice vibrations on p_F.

E. Zero-field Resonance Measurements in Ferromagnetic and Antiferromagnetic Materials

In a ferromagnetic or antiferromagnetic substance, the magnetic field which removes the degeneracy of the magnetic energy levels is produced by unpaired electron-spins within the material itself. For example, in iron these internal fields average about 330 500 gauss at 295° K, giving a ^{57}Fe NMR frequency of about 45 Mc/s. No external magnetic field is therefore necessary in the experiment, although with conductors, finely-powdered samples must be used, e.g. with iron a particle diameter of 10 microns is needed. ^{57}Fe resonance in enriched iron powder has been studied at 196, 273, and 357·2° K at pressures up to 10^4 kg/cm² (Benedek and Armstrong, 1961). The *mean* field experienced by the iron nucleus is assumed to be proportional to the mean spin per atom, so that the ^{57}Fe NMR frequency ν is written

$$\nu = A'\sigma, \tag{12}$$

in which σ is the saturation magnetization and A' is a hyperfine coupling coefficient which governs the magnitude of the local field produced by lattice magnetization at the iron nucleus. σ is expected to be a function of temperature and volume, A' of volume alone, but high pressure studies have shown that A' also has an explicit temperature dependence. Thus, the volume dependence of ν, $(\partial \ln \nu / \partial \ln V)_T$, obtained by dividing $(1/\nu)(\partial \nu/\partial p)_T$ by the compressibility, $(1/V)(\partial V/\partial p)_T$, turns out to be independent of temperature and so can be used (as in Eq. (11)) to eliminate the thermal expansion term from $(\partial \ln \nu / \partial T)_p$, giving A' as an explicit function of temperature, in which form it can be compared with theoretical estimates.

A similar problem is encountered in ^{19}F resonance studies on MnF_2 (Benedek and Kushida, 1960), which is anti-ferromagnetic below 68° K; the ^{19}F resonance frequency in zero-field experiments is near to 160 Mc/s, corresponding to a physically significant field at the ^{19}F nucleus produced by complete sublattice alignment (H_∞) of 40 470 gauss. This resonance frequency (ν) has been studied at temperatures of 4·2, 20·4, and 35·7° K and increases linearly with pressure in the range up to 10^3 kg/cm². In this compound, ν depends not only on the sublattice magnetization $M(T)$ at temperature T but on a hyperfine coefficient A'' which in this case expresses the magnitude of the internal fields at the ^{19}F nucleus;

$$h\nu = \tfrac{5}{2}A''(M(T)/M_\infty). \tag{13}$$

A'' contains two important terms. The first is the dipolar term, A''_{dip}, and its magnitude and pressure dependence can be calculated from the known crystal structure of MnF_2 with the approximation that the one structural parameter determining the fluorine co-ordinates is not changed by pressure; the nearest neighbour contribution to A'' in gauss is calculated as 12 800. The second, larger, term, the isotropic hyperfine interaction or contact term A''_{hyp}, arises predominantly from the overlap of the 3d orbitals on Mn^{++} with the 2s orbital on F^- and produces an unpaired spin density on the latter through exchange polarization; its magnitude is calculated as 24 070 gauss. Both A'' and $M(T)$ may be functions of pressure, and from Eq. (13),

$$\frac{1}{\nu}\left(\frac{\partial \nu}{\partial p}\right)_T = \left(\frac{\partial \ln A''}{\partial p}\right)_T + \left(\frac{\partial \ln M}{\partial p}\right)_T. \tag{14}$$

With the assumption that $(\partial \ln A''/\partial p)_T$ is independent of temperature and that M depends on pressure only through its dependence on T_N (the Néel temperature), the results at three different temperatures can be combined to give a self-consistent set of values for $(\partial \ln A''/\partial p)_T$ of $1 \cdot 9 \pm 0 \cdot 1 \times 10^{-6}/\mathrm{kg/cm^2}$ and $(\partial \ln T_N/\partial p)_T$ of $4 \cdot 4 \pm 0 \cdot 3 \times 10^{-6}/\mathrm{kg/cm^2}$. The interesting quantities A''_{hyp} and $(\partial \ln A''_{\mathrm{hyp}}/\partial p)_T$ may then be compared with theoretical estimates based on modified Hartree-Fock wavefunctions, which are affected by overlap through the exclusion principle.

III. Nuclear Quadrupole Resonance Spectroscopy

All nuclei with a spin quantum number I greater than $\frac{1}{2}$ can have a quadrupole moment eQ (either positive or negative) which will interact with the gradients of electric fields produced by charge distributions external to the nucleus. The permitted energy levels of the nuclear quadrupole moment depend on the size and symmetry of the electric field gradients within the crystal. When this splitting is much greater than the Zeeman splitting in normal laboratory magnetic fields, we can dispense with the latter altogether and study the transitions induced by the oscillating magnetic dipole of the rf radiation between the electric quadrupole levels. This form of spectroscopy is known as nuclear quadrupole resonance (NQR) (Das and Hahn, 1958). As an example, we take ^{35}Cl, for which $I = 3/2$. At 10^4 gauss, its NMR frequency in liquids (in which the quadrupolar splitting is averaged to zero) is near $4 \cdot 2$ Mc/s; in polycrystalline trans-dichloroethylene, NQR lines can be detected at $28 \cdot 0$ and $35 \cdot 4$ Mc/s with zero d.c. magnetic field (Dehmelt and Krüger, 1950). If we represent the electric field gradient near the nucleus by the second derivative of the electrostatic potential Φ, and with the assumption that this field is axially symmetrical, i.e.

$$\frac{\mathrm{d}^2\Phi}{\mathrm{d}x^2} = \frac{\mathrm{d}^2\Phi}{\mathrm{d}y^2} \quad \left(\neq \frac{\mathrm{d}^2\Phi}{\mathrm{d}z^2} \right), \tag{15}$$

then the energy levels of the nucleus in the general case are given by

$$E_{I_z} = \frac{e^2qQ}{4I(2I-1)} \left\{ 3I_z^2 - I(I+1) \right\}. \tag{16}$$

I_z is now the component of nuclear spin along the symmetry axis (z), $eq = \mathrm{d}^2\Phi/\mathrm{d}z^2$, and eQ is the electric quadrupole moment of the nucleus (Q has the dimensions of cm²); the product e^2qQ is called the quadrupole coupling constant and is often quoted in units of Mc/s. For $I = 3/2$ (as in ^{35}Cl), there are two levels only, with $I_z = \pm \frac{1}{2}$ or $\pm 3/2$, and with a selection rule $\Delta I_z = \pm 1$, only one NQR line will be observed at a frequency of

$$\nu = e^2 qQ/2h, \tag{17}$$

from which the quadrupole coupling constant is immediately derived.

The measured value of e^2qQ contains the average value of q, $\langle q \rangle$, over the lattice vibrations of the crystal, even at the very lowest temperatures, and therefore depends not only on volume, but also on temperature because of the simultaneous volume change, *and* on the effects of both volume and temperature on the amplitudes of the lattice vibrations. The quantity which really governs the internal field gradients is q_0, the value of q in a rigid lattice unaffected by vibrations; by a combination of NQR measurements at both variable temperature and pressure, this important quantity can be measured. If we write ν as a function of both q_0 and $\xi_i{}^0$, the latter being the amplitude of the ith normal vibrational mode, the equations governing its temperature and pressure dependence in the case of axial symmetry may be written

$$\frac{1}{\nu}\left(\frac{\partial \nu}{\partial p}\right)_T = \frac{V}{\nu}\left\{ \frac{\partial \nu}{\partial q_0} \cdot \frac{\partial q_0}{\partial V} + \sum_i \frac{\partial \nu}{\partial \xi_i{}^0}\left(\frac{\partial \xi_i{}^0}{\partial V}\right)_T \right\} \frac{1}{V}\left(\frac{\partial V}{\partial p}\right)_T \tag{18}$$

and

$$\frac{1}{\nu}\left(\frac{\partial \nu}{\partial T}\right)_p = \frac{V}{\nu}\left\{ \frac{\partial \nu}{\partial q_0} \cdot \frac{\partial q_0}{\partial V} + \sum_i \frac{\partial \nu}{\partial \xi_i{}^0}\left(\frac{\partial \xi_i{}^0}{\partial V}\right)_T \right\} \frac{1}{V}\left(\frac{\partial V}{\partial T}\right)_p$$
$$+ \frac{1}{\nu}\sum_i \frac{\partial \nu}{\partial \xi_i{}^0}\left(\frac{\partial \xi_i{}^0}{\partial T}\right)_V. \tag{19}$$

The pressure dependence of ν is governed by two terms; one contains the volume dependence of q_0, and the other that of the amplitudes of the lattice vibrations. Both reappear in that part of the equation for $(1/\nu)(\partial \nu/\partial T)_p$ that governs the volume changes that always occur when the temperature varies, together with a third term, first discussed by Bayer (1951) and generally called the Bayer term, which expresses the explicit temperature variation of the $\xi_i{}^0$'s. In ^{35}Cl resonance in $NaClO_3$, the Bayer term accounts for 80% of the observed temperature dependence at constant pressure. In order to separate these various factors, both variable temperature and pressure measurements are necessary, together with a knowledge of the coefficients of thermal expansion and the compressibilities.

The methods that may be used to analyse the experimental data have been discussed by several authors (Kushida *et al.*, 1956; Gutowsky and Williams, 1957) and we give here a resumé of the type of information that one may expect to derive in the best cases;

(*a*) the absolute magnitude and volume dependence of q_0—or n in $q_0 \propto V^n$;

(*b*) the magnitudes and volume dependences of important vibrational frequencies, i.e. low frequency oscillational modes in molecular crystals and in some cases their effective moments of inertia;

(c) the contributions to $(\partial \ln \nu / \partial \ln V)_T$ of both the volume dependence of q_0 and that of the vibrational frequencies; and

(d) the contributions to $(\partial \nu / \partial T)_p$ of both the volume expansion term and the Bayer term.

For example, the volume dependence of q_0 is known for at least six crystals, and the coefficients n in $q_0 \propto V^n$ are listed in Table III (Bernheim and Gutowsky, 1960).

TABLE III. Volume Dependence of the Electric Field Gradient q_0

Compound	Nucleus	n in $q_0 \propto V^n$	Reference
Cu_2O	^{63}Cu	-0.96	Kushida et al. (1956)
$NaClO_3$	^{23}Na	-1.9	Gutowsky and Williams (1957)
$NaClO_3$	^{35}Cl	-0.10	Bernheim and Gutowsky (1960)
$KClO_3$	^{35}Cl	-0.025	Kushida et al. (1956)
$NaBrO_3$	^{23}Na	-2.0	Bernheim and Gutowsky (1960)
$NaNO_3$	^{23}Na	-3.8	Bernheim and Gutowsky (1960)

In Cu_2O, a cubic crystal, the value of n shows that q_0 depends on the interionic distances as r^3, as would be expected if the electric field gradients in the crystal were due entirely to Cu^+ and O^{2-} ions. On the other hand, the very low values of n for ^{35}Cl resonance in $KClO_3$ and $NaClO_3$ arise because the major part of the field gradient is caused by the anisotropy of the charge distribution of the ClO_3^- ion, which is little affected by changes in volume and temperature. The measured values

TABLE IV. Some NQR Studies at High Pressures

Compound	Nucleus	Comments	Reference
p-dichlorobenzene	^{35}Cl	NQR frequency increases linearly with pressure in all 3 phases at room temperature. Some evidence that $\partial \nu / \partial p$ becomes negative in the γ-phase about 8 500 kg/cm²	Dauthreppe and Dreyfus (1955) Kushida et al. (1956)
Mercuric chloride	^{35}Cl	Two NQR lines with negative pressure coefficients but different magnitudes.	Dauthreppe and Dreyfus (1956)
Titanium tetrabromide	^{81}Br	Maximum in $\partial \nu / \partial T$ caused by a negative $\partial \nu / \partial p$.	Barnes and Engardt (1958)
Stannic Iodide	^{127}I	Careful discussion of factors (a) to (d) in the text.	Fuke (1961)
p-Dibromobenzene	^{81}Br		
Arsenious oxide	^{75}As		

of n can then be used to study the charge distribution within the ClO_3^- ion, provided that an accurate crystal structure analysis is available (Bernheim and Gutowsky, 1960). As an example of (b), the analysis of the NQR data for $KClO_3$ gave an average low-frequency vibration $\langle v \rangle$ of 102 cm^{-1}, which is identified with the Raman line at 98 cm^{-1} attributed to a tilting motion of the ClO_3^- ion. The derived value of the moment of inertia (for two such orthogonal modes) is 84×10^{-40} g cm^2; the calculated value for the ClO_3^- ion is $85 \pm 2 \times 10^{-40}$ g cm^2 (Kushida et al., 1956). The terms mentioned in (c) and (d) are useful in explaining the unusual temperature dependences that are occasionally observed; examples of this type of NQR study are summarized briefly in Table IV.

IV. ELECTRON SPIN RESONANCE SPECTROSCOPY

In this form of spectroscopy, the energy levels are derived from the interaction of the applied magnetic field with the spin and orbital moments of unpaired electrons in the crystal. The equation corresponding to Eq. (2) is now

$$hv = g\beta H, \tag{20}$$

in which β is the Bohr magneton ($eh/4\pi mc$) and g is the spectroscopic splitting factor. For free electron spins, $g = 2 \cdot 0023$, so that in a field of 10^4 gauss v is near to 28 000 Mc/s in the microwave region; for pure orbital motion, $g = 1$. These limiting cases rarely hold in crystalline materials and a range of g-values is encountered, often with temperature and pressure shifts and a marked anisotropy in single crystals. The kind of information that can be obtained from high pressure studies is best discussed in terms of specific examples.

The electron spin resonance (ESR) spectra of transition metal ions of the first long row are very sensitive to their electrical environment in the crystal. Direct advantage of this dependence has been taken to follow the pressure-induced transition of wurtzite (ZnS, hexagonal) into zinc-blende (ZnS, cubic) by means of the ESR spectrum of small quantities of Mn^{2+} in solid solution (Van Wieringen, 1953). The detailed pressure changes of a spectrum provide very much more information. The first case to be discussed is that of the cubic MgO lattice in which about $0 \cdot 01$ atomic % of the Mg^{2+} sites is replaced by a paramagnetic ion, whose ESR spectrum is then studied (Walsh, 1961). Provided that the lattice distortion at these sites is negligible, the paramagnetic ion is then subjected to an electric field of octahedral cubic symmetry. In the case of F-state ions like Cr^{3+}(^{4}F, $3d^3$) and Ni^{2+}(^{3}F, $3d^8$), the cubic electric field of neighbouring O^{2-} and Mg^{2+} ions splits the seven-fold orbitally degenerate F-state of the free paramagnetic ion into two orbital triplets and an orbital singlet, the latter lying lowest and retaining a quadruple (Cr^{3+}) or a triple (Ni^{2+}) spin degeneracy in a purely cubic electric field (Bleaney and Stevens, 1953); the smaller singlet-triplet separation is written as Δ and is proportional to the cubic moment of the lattice potential at the position of the paramagnetic ion, that is, to the fourth-order terms in a Taylor expansion of the potential energy of a given electron in the external field of neighbouring ions. Spin-orbit coupling tends to mix with the wave-function of the singlet ground state a small contribution from the higher triplet, which has different values of m_L and m_S (the orbital and spin angular momentum quantum numbers); the predicted result is an isotropic shift of the g-value by an amount

$$g - g_0 = -4\lambda g_0/\Delta, \tag{21}$$

in which λ is the spin-orbit coupling constant, usually assumed to be of the same form as it is in the related Russell-Saunders term of the free ion. Various other effects may occur, such as small departures from full cubic symmetry, or the existence of a small zero-field splitting (as is suggested by the doublet structure of the Ni^{2+} spectrum); but the main attention has been devoted to the effect of high pressure on g and its interpretation in terms of Eq. (21). From a point-charge model, Δ can be calculated as

$$\Delta = 10e^2 \langle r^4 \rangle / 3d^5, \tag{22}$$

in which $\langle r^4 \rangle$ is the average value of r^4 over the radial part of the $3d$ orbitals and d is the anion-cation distance; from Eqs. (21) and (22), the volume dependence ($V \propto d^3$) of $g - g_0$ can be calculated as $(\partial \ln (g - g_0)/\partial \ln V)_T = 1\cdot67$ for Ni^{2+} and $1\cdot84$ for Cr^{3+}, provided that radial scale of the Hartree-Fock wave functions for the free ion used in calculating $\langle r^4 \rangle$ is expanded by about 10% (a similar correction was also needed in the theoretical interpretation of antiferromagnetic resonance in MnF_2) and some correction is made for induced dipoles on O^{2-} in the case of Cr^{3+}. Theoretically, therefore, the approximation is made that the compression acts only on Δ. Experimentally, g is determined as a function of pressure by measurement of the resonant field strength at constant frequency and converted to the volume dependence by means of the compressibility. The pressure variation for both ions is linear and $(\partial \ln (g - g_0)/\partial \ln V)_T$ is found to be $1\cdot9 \pm 0\cdot3$ for Ni^{2+} and $2\cdot0 \pm 0\cdot2$ for Cr^{3+}, in reasonable agreement with the theory. With S-state ions like Mn^{2+} and Fe^{3+} (both ^6S, $3d^5$), the crystal field effects enter through a term involving the hexadecapole moment of the lattice potential (the 16th-order terms) and the experimental value of its pressure variation is again in reasonable agreement with a point-charge model, although the relative magnitudes are not. An additional parameter in the case of Mn^{2+} $(I = 5/2)$ is the nuclear hyperfine structure, whose pressure dependence can be measured. In d^5 ions, the splitting is largely isotropic and appears in the spin Hamiltonian as a term $A\mathbf{I.S}$, in which A is the hyperfine coupling constant; it is represented as a contact term originating in an exchange polarization of the inner s-orbitals on Mn^{2+} by its unpaired 3d electrons. The interesting possibility that the pressure dependence of $A(\ (\partial \ln A/\partial V)_T = 0.06$ for Mn^{2+} in MgO) arises from pressure distortion of the 3d-orbital radial distribution has yet to be explored.

In single crystals of $NiSiF_6.6H_2O$ (Walsh, 1959a), the situation is more complicated. Firstly, the crystal is trigonal, so that the Ni^{2+} must now be thought of as lying in a cubic field with a trigonal distortion, and this acting in conjunction with the spin-orbit coupling lifts the triple spin degeneracy of the orbital singlet ground state and produces a spin doublet and a spin singlet; this so-called zero-field splitting D is -0.52 cm^{-1} at room temperature and atmospheric pressure, the negative sign indicating that the spin doublet lies lower. D varies with temperature and pressure; its pressure dependence at room temperature is given by $(\partial D/\partial p)_T = 0.834 \times 10^{-4}$ $cm^{-1}/kg/cm^2$, so that near 6200 kg/cm^2 it passes through zero and becomes positive. In this crystal, the cubic part of the internal crystalline field changes slowly while the trigonal part varies rapidly with pressure. However, the theoretical interpretation in terms of a point-charge model is extremely difficult, since the lattice parameters of the various ions change by different amounts on compression; an accurate crystal structure analysis is required at each pressure. Similar difficulties arise in the interpretation of the effect of pressure on the crystal field splitting of Cr^{3+} in solid solution in ammonium alum and $K_3Co(CN)_6$ (Walsh, 1959b). A second complication in $NiSiF_6.6H_2O$ is that the paramagnetic ions are now closer and exchange interactions between neighbouring Ni^{2+} ions (both isotropic and anisotropic) must be allowed for; compression changes the Ni^{2+}---Ni^{2+} separations, which appears in the ESR experiments as a strong pressure dependence of the line width, which approximately doubles at pressures of 10^4 kg/cm^2. These exchange interactions must be related to the amount of charge transfer that occurs from Ni^{2+} to neighbouring diamagnetic ions, i.e. to the degree of covalent bonding in the complex, and their study and quantitative interpretation should be of considerable chemical importance.

Exchange interactions assume a predominant importance in ferromagnetics and ferrimagnetics. Ferrimagnetic materials like erbium iron garnet, $Er_3Fe_2(FeO_4)_3$, show strong resonance absorption in the microwave region when placed in d.c. magnetic fields. The effective magnetic field acting on the unpaired electrons is very different from the applied d.c. field and contains additional contributions from the demagnetizing field, the magnetic anisotropy, and spin exchange, among others. Factors like size, shape, and surface smoothness may also affect the spectrum. Despite this complexity, some progress has been made in sorting out the various pressure dependences (Kaminov and Jones, 1961). For example, from a study of the pressure variation of the effective g-factor, g_{eff}, in erbium and yttrium iron garnets, $M_3Fe_2(FeO_4)_3$ (M = Er or Y), and with the assumption of identical compressibilities, it has been possible to derive the volume dependence of the composite exchange constant λ_{AB} which couples the erbium and ferric sub-lattices and is a measure of the exchange field. λ_{AB} increases rapidly as neighbouring ions approach each other, i.e.

$$(\partial \ln \lambda_{AB}/\partial \ln V)_T = -7\cdot 0.$$

In nickel cobalt ferrite $Ni_{1-z}Co_zFe_2O_4$, the pressure dependence of the magnetic anisotropy around each Co^{2+} ion has also been derived from high pressure studies. Once again, the complexibility of crystal structure changes at high pressure is a limiting factor and more structure analyses under such conditions are required.

ACKNOWLEDGMENT

The author thanks Dr. E. F. W. Seymour, Department of Physics, University of Leeds, for helpful comments.

REFERENCES

Abragam, A. (1961). " The Principles of Nuclear Magnetism ", 599 pp., Oxford University Press, London.
Andrew, E. R. (1955). " Nuclear Magnetic Resonance ", pp. 265, Cambridge University Press, London.
Barnes, R. G., and Engardt, R. D. (1958). *J. chem. Phys.* **29**, 248.
Barnes, R. G., Engardt, R. D., and Hultsch, R. A. (1959). *Phys. Rev. Letters*, **2**, 202.
Bayer, H. (1951). *Z. Phys.* **130**, 227.
Benedek, G. B. (1961). *In* " Progress in Very High Pressure Research " (F. P. Bundy, W. R. Hibbard, Jr., and H. M. Strong, eds.), pp. 288–289, Wiley, New York.
Benedek, G. B., and Armstrong, J. (1961). *J. appl. Phys.* **32**, 106 (S).
Benedek, G. B., and Kushida, T. (1960). *Phys. Rev.* **118**, 46.
Benedek, G. B., and Purcell, E. M. (1954). *J. chem. Phys.* **22**, 2003.
Bernheim, R. A., and Gutowsky, H. S. (1960). *J. chem. Phys.* **32**, 1072.
Billings, J. J., and Nolle, A. W. (1958). *J. chem. Phys.* **29**, 214.
Bleaney, B., and Stevens, K. W. H. (1953). *Rep. Progr. Phys.* **16**, 108.
Bloembergen, N., Purcell, E. M., and Pound, R. V. (1948). *Phys. Rev.* **73**, 679.
Bloom, M. (1957). *Physica 's Grav.* **23**, 237.

Das, T. P., and Hahn, E. L. (1958). " Nuclear Quadrupole Resonance Spectro-
    scopy ", 223 pp., Academic Press, New York.
Dauthreppe, D., and Dreyfus, B. (1955).   *C. R. Acad. Sci., Paris* **241**, 795.
Dauthreppe, D., and Dreyfus, B. (1956).   *C. R. Acad. Sci., Paris* **242**, 766.
Dehmelt, H. G., and Krüger, H. (1950).   *Naturwissenschaften*, **37**, 111.
Fuke, T. (1961).   *J. phys. Soc. Japan*, **16**, 266.
Gutowsky, H. S., and Williams, G. A. (1957).   *Phys. Rev.* **105**, 464.
Johnson, C. S., and Waugh, J. S. (1961).   *J. chem. Phys.* **35**, 2020.
Kaminov, I. P., and Jones, R. V. (1961).   *Phys. Rev.* **123**, 1122.
Kushida, T., and Benedek, G. B. (1958).   *J. Phys. Chem. Solids*, **5**, 241.
Kushida, T., Benedek, G. B., and Bloembergen, N. (1956).   *Phys. Rev.* **104**, 1364
Lemanov, V. V. (1961).   *Soviet Phys. JETP*, **13**, 543.
Lipsicas, M., and Bloom, M. (1961).   *Canad. J. Phys.* **39**, 881.
McCall, D. W., Douglas, D. C., and Anderson, E. W. (1959).   *J. chem. Phys.* **31**,
    1555.
McGarvey, B., and Gutowsky, H. S. (1953).   *J. chem. Phys.* **21**, 2114.
Nolle, A. W., and Billings, J. J. (1959).   *J. chem. Phys.* **30**, 84.
Nolle, A. W., and Mahendroo, P. P. (1960).   *J. chem. Phys.* **33**, 863.
Pines, D. (1955).   *Solid State Physics*, **1**, 367.
Shulman, R. G., Wyluda, B. J., and Anderson, P. W. (1957).   *Phys. Rev.*, **107**,
    953.
Smith, G. W., and Squire, C. F. (1958).   *Phys. Rev.* **111**, 188.
Van Wieringen, J. S. (1953).   *Physica, 's Grav.* **19**, 397.
Walsh, W. M. (1959a).   *Phys. Rev.* **114**, 1473.
Walsh, W. M. (1959b).   *Phys. Rev.* **114**, 1485.
Walsh, W. M. (1961).   *Phys. Rev.* **122**, 762.
Watkins, G. D., and Pound, R. V. (1953).   *Phys. Rev.* **89**, 658.

Chapter 10.ii

STRUCTURAL DETERMINATIONS BY X-RAYS OF SYSTEMS AT HIGH PRESSURE

D. C. MUNRO

School of Chemistry, University of Leeds, England

I. INTRODUCTION

Pressure-induced phase transformations which do not revert on release of pressure in the cold, and which persist as meta-stable structures such as diamond, may present their problems in determination of crystal structure, but these are not generally different from problems with other crystalline materials. However, some phase changes are reversed when the pressure is released, notably transitions in molecular solids and simple ionic solids. Attempts to study these new phases have lent incentive to the development of apparatus in which material may be studied while still under pressure, either for determination of crystal structures or for precise compressibility measurements.

At ordinary pressure there may be difficulties in securing satisfactory powder diffraction photographs for particular substances. At high pressures there are additional difficulties caused by X-ray reflection and absorption in the material supporting the pressure in the sample. Some of the relevant considerations are reviewed below.

II. Apparatus

A. *Materials for Pressure Vessels*

A number of materials are available for construction of pressure plugs which are relatively transparent to X-radiation and enable diffraction patterns to be transmitted. They may be used in the form of a plug or window in a pressure vessel mainly constructed of other materials; however the simplest system is that of a cylinder consisting entirely of transparent material and which contains the material under pressure, as in Lawson and Riley's simple beryllium vessel or Jamieson's diamond.

For materials which are not too brittle a limit is reached when the pressure stresses the material of the vessel to a plastic state throughout, resulting in a slow swelling and eventual breakage with a crack which usually starts in the outer layer of the vessel. In the plastic state the inner layers of the vessel still contribute to the containing force, a definite stress being required to keep them in the " creeping " state. For metals this corresponds very roughly with the ultimate tensile strength.

The pressure decrement due to the tension in a thin cylindrical element, stressed to s kb, is given by the equation,

$$-\,\mathrm{d}p = s \,.\, \mathrm{d}r/r \tag{1}$$

where $\mathrm{d}r$ is the thickness of the cylindrical shell, and r its radius. For a thick cylinder, made up of such elements all stressed to slow plastic flow, for which S (kb) is the ultimate tensile strength, the maximum difference in pressure between outside (p_e) and inside (p_i) is given by the equation,

$$p_i - p_e = S \,.\, \ln\,(r_e/r_i), \tag{2}$$

where r_e, r_i, are the corresponding radii. For most purposes p_e, the pressure outside the vessel, may be neglected.

Decrease in intensity of radiation due to absorption in the vessel walls takes place according to the equation:

$$I/I' = \exp\,(-\,\mu t), \tag{3}$$

I and I' are initial and final intensities, μ is the linear absorption coefficient, and t is the thickness of the cylinder wall; the latter may be equated with $(r_e - r_i)$. For most pressure vessels of the sort considered the bore is small, so that for a diffracted beam emerging from the centre t is approximately the same as r_e.

The suitability of materials for X-ray pressure vessels is indicated concisely by the values of S and μ. Values of the former are not available for all the materials of possible use in this field, but values of μ

can be obtained; the values of this quantity are compared in Table I for a number of materials.

TABLE I. Basic Data for Pressure Window Materials

Material	Absorption coefficient μ in cm^{-1}	
	for Mo Kα	for Cu Kα
Li metal	0·12	0·36
LiH	0·15	0·46
Li$_3$N	0·79	5·30
Be metal	0·54	2·43
Be$_2$C	0·87	5·71
Be$_3$N$_2$	1·92	13·5
BeO	3·22	25·8
B	1·05	7·15
B$_4$C	1·26	8·99
BN (borazon)	2·82	21·2
C (diamond)	2·45	19·3

These calculated values are based on mass absorption coefficients given in " International Tables for Determination of Crystal Structure " (1935). Vol. II, p. 577. G. Bell and Sons, London.

B. *Absorption by the Sample*

The precision of X-ray powder photographs may be impaired by absorption of radiation by the specimen itself; this may reduce the intensity of the diffracted beam below that of the background radiation scattered by the pressure vessel. Absorption of radiation is governed by Eq. (3) above. Cylindrical samples can be compared using the value of the product $2\mu r$, where r is the radius of the sample, and μ is the linear absorption coefficient. The intensity of the diffracted beam is proportional to the quantity $\exp(-2\mu r)$.

In addition, the effect of high absorption by the sample is to distort the intensity distribution within the diffracted beam, (cf. Nelson, 1955). In moderately absorbing specimens, (μr values of 1 to 4), there is some distortion of diffraction line shapes, and for low diffraction angles (2θ values from 0° to 15°) some diffraction lines may appear as doublets, as the reflected beam from either side of the sample is recorded on the film while that from the centre is absorbed within the sample.

In strongly absorbing samples, (with μr values of 4 to 10 or more) there may be quite serious interference with the formation of the diffraction pattern.

In Table II are compared the absorption coefficients, and μr values for cylindrical specimens of $r = 0.4$ mm, for the substances whose study has been attempted. These values indicate the magnitude of sample absorption effects. The figures are of limited precision since they are proportional to density which varies on compression and also varies from one crystal form to another, as for instance with potassium nitrate.

TABLE II. X-ray Absorption Coefficients of Sample Materials

Material	Mo Kα radiation		Co Kα radiation	
	μ cm^{-1}	μr	μ cm^{-1}	μr
CsI	347	13·9	1 122	44·9
CsClO$_4$	222	8·9	418	16·7
RbI	218	8·7	820	32·8
RbCl	193	7·7	296	11·9
KI	106	4·2	1 175	47·0
KNO$_3$	15·4	0·6	132	5·3
AgI	194	7·8	1 542	60·2
HgSe	925	37	1 468	59
Bi	1 422	57	2 480	99
Cd	258	10·3	2 020	81
Ce	359	14·4	2 810	112
94% WC–6% Co	1 427	57	2 585	103
Zinc stearate	6·3	0·25	11·1	0·45

Values of μr are calculated for $r = 0.04$ cm.

C. Practical Designs

A number of attempts have been made to combine the conflicting requirements of a strong pressure wall and minimal interference with transmission of radiation.

In an early approach, Frevel (1935) proposed the use of pyrex glass capillary tubes to contain materials for study with copper radiation while under pressure. Experiments with CsI showed that pressures of about 1 kb could be reached, enough for some compressibilities to be studied by changes in lattice constant.

In a later development, Jacobs (1938) filled a powder camera assembly with helium under pressure, and studied transformations in AgI, and RbI; copper K radiation was used for studies up to 5 kb. For this assembly, it was essential to purify the helium filling the camera. Even at a purity of 99·72%, the remaining 0·28% of other gases was still responsible for nearly 20% of the X-ray absorption in the pressure medium.

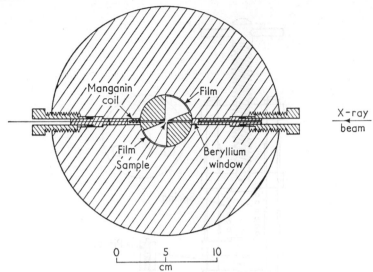

FIG. 1. Pressurized Camera used by Jacobs. (Reproduced with permission from Jacobs, 1938.)

Figure 1 shows, in horizontal cross-section, the system used by Jacobs. To reduce the volume of compressed helium two quadrants of the camera were filled in. Slow decompression of the contents of the pressure vessel was necessary to avoid stripping emulsion from the film support.

However, Jacobs' system has a number of advantages. The X-ray beam encounters the beryllium pressure window before meeting the camera collimator system, so that much of the radiation scattered by the beryllium does not affect the film. A small manganin gauge within the camera pressure system makes fairly accurate measurement of pressure possible; and further, the diameter of the sample may be varied to control the effects of absorption by the sample.

Muller (1941) constructed a cylindrical containing-apparatus of beryllium powder and bakelite surrounded by a steel jacket. Pressure was transmitted to the system by oil which supplied the force to a steel piston bearing on the sample. Radiations from silver and copper targets were used to study the compression of crystalline paraffins up to pressures of 1·5 kb.

Much greater pressures were reached by Lawson and Riley (1949) who constructed a pressure vessel of large-grained beryllium metal and developed the pressure by the thrust on a piston moved by a simple press screwed by hand: the apparatus, with the camera removed, is shown in Fig. 2. They used this assembly with molybdenum radiation to study silver iodide, and cerium and cadmium metals, up to 15 kb.

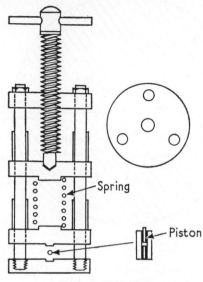

Beryllium bomb

Fig. 2 Lawson and Riley's beryllium vessel and press. (Reproduced with permission from Lawson and Riley, 1949.)

The large-grained beryllium gave rise to " splotchy " background exposure of the photographic film. Fine-grained beryllium gave a more even background exposure, but often obliterated all diffraction lines from the sample.

A single crystal beryllium vessel gives much more satisfactory photographs. Lawson and Ting Yuan Tang (1950) used a monocrystalline beryllium pressure vessel, and reached 10 kb. However, the hole which contains the sample needs to be drilled along the direction of the six-fold axis of symmetry, otherwise the beryllium may split when pressure is applied (Guengant and Vodar, 1954).

In distinction from Jacobs' apparatus, in which the sample diameter may be varied, the systems used by Lawson and Riley and by Guengant and Vodar, among others, imply a standard sample diameter of 0·8 mm and difficulties are found with strongly absorbing samples. To some extent sample absorption can be overcome by using a mixture of sample substance and zinc stearate, in which the latter provides a solid lubricant and at the same time dilutes the sample making it less absorbent towards the radiation.

With this arrangement, Guengant and Vodar (1954) reached 10 kb pressure, and confirmed the observations by Jacobs (1938) of changes in AgI and RbI, also the transformation in KNO_3 at 3·7 kb. This study used molybdenum radiation.

Vereshchagin and Brandt (1956) constructed a steel-supported beryllium pressure vessel with pistons moved by a built-in hydraulic ram system, and with lithium metal to transmit the pressure. Capable of reaching 30 kb, this apparatus was used to examine the crystalline forms of bismuth above 25 kb.

A different form of high pressure X-ray camera (Kabalkina, 1959) in which a supported beryllium piston in a hydraulic system also acts as container for the sample, has been used to study the compression of normal paraffins to 13·5 kb.

This apparatus has also been used by Kabalkina and Vereshchagin (1960) to study the compressibility of graphite and boron nitride up to 16 kb; copper radiation was used.

A diamond pressure vessel offers some advantages over beryllium, particularly at extreme pressures. Lawson and Ting Yuan Tang (1950) found that a cylinder made from two diamonds clamped together extended their range of pressure to 23 kb.

A pressure vessel made from a single diamond drilled by wire-die techniques was developed by Jamieson (1957), who used molybdenum radiation to confirm transformations in potassium iodide at 18 kb.

These forms of apparatus use a cylindrical vessel, with a sample of standard diameter which may be diluted with zinc stearate. For some materials the high degree of dilution required reduces the intensity of reflections so much that they are masked by the pressure vessel absorption and scattering; no diffraction pattern at all can be obtained for mercuric selenide.

Jamieson and Lawson (1962) describe a much improved diamond cell constructed by Kasper and others. The system of a cylindrical hole through the diamond, terminating at ground flat surfaces, which characterizes Jamieson's pressure cell, is modified by the introduction of 60° conical entries which leave only a short cylindrical centre section 0·75 mm long and 0·38 mm diameter. A correspondingly conical piston, with short cylindrical termination, must be used.

This system reduces friction between piston, sample, and cylinder walls, and among other advantages it enables a piston of smaller end-diameter to be used without encountering difficulties from increased fragility. The system is shown in Fig. 3.

Jamieson and others (1959) have developed a radically different type of X-ray device. This uses a clamping technique to maintain the force in a pressure assembly of the " squeezer " type. Used with diamond anvils, as shown in Fig. 4, this apparatus overcomes some of the disadvantages due to absorption of radiation by the sample: one of the diamonds may be replaced by sapphire (corundum).

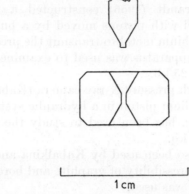

FIG. 3. Kasper's diamond cell, with one of the two conical pistons.
(Reproduced with permission from Kasper, *et al.*, 1960.)

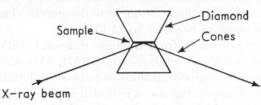

FIG. 4. Diamond anvil system. (Reproduced with permission
from Jamieson *et al.*, 1959.)

The apparatus may be used with a number of commercially made counter-diffractometers. A disadvantage of the system compared with Jamieson's single diamond containers is that the anvil system makes it more difficult to distinguish between intensity maxima due to the diamond and reflections due to the sample. A very high rate of failure of the diamond pistons is also a drawback.

With molybdenum radiation, the apparatus has been used successfully to record diffraction patterns up to pressures of 35 kb. Traces for bismuth are shown in Fig. 5. However, Jamieson (1961) notes inconsistencies between results obtained with a single diamond vessel and those obtained with diamond anvils which throw doubt on results from the latter apparatus.

A recent review by Jamieson and Lawson (1962) describes some of the more recently designed apparatus together with some of the results obtained by their use. These authors conclude that the single diamond cell constructed by Kasper and others is, so far, the most successful design.

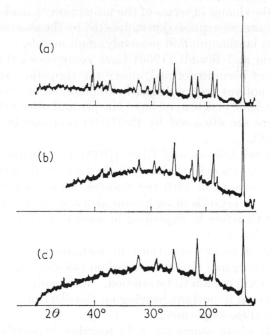

FIG. 5. Diffraction traces from Bismuth (*a*) Sample on sapphire, diamond removed. (*b*) Bi I, after exposure to pressure. (*c*) Bi II, at 27 kb. (Reproduced with permission from Jamieson *et al.*, 1959).

III. Results and Developments

A. *General Remarks*

Although a substantial number of papers have described apparatus for X-ray studies at high pressures, in comparison the structural information published has been dissappointingly sparse. The results may be summarized under headings divided according to the different types of bonding.

B. *Metallic and Covalent Crystals*

In earlier studies, notably those of Bridgman, a number of phase changes in metals were revealed by discontinuous changes of volume or electrical conductivity with rising pressure.

Lawson and Ting Yuan Tang (1949) reported that metallic cerium crystallized with the face-centred cubic structure both above and below the transition at 12·5 kb, although with a large change in lattice constant. This transition is therefore attributed to some rearrangement in the electronic structure of the cerium atoms. These authors (1950) account for the change in terms of the promotion of an electron from the 4f to the 5d state, an explanation supported by the absence of observable transitions in lanthanum and praseodymium metals.

Vereschagin and Brandt (1956) have commenced the study of the solid phases of bismuth formed above the transition at 25 kb; their results have not yet been published. Jamieson and others (1959) have attacked the same problem, as have Kasper and others (1960); some of the difficulties are discussed by the latter and also by Jamieson and Lawson (1962).

Jacobs (1938), Lawson and Riley (1949), and Jamieson (1957) have all observed that there is no change in pattern of diffraction for metallic cadmium to correspond with the volume change noted by Bridgman (1925) for single crystals of cadmium at 3 kb. This apparent volume change must therefore be explained in some terms other than a change of crystal lattice.

A number of other transitions in metallic phases, notably those reported by Bridgman (1949) for caesium (45 kb), barium (60 kb), and antimony (85 kb) remain to be studied. The results of such studies are likely to have an important bearing on the electronic configuration of the atoms in these structures.

In crystals whose atoms are held together by continuous chemical bonding, extending throughout the crystal and largely covalent in character, the rearrangement of bonding to form a new phase requires a considerable activation energy. Phase changes may be brought about by elevated temperatures in addition to high pressures, but rarely by the latter alone. However, the resulting changes do not revert when the pressure is released after cooling. In consequence, phase changes in this type of material can be studied by the usual procedures of crystal investigation and do not require special apparatus for studies under pressure. The conversions of hexagonal boron nitride into cubic borazon, and of graphite into diamond, are phase changes of this type, as are the formation of dense varieties of silica: coesite, keatite, and stishovite.

C. *Ionic Crystals*

Many substances in this group have been investigated, often for the geological significance of the results. Jacobs (1938) obtained a series of lattice spacing values for the high pressure form of AgI, (above 3 kb), showing this to have the rock salt structure; at normal pressure and room temperature this compound has the zinc blende structure. Lawson and Riley have confirmed this observation.

Jacobs also obtained diffraction patterns for the high pressure form of $CsClO_4$ (at 2·5 kb) but without being able to work out the structure: this remains to be done. For RbI the results confirmed earlier suppositions that the form above 4·5 kb had the CsCl type of structure, as opposed to the NaCl type at low pressures.

Guengant and Vodar (1954) confirmed that the transitions in AgI and RbI can be studied by X-ray techniques under pressure. They also observed diffraction lines from KNO_3 above the transition at 3·7 kb, but obtained data insufficient for determination of the structure.

Jamieson (1957) used diamond vessels to observe the transformation of KI at 18 kb from the NaCl to the CsCl form. He also studied the transitions in KNO_3, which may be analogous to the geologically important $CaCO_3$. The structures of KNO_3 I and KNO_3 III are known; further, at room temperature and pressure the stable form (KNO_3 II) has the aragonite structure. For comparison with this, Jamieson (1956) obtained diffraction patterns from KNO_3 IV at 4·7 kb and at 12 kb. An orthorhombic structure was indicated, which is analogous to the structure of $RbNO_3$ at atmospheric pressures.

When aragonite or vaterite (a hexagonal form of $CaCO_3$) were taken to 24 kb at room temperature, no transitions were observed. However, the diffraction pattern of calcite showed a slow modification starting at 15 kb and continuing to 22 kb: the transition from calcite I to calcite II is involved. Jamieson concluded that calcite II may be an anion-disordered form of normal calcite.

D. *Molecular Crystals*

Together with the ionic systems, it is with molecular crystals that X-ray studies of materials while under pressure should be of most value from the structural point of view. However there has been a disappointing absence of results in this field.

Particular interest attaches to the high pressure forms of ice. McFarlan (1936) produced ice forms II and III under pressure and stabilized them by cooling in liquid air. His conclusions from X-ray diffraction studies are contradicted by more recent findings of Kamb and Datta (1960). In Chapter 5.iii of this book, Dr. R. S. Bradley reviews the structural data obtained for ice by these investigators.

Besides structural information, the study of molecular crystals has yielded information on the intermolecular repulsion forces. Muller (1941) studied *n*-paraffins up to 1·5 kb, and found that the linear compressibilities were much higher in a plane normal to the chain axis (3 to 12×10^{-12} cm²/dyn) than in the direction of the chain (3×10^{-13} cm²/dyn).

Kabalkina (1959) studied the variation in lattice dimensions for

L

crystalline specimens of the even paraffins n-$C_{30}H_{62}$ and n-$C_{32}H_{66}$ up to 13·5 kb, and found that the compression along the direction of the molecular chain is negligible in comparison with that perpendicular to the chain. This agrees with Muller's results which were for the odd paraffins n-$C_{23}H_{48}$ and n-$C_{29}H_{60}$.

Kabalkina found that at 7 kb there appears to be a sharp change in the compressibility although there is no abrupt volume change. Both at high and low pressures, when these are isotropic, the even paraffins exhibit a rhombic sub-cell. However, under conditions in which pressures of 7–10 kb are non-isotropic, both rhombic and triclinic modifications appear together.

The compression of graphite in a direction perpendicular to the planes, that is along the c axis, is similar in some ways to the compression of molecular crystals. This compression has been studied by Kabalkina and Vereshchagin (1960) both for graphite and for the hexagonal form of boron nitride. The results for graphite indicate that the van der Waals radius of the carbon atom decreases from 1·68 Å at 1 bar to 1·63 Å at 15 kb.

These authors find that the compression data are expressed satisfactorily by a second order equation.

$$\Delta c/c = ap - bp^2. \tag{4}$$

For pressure in kb, $a = 28·5 \times 10^{-4}$, $b = 46·6 \times 10^{-6}$ for graphite, and $a = 34·6 \times 10^{-4}$, $b = 55·9 \times 10^{-6}$ for boron nitride.

E. *Further Developments*

1. *Single Crystal Work*

There is an interesting possibility that X-ray diffraction work with single crystals might be done at these high pressures. As Jamieson (1956, p. 71) has pointed out, this becomes feasible when recrystallization takes place in the pressure vessel, yielding a small number of large crystals of the high pressure phase, as with KNO_3. This possibility is both real and important for substances such as KNO_3, and for molecular crystals such as those of the ice–water system; its realization will require much further work.

REFERENCES

Bridgman, P. W. (1925). *Proc. Amer. Acad. Arts Sci.* **60**, 303.
Bridgman, P. W. (1949). " The Physics of High Pressure ", (Second Printing) p. 421, G. Bell and Sons, London.
Frevel, L. K. (1935). *Rev. sci. Instrum.* **6**, 214.
Guengant, L., and Vodar, B. (1954). *C. R. Acad. Sci., Paris* **239**, 431.

Jacobs, R. B. (1938). *Phys. Rev.* **54**, 325, 468.

Jamieson, J. C. (1956). *Z. Kristallogr.* **107**, 65.

Jamieson, J. C. (1957). *J. Geol.* **65**, 334.

Jamieson, J. C. (1961). *In* " Progress in Very High Pressure Research ", Proceedings of a conference at Bolton Landing, Lake George, N.Y. U.S.A. June 1960, John Wiley, New York.

Jamieson, J. C., and Lawson, A. W. (1962). *In* " Modern Very High Pressure Techniques ", (R. H. Wentorf, ed.) pp. 70–92, Butterworths, London.

Jamieson, J. C., Lawson, A. W., and Nachtrieb, N. D. (1959). *Rev. sci. Instrum.* **30**, 1016.

Kabalkina, S. S. (1959). *C. R. Acad. Sci. U.R.S.S.* **125**, (1) 114.

Kabalkina, S. S., and Vereshchagin, L. F. (1960). *C. R. Acad. Sci. U.R.S.S.* **131**, (2) 300; **134**, (2) 330. (*Soviet Physics—Doklady* **5**, 373; 1065.)

Kamb, W. B., and Datta, S. K. (1960). *Nature, Lond.* **187**, 140.

Kasper, J. S., Hilliard, J. E., Cahn, J. W., and Phillips, V. A. (1960). WADC Technical Report No. 59–747, General Electric Co. Schenectady, U.S.A.

Lawson, A. W., and Riley, N. A. (1949). *Rev. sci. Instrum.* **20**, 763.

Lawson, A. W., and Ting Yuan Tang, (1949). *Phys. Rev.* **76**, 301. (1950). *Rev. sci. Instrum.* **21**, 815.

McFarlan, R. L. (1936). *J. chem. Phys.* **4**, 60; 253.

Muller, A. (1941). *Proc. roy. Soc.* **178**, 227.

Nelson, J. B. (1955). *In* " X-ray Diffraction by Polycrystalline Materials " (H. S. Peiser, H. P. Rooksby and A. J. C. Wilson, eds.) pp. 78–121, Chapman and Hall, London.

Vereshchagin, L. F., and Brandt, I. V. (1956). *C. R. Acad. Sci. U.R.S.S.* **108**, (3) 423. (*Soviet Physics—Doklady* **1**, 312).

Chapter 10.iii

OTHER MISCELLANEOUS EFFECTS OF PRESSURE

R. S. BRADLEY

School of Chemistry, University of Leeds, England

I. ELECTRICAL POLARIZATION AT HIGH PRESSURES

A. *The Dielectric Constant and Refractive Index of Gases*

A typical apparatus for measuring the dielectric constant of gases up to 3 000 Mc and 500 atm is described by Vallauri and Fosbergh (1957) and is shown in Fig. 1; a quartz-metal seal was used.

According to the theory of Debye the Clausius-Mosotti function $(\epsilon - 1)V/(\epsilon + 2)$, where ϵ is the dielectric constant at static field and V the molar volume, should remain constant with increasing pressure, and should be given by

$$(\epsilon - 1)V/(\epsilon + 2) = \tfrac{4}{3}\pi N[\alpha_0 + \mu_0^2/(3kT)], \tag{1}$$

where α_0 is the mean molecular polarizability and μ_0 the dipole moment. Experiment shows that $(\epsilon - 1)V/(\epsilon + 2)$ rises and then falls with increasing pressure. Departures from constancy arise from molecular interactions and are expressed by the equation

$$(\epsilon - 1)V/(\epsilon + 2) = \tfrac{4}{3}\pi N[\alpha_0 + \mu_0^2/(3kT)] + B/V + C/V^2. \tag{2}$$

The coefficients B, C etc. have been called " dielectric virial coefficients " by Buckingham and Pople (1956) by analogy with the coefficients in the virial expansion of the equation of state.

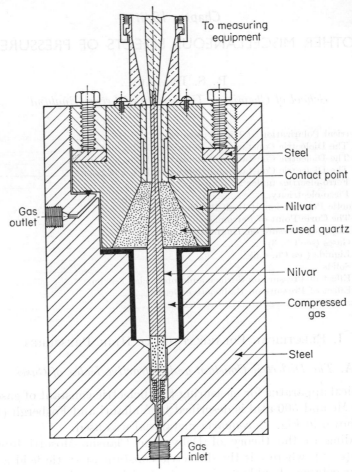

Fig. 1. Apparatus of Vallauri and Forsbergh for measuring the dielectric constant of gases at high pressure. (Reproduced with permission from Vallauri and Forsbergh, 1957.)

For non-dipolar gases and for those which also have no permanent multipoles the value of B has been derived by Kirkwood (1936) and has been discussed by Böttcher (1952), by de Boer and others (1953), by Jansen and Mazur (1955) and by Buckingham (1956). The term containing B arises partly from a change of polarizability of a molecule in the neighbourhood of another, and partly by the induction of a dipole in a neighbouring molecule, and these effects are usually small; B has been found experimentally to be nearly zero for helium and argon (Oudemans and Cole, 1959).

For dipolar gases Buckingham and Pople (1956) showed that

$$3\Omega B = 4\pi N^2 \int \{ [\tfrac{1}{2}\alpha_{12} - \alpha_0] + [\tfrac{1}{2}(\mu_1 + \mu_2)^2 - \mu_0^2]/(3kT) \} \exp[-u(\tau)/kT] \, d\tau \quad (3)$$

where α_{12} is the polarizability of an interacting molecular pair, $\mu_1 + \mu_2$ the corresponding resultant dipole moment, μ_0 the permanent dipole moment, τ the molecular configuration, Ω the integral over angular co-ordinates, and $u(\tau)$ the intermolecular potential energy.

For molecules with permanent dipoles the temperature dependent term of B should be dominant and should be positive. Observed negative values, as with methyl fluoride, can be explained by the formation at high pressures of dimers with balanced dipoles.

There is also a temperature dependent dipolar term in B with molecules such as carbon dioxide, which has a permanent quadrupole moment. This quadrupole moment induces a dipole moment in a neighbouring molecule (Buckingham and Pople, 1955). The contributions to B from the temperature independent and dependent terms are respectively 8 and 38 cm^6/mole^2 for carbon dioxide, in comparison with 36 ± 3 cm^6/mole^2 observed experimentally for B.

The refractive index (n) at optical frequencies may be treated in a similar manner and the Lorentz-Lorenz function $(n^2 - 1)V/(n^2 + 2)$ may be expanded in terms of virial coefficients, giving a value of B as before, with the omission of terms in μ (strictly n should be extrapolated to the value at zero frequency). The work of Michels and co-workers (1937, 1947a, b, 1949) shows that the Lorentz-Lorenz function decreases at high pressures as the pressure increases. With ethylene the Lorentz-Lorenz function passes through a maximum (Michels et al., 1947b). Part of this change arises from a decrease in polarizability by the influence of the field of neighbouring molecules. With polar gases these effects become apparent in the range 0–50 cm of Hg (Blythe et al., 1960).

Ashton and Guggenheim (1956) suggest that with sufficient accuracy

$$\frac{n^2 - 1}{n^2 + 2} \frac{RT}{p} = P_0 \left(1 - \frac{B'p}{RT} \right), \quad (4)$$

where P_0 is independent of temperature and B' is the virial coefficient of the equation $pV = RT(1 + B'/V + C'/V^2)$. In this way, on this assumption, second virial coefficients B' may be calculated from measurements of n and p, without the necessity for measurements of density. It should be noted that the coefficient B of Buckingham and Pople has not the same dimensions as B'.

B. *The Dielectric Constant and Refractive Index of Liquids*

The static dielectric constant of liquids increases and the Clausius-Mosotti function decreases with increasing pressure. Owen and Brinkley (1943) and Owen (1944) showed that the data of Kyropoulos (1926) and of Danforth (1931) could be fitted to the equation

$$1/\epsilon_1 - 1/\epsilon_p = A \ln (B_1 + p)/(B_1 + H), \qquad (5)$$

where A is approximately independent of temperature and A and B_1 are independent of pressure. This equation is analogous to Tait's equation giving the density (ρ) as a function of the pressure for liquids

$$1/\rho_1 - 1/\rho_p = C_1 \ln (B_1 + p)/(B_1 + 1), \qquad (6)$$

where C_1 is constant. It is remarkable that B_1 is the same for both sets of data. Even for such an abnormal liquid as water the data fit Eq. (5) up to 6 000 atm (Scaife, 1955 and Hamann, 1957b). According to Rosen (1949) a somewhat better fit of the data for a number of liquids is obtained by the use of the equation

$$(\epsilon_p + 2)/(\epsilon_p + 1) - (\epsilon_1 + 2)(\epsilon_1 + 1) = A' \ln (B_1' + p)/(B_1' + 1). \qquad (7)$$

The Lorentz-Lorenz function for liquids decreases with increasing pressure. Rosen (1947) has measured the refractive indices of ethyl alcohol and of water and mixtures of these at 25° C and up to 1 800 atm. A good fit with the experimental data is obtained using a modified Tait equation as above, with n^2 replacing ϵ.

C. *The Dielectric Constant and Refractive Index of Solids*

In contrast to the effect of pressure on the dielectric constant of gases and liquids the dielectric constant of solids decreases with increasing pressure. This is because the density changes much less than with a gas or liquid and the main effect arises from a decrease in polarizability and from a change in the inner field.

With ionic solids the change in polarizability of the ions is revealed by photo-elastic studies (Mueller 1935; see below), and the relative change in polarizability is about half the relative change in density. Mayburg (1950, 1951) has measured the dielectric constant of a number of alkali halides and of magnesium oxide at 1 000 c/s at room temperature and up to 8 000 bars. At these long wavelengths most of the polarization arises from the relative movement of positive and negative ions. If α_0 is the polarizability of the ions per unit volume and α the lattice polarizability per unit volume, Mott and Littleton (1938; cf. Mayburg, 1950) showed that

$$(\epsilon - 1)/4\pi = [24\pi\alpha\alpha_0(\gamma - 1) + 9(\alpha + \alpha_0)]/[9 - 12\pi(\alpha + \alpha_0) + 16\pi^2\alpha\alpha_0(1 - \gamma^2)], \quad (8)$$

where γ is a parameter which changes with pressure and which allows for departure from the Lorentz field, for which $\gamma = 1$, in terms of overlap between adjacent ions. The effective polarizing field F is then related to the electric field E in the medium by the equation

$$F = E + \tfrac{4}{3}\gamma P, \quad (9)$$

where P is the total polarization per unit volume. Unfortunately γ is not known and must be determined by comparing theory and experiment. The value of γ is found to be considerably less than unity and decreases with increasing pressure, as would be expected from the increasing ionic overlap.

Reitzel (1956) found that the Clausius-Mosotti function for vitreous silica decreased linearly with increasing pressure up to $4\,000$ kg/cm^2 at $2\,500$ c/s with a slope independent of temperature.

Under hydrostatic pressure the optical refractive index (n) of ionic crystals increases. The observed value of n is less than that calculated by means of the Lorentz-Lorenz function, and experimental results can be explained by assuming a decrease in polarizability of the ions as the pressure increases (Mueller, 1935). These changes of refractive index for a crystal under hydrostatic pressure may be calculated from observations of the photo-elastic effect. When a cubic crystal is compressed by a thrust normal to a cube face the crystal becomes doubly refracting, partly because of the anisotropy of the electrical forces, partly because of the anisotropy of the polarization at optical frequencies arising from the compression.

Waxler and Adams (1961) have studied the effect of uniaxial pressure up to $10\,000$ bars on the rate of relaxation of birefringence in glassy polymers. The rate of decay is reduced by increase in pressure and is inhibited completely by a pressure of $10\,000$ bars with poly-allyl-diglycoll-carbonate.

D. *Ferro-electrics under Pressure*

A number of crystals such as potassium dihydrogen phosphate, barium titanate and Rochelle salt show spontaneous polarization below a so-called Curie temperature (Rochelle salt has two such points). Just above this temperature (T_c) a large rise in static dielectric constant occurs, as represented by the equation

L*

$$\epsilon = \text{const} + \text{const}/(T - T_c), \tag{10}$$

which is similar to the Curie-Weiss law of ferromagnetism.

Bancroft (1938) showed that both Curie temperatures of Rochelle salt were raised linearly with increasing pressure up to 10 000 atm, and these results were interpreted by Merz (1950) in terms of second-order theory. Merz calculates from the equation (cf. Eq. 38, Ch. 5.iii)

$$\mathrm{d}p/\mathrm{d}T = \Delta C_p/(VT\Delta\alpha), \tag{11}$$

where V is the molar volume at T_c and ΔC_p and $\Delta\alpha$ are the changes in molar specific heat and volume expansion coefficient on passing through the Curie point, that the change in specific heat is 14×10^{-3} and $4\cdot1 \times 10^{-3}$ cal/g degree for the upper and lower Curie points respectively, in good agreement with the experiments of Wilson (1938). Merz studied barium titanate up to 5 000 atm and calculated in the same way on the assumption that the transition is second order that a specific heat change of $4\cdot9 \times 10^{-3}$ cal/g degree occurs. The Curie temperature is lowered by increasing pressure, in contrast to the results of Forsbergh (1954) who found that if a disc of barium titanate is subjected to a pressure exerted along the edge and not on the face, so that there is no thrust along the c axis, the transition temperature is raised. Jaffe and co-workers (1957) found that the Curie temperature of a polycrystalline barium titanate ceramic is raised quadratically by an increase in pressure. They interpreted their results in terms of a combined linear and quadratic effect, the latter arising from domain alignment. Presumably domain alignment contributes to the results of Forsbergh.

Jona and Shirane (1960) have measured the effect of hydrostatic pressures up to 2 700 atm on the transition temperature of triglycine sulphate $(CH_2.NH_2.COOH)_3.H_2SO_4$ and the isomorphous selenate. Although the transition temperatures are raised linearly by increasing pressure there is no change in the Curie-Weiss constant. The square of the spontaneous polarization is a linear function of pressure at constant temperature.

E. *Piezo-electricity* (cf. Cady 1946; Mason 1950)

Piezo-electricity was discovered by J. and P. Curie in 1880. Certain crystals when compressed in one particular direction, or when twisted, develop electrification on some of the crystal faces, examples being quartz, Rochelle salt, potassium dihydrogen phosphate, tourmaline, lactose, zinc blende, ammonium chloride and sodium chlorate. Voigt developed the phenomenological theory and interest in the subject was revived by its application by Langevin to ultrasonics. The polarization is proportional to the field and changes sign with it, and it follows as a reciprocal effect that a piezo-electric crystal will be strained by an electric field. This distinguishes the converse piezo-electric effect from electrostriction, which is common to solids, liquids and gases, and for which the deformations are proportional to the square of the field. Piezo-electric crystals lack a centre of symmetry, but the molecular theory is still in a rudimentary state. Gibbs (1926) gave an estimate of the polarization in terms of the displacement of charges and obtained a result for quartz which was four times too large. However, he assumed that the binding was entirely ionic, and later calculations by Machlup and Christopher (1961) show that the piezo-electric effect may be explained on the basis of an effective charge about one-sixth of that for pure ionic binding. The resonance frequency (f) of a quartz crystal changes under hydrostatic pressure because of changes in the dimensions and in the elastic constants. Michels and Pérez (1951) using nitrogen as a pressure medium up to $1\,000$ kg/cm^2 found that $\Delta f/(f \Delta p)$ is $8\cdot03 \times 10^{-6}$ cm^2/kg for the AT cut and $-2\cdot03 \times 10^{-6}$ cm^2/kg for the BT cut. Susse (1955) calculated from her measurements on the AT, BT and γ cut crystals at pressures up to $1\,000$ kg/cm^2 the changes in the elastic constants. These experiments suggest a method for measuring high pressures.

Many of these effects of pressure are inter-related, although it is often convenient to consider them separately. The mechanical, thermal, electric and magnetic effects form a thermodynamic network. There are also many close analogies between electric and magnetic phenomena and a brief account will be given in the next section of the effect of pressure on the magnetic Curie point, which is of considerable importance in geophysics.

II. MAGNETIC POLARIZATION AT HIGH PRESSURE

A. *The Curie Point of Ferromagnetic Crystals*

According to Heisenberg's theory ferromagnetism arises from a positive exchange interaction which is necessarily pressure-dependent, since the interaction is sensitive to interatomic distance. The exchange interaction is usually represented qualitatively by a curve of the type due to Bethe (1933), which gives the interaction in terms of the ratio interatomic distance/diameter of the unfilled shell, and which is shown for a number of elements in Fig. 2. Ferromagnetism is not possible for very small or very large values of this ratio. A similar type of curve is obtained by plotting the Curie temperatures *versus* the same abscissa (Bozorth, 1940). An effect of pressure on the Curie temperature necessarily implies the reciprocal effect of volume magnetostriction. Moreover, the loss of ferromagnetism above the Curie point gives an abnormal expansion coefficient just above this point.

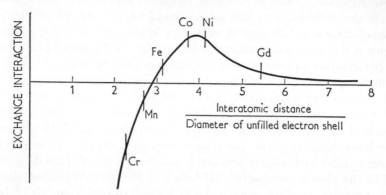

FIG. 2. Exchange interaction curve for ferromagnetics. (Reproduced with permission from Lee, 1955.)

Slater (1940) discussed the transition at the Curie point in terms of first order thermodynamics, and having estimated the volume and entropy change calculated that dT/dp would be 0·05° per 1 000 atm for nickel. A more realistic approach in terms of second-order theory gives a theoretical value of 0·35° per 1 000 atm (Michels and de Groot, 1950). An attempt has been made by Kornetzki (1935) to relate dT/dp to his measurements of volume magnetostriction at 20–100° C, which gives $dT/dp = 5$–$10°$ per 1 000 atm for iron. It should be remembered, however, that these measurements were made at a much lower temperature than the Curie temperature of iron, 770° C.

Most of these theoretical predictions are incorrect in the light of the experiments of Patrick (1954) in which, following Adams and Green (1931), the sample was made the core of a transformer. A constant 1 000 cycle a.c. was supplied to the primary and there was a sharp drop in the output in the secondary at the Curie temperature. Pressure equipment made use of a liquid medium with external heating up to 400° C, and argon with internal heating up to 1 120° C; pressures up to 9 000 atm were used. Values of dT/dp for Fe, Co, Ni and Gd were respectively $0 \pm 0·1°$, $0 \pm 1°$, $0·35 \pm 0·02°$ and $-1·2 \pm 0·05°$, all per 1 000 atm, which may be compared with the theoretical values above. It appears that although the form of interaction curve for any one substance is correct, the positions of the elements on the generalized curves of Bozorth and of Néel need revision (for a further discussion see Smoluchowski, 1941a, b, 1954; Lee, 1955).

III. THE EFFECT OF PRESSURE ON THERMAL CONDUCTIVITY

A. *Gases* (see Chapter 3)

B. *Liquids* (see Chapter 4.ii)

C. *Solids*

Thermal conduction in solids arises partly from electronic and partly from atomic motion, and at high temperatures there may be a significant contribution from radiation passing through the solids. The theory is one of the most difficult and complex in physics.

With insulators at a sufficiently low temperature the electronic contribution is negligible. Measurements may be made by a modification of the method used by Bridgman for liquids; the solid is machined into a cylindrical tube through which heat passes radially. The effect of pressure on the thermal conductivity is much less than with liquids.

These measurements and the theoretical background are of importance in calculating the flow of heat in the Earth. The theory is based on the early work of Debye, who regarded the solid as a system of coupled oscillators transmitting thermo-elastic waves. Whereas for an ideal lattice with simple harmonic motion of the atoms the conductivity would be infinite, in actual lattice anharmonic motion decreases the conductivity by the coupling of the vibrations. This work was extended in terms of quantum theory by Peierls (1955). At temperatures large compared with the Debye characteristic temperature the conductivity is inversely proportional to the absolute temperature. Pomeranchuk (1941) however, derives a proportionality to $T^{-3/2}$ on the basis of an interatomic potential expressed as a power series of atomic displacement and taken as far as the fourth power in displacement; according to Herring (1954) this work is vitiated by a neglect of elastic anisotropy. The pressure effect according to these theories follows from the effect on the lattice spacing and on the velocity of sound.

Provided that the opacity is assumed to be independent of wavelength, radiative transfer gives a thermal conductivity $\lambda = \frac{16}{3} n^2 s T^3 / E$, where E is the extinction coefficient, n the refractive index and s the Stefan-Boltzmann constant. The pressure effect follows from the effect on n and on E. Although radiative and other forms of conduction are treated independently they are, in fact, inter-related. (For discussions of radiative transfer, see Kellett, 1952; Clark, 1956, 1957; McQuarrie, 1954).

With metals the contribution from electrons predominates, the conductivity arising from free electrons being given by $\lambda = \frac{1}{3} \pi^2 (k/e)^2 \sigma T$, where σ is the specific electrical conductivity and e the electronic charge. Experiments on the pressure effect are mainly of interest with respect to variation of $\lambda/(\sigma T)$. Because of the high thermal conductivity it is necessary to use a longitudinal method in which the specimen, in the form of a long rod, is mounted in the centre of a pressure cylinder with one end in a copper block and the other containing a small heating coil. Starr (1938) found that the ratio of thermal to electrical conductivity did in fact remain substantially constant with increasing pressure at constant temperature, up to $12\,000$ kg/cm². This work supersedes that of Bridgman (1922) who found that the Wiedmann-Franz ratio could either increase or decrease with increasing pressure. The dependence of thermal conductivity of metals on pressure can thus be related directly to the dependence of electrical resistance, already discussed.

IV. THE EFFECT OF PRESSURE ON SURFACE AND INTERFACIAL TENSION

According to thermodynamics the change of surface tension γ with pressure is given by

$$(\partial\gamma/\partial p)_{A,\,T} = (\partial V/\partial A)_{p,\,T}, \tag{14}$$

where A is the area of the interface and V the total volume. For a one-component system, in equilibrium with its vapour, change in surface tension with increasing pressure at constant temperature appears meaningless. The use of a second component to act as a " pressure transmitting medium " gives a solution in the liquid and adsorption at the interface of the second component.

Some experimental work has been done on interfacial tension at a range of pressure for liquids such as benzene and water, for which, it should be remembered, mutual solution occurs. Harvey (1958) studied this system by the use of the pendant drop method at 31–95° C and up to 1 360 atm. This work extends the range of pressure used by Michaels and Hauser (1951). Other hydrocarbon–water systems have been studied by Hough et al. (1951) and by Hassan et al. (1953).

V. THE EFFECT OF PRESSURE ON RADIOACTIVE DECAY

Radioactive decay rates are usually considered to be independent of the environment and to be unaffected by changes in pressure and temperature. This, however, is a matter of degree, and in recent years certain decay constants have been found to be dependent on the chemical environment and to change with the ambient pressure.

Bainbridge and co-workers (1951, 1953) studied the isomeric transition in ^{99}Tc, which occurs with internal conversion, i.e. the γ-ray photon emerging from the nucleus has a certain probability of ejecting an electron from the K, L etc., shell. It was found that the decay constant of Tc in KTcO$_4$ was greater than that of the metal by a factor $1 + 0 \cdot 0030 \pm 0 \cdot 0001$. Slater (1951) suggested that only those electrons within $0 \cdot 2$ Å of the nucleus contributed effectively to the probability of conversion. The Tc atom in KTcO$_4$ behaved as if it were compressed in comparison with that in Tc metal.

Bainbridge (1952) made a brief report on the effect of pressure on the isomeric transition of ^{99}Tc and later provided experimental data for comparison with the theory of Porter and McMillan (1960). These authors calculated that the contribution to internal conversion comes mainly from the 3p and 3d levels, but that the principal contribution to the change with pressure comes from the valency electrons, particularly 4p, 4d and 5s. They assumed that the internal conversion coefficient which gives the ratio of the number of electrons to γ-photons emitted per second, is a linear function of pressure, and found for 100 000 bars a fractional decrease in half life of $(2-4) \times 10^{-4}$ in good agreement with Bainbridge's experimental result of $2 \cdot 3 \pm 0 \cdot 5 \times 10^{-4}$.

Radioactive decay by K-capture is also a process affected by the chemical environment and ambient pressure. Christiansen et al. (1962) found for ^{7}Be and ^{131}Ba respectively fractional increases in the decay constants of $2 \cdot 5 \times 10^{-8}$ and $1 \cdot 3 \times 10^{-8}$ per atmosphere.

REFERENCES

Adams, L. A., and Green, J. W. G. (1931). *Phil. Mag.* **12**, 361.
Ashton, N. H. M., and Guggenheim, E. A. (1956). *Proc. Phys. Soc. B* **69**, 693.
Bainbridge, K. T. (1952). *Phys. Rev.* **86**, 582T.
Bainbridge, K. T., Goldhaber, M., and Wilson, E. (1951). *Phys. Rev.* **84**, 1260.
Bainbridge, K. T., Goldhaber, M., and Wilson, E. (1953). *Phys. Rev.* **90**, 430.
Bancroft, D. (1938). *Phys. Rev.* **53**, 587.
Bethe, H. (1933). "Handbuch der Physik". Vol. 24. Springer, Berlin.
Blythe, A. R., Lambert, J. D., Petter, P. J., and Spoel, H. (1960). *Proc. roy. Soc.* *A***245**. 427.
Bottcher, C. J. F. (1952). "The Theory of Electric Polarisation", Elsevier, Amsterdam.
Bozorth, R. M. (1940). *Bell Syst. tech. J.* **19**, 1.
Bridgman, P. W. (1922). *Proc. Amer. Acad. Arts Sci.* **57**, 77.
Buckingham, A. D. (1956). *Trans. Faraday Soc.* **52**, 1035.
Buckingham, A. D., and Pople, J. A. (1955). *Trans. Faraday Soc.* **51**, 1029.
Buckingham, A. D., and Pople, J. A. (1956). *Disc. Faraday Soc.* **22**, 17.
Cady, W. G. (1946). "Piezo-electricity", McGraw-Hill, New York.
Chapman, S., and Cowling, T. G. (1939). "The Mathematical Theory of Non-Uniform Gases ", p. 288. Cambridge University Press, London.
Christiansen, E. B., Kistler, S. S., and Gogarty, W. B. (1963). To be published.

Clark, S. P., Jr. (1956). *Bull. geol. Soc. Amer.* **67**, 1123.

Clark, S. P., Jr. (1957). *Trans. Amer. geophys. Union* **38**, 931.

Danforth, W. E. (1931). *Phys. Rev.* **38**, 1224.

de Boer, J., van der Maesen, F., and Ten Seldam, C. A. (1953). *Physica 's Grav.* **19**. 265.

Forsbergh, P. W., Jr. (1954). *Phys. Rev.* **93**, 686.

Gibbs, R. E. (1926). *Proc. roy. Soc.* A**110**, 443.

Hamann, S. D. (1957). " Physico-chemical Effects of Pressure ", p. 104, Butterworths, London.

Harvey, R. R. (1958). *J. phys. Chem.* **62**, 322.

Hassan, M. E., Nielsen, R. F., and Calhoun, J. C. (1953). *Trans. Amer. Inst. Min. (Metall.) Engrs.* **198**, 299.

Herring. C. (1954). *Phys. Rev.* **95**, 954.

Hough, E. W., Rzasa, M. J., and Wood, B. B. (1951). *Trans. Amer. Inst. Min. (Metall.) Engrs.* **192**, 57.

Jaffe, H., Berlincourt, D., and McKee, J. M. (1957). *Phys. Rev.* **105**, 57.

Jansen, L., and Mazur, P. (1955). *Physica 's Grav.* **21**. 193; 208.

Johannin, P., and Vodar, B. (1957). *Industr. Engng. Chem. (Industr.)* **49**, 2040.

Jona, F., and Shirane, G. (1960). *Phys. Rev.* **117**, 139.

Kellett, B. S. (1952). *J. opt. Soc. Amer.* **42**, 339.

Kirkwood, J. G. (1936). *J. chem. Phys.* **4**, 592.

Kirkwood, J. G. (1946). *J. chem. Phys.* **14**, 180; 347.

Kornetzki, M. K. (1935). *Z. Phys.* **98**, 289.

Kyropoulos, H. (1926). *Z. Phys.* **40**, 507.

Lambert, J. D., Staines, E. N., and Woods, S. D. (1950). *Proc. roy. Soc.* A**200**, 262.

Lee, E. W. (1955). *Rep. Progr. Phys. Lond.* **18**, 184.

Machlup, S., and Christopher, E. (1961). *J. appl. Phys.* **32**, 1387.

Mason, W. P. (1950). " Piezo-electric Crystals and Their Application to Ultrasonics ", van Nostrand, New York.

Mayburg, S. (1950). *Phys. Rev.* **79**, 375.

Mayburg, S. (1951). *Phys. Rev.* **83**, 1072.

McQuarrie, M. (1954). *J. Amer. ceram. Soc.* **37**, 91.

Merz, W. J. (1950). *Phys. Rev.* **78**, 52.

Michaels, A. S., and Hauser, E. A. (1951). *J. phys. Chem.* **55**, 408.

Michels, A., and Botzen, A. (1949). *Physica 's Grav.* **15**. 769.

Michels, A., and Botzen, A. (1952). *Physica 's Grav.* **18**. 605.

Michels, A., and Botzen, A. (1953). *Physica 's Grav.* **19**. 585.

Michels, A., and de Groot, S. R. (1950). *Physica 's Grav.* **16**. 249.

Michels, A., and Hamers, J. (1937). *Physica 's Grav.* **4**. 995.

Michels, A., and Pérez, J. P. (1951). *Physica 's Grav.* **17**. 563.

Michels, A., Lebesque, L., and de Groot, S. R. (1947a). *Physica 's Grav.* **13**. 337.

Michels, A., Botzen, A., and de Groot, S. R. (1947b). *Physica 's Grav.* **13**. 343.

Michels, A., Botzen, A., Friedman, A. S., and Sngers, J. V. (1956). *Physica 's Grav.* **22**. 121.

Mott, N. F., and Littleton, M. J. (1938). *Trans. Faraday Soc.* **34**, 485.

Mueller, H. (1935). *Phys. Rev.* **47**, 947.

Oudemans, G. J., and Cole, R. H. (1959). *J. chem. Phys.* **31**, 843.

Owen, B. B. (1944). *J. chem. Educ.* **21**, 58; 84.

Owen, B. B., and Brinkley, P. R. (1943). *Phys. Rev.* **64**, 32.

Patrick, L. (1954). *Phys. Rev.* **93**, 384.

Peierls, R. E. (1955). " The Quantum Theory of Solids ", Oxford University Press, London.

Pomeranchuk, J. (1941). *Phys. Rev.* **60**, 820.

Porter, R. A., and McMillan, W. G. (1960). *Phys. Rev.* **117**, 795.

Reitzel, J. (1956). *Nature, Lond.* **178**. 940.

Rosen, J. (1947). *J. opt. Soc. Amer.* **37**, 932.

Rosen, J. (1949). *J. chem. Phys.* **17**, 1192.

Saurel, J., Bergeon, R., Johannin, P., Dapoigny, J., Kieffer, J., and Vodar, B. (1956). *Disc. Faraday Soc.* **22**, 64.

Scaife, B. K. P. (1955). *Proc. phys. Soc.* B**68**, 790.

Schäfer, K., and Foz Gazula, O. R. (1942). *Z. phys. Chem.* B**52**, 299.

Sengers, J. V., and Machlup, S. (1958). *In* " Transport Processes in Statistical Mechanics " (I. Prigogine, ed.) pp. 376–381, Interscience, New York.

Slater, J. C. (1940). *Phys. Rev.* **58**, 54.

Slater, J. C. (1951). *Phys. Rev.* **84**, 1261.

Smoluchowski, R. (1941a). *Phys. Rev.* **59**. 309.

Smoluchowski, R. (1941b). *Phys. Rev.* **60**. 249.

Smoluchowski, R. (1954). *Phys. Rev.* **93**, 392.

Starr, C. S. (1938). *Phys. Rev.* **54**, 210.

Susse, C. (1955). *J. Phys. Rad.* **16**, 348.

Vallauri, M. G., and Forsbergh, P. W., Jr. (1957). *J. sci. Instrum.* **28**, 198.

Vines, R. G. (1953). *Austral. J. Chem.* **6**, 1.

Waxler, R. M., and Adams, L. H. (1961). *J. Res. nat. Bur. Stand.* **65**, 283.

Wilson, A. J. C. (1938). *Phys. Rev.* **54**, 1103.

AUTHOR INDEX

Numbers in italics refer to pages on which references are listed in full;
numbers in parentheses refer to to references listed in tables.

SUBJECT INDEX

A

Absorption coefficient, 314
 linear, 312, 313
Absorption of X-rays, 312–314
Acentric factor, 105
Acetals, 198
Acetic acid, 152, 155
Aceto-acetic ester, 145–146
Acid magmas, 11
Acoustic approximation, 223
 impedance relation, 221
Activation volume, 166–172, 173, 186,
 189–193, 201
Activity, 95–100, 134
Acyl azides, 175–176
Adiabat, curvature, 258
Adiabatic dissociation, 167
 sound velocity, 219
Aegirine, 65
Air, 101
Airshocks, 239
Albite, 22, 23, 34, 41, 284
 nepheline-quartz-jadeite system, 20–
 21
 orthoclase-water system, 23, 26
 water system, 26, 44
 carbon dioxide system, 30
 water-hydrogen fluoride system, 34–
 35, 46, 48
 orthoclase-quartz system, 58
 orthoclase-quartz-water system, 58,
 59
Alcohols, 92, 144–145
Aldehydes, 92
Alkali,
 ion-exchange, 63
 magmas, 67, 68
 salts, 63
Alkali feldspars, 23, 26, 33
 leucite-nepheline system, 67
Alkali halides, 63, 147, 328
Alkaline rocks, 64–69

Alkyl halides, 185–188
Allyl vinyl ethers, 183–184
Aluminium, 265, 269, 300
 oxide, 21, 296
 oxide-magnesium oxide-silica-water
 system, 25
 calcium oxide system, 27
Amine bases, 153–154
Ammonia, 34, 92, 93, 101, 106–107, 152,
 154
Ammonium,
 alum, 308
 cyanate-urea system, 196
 salts, quaternary, 195
Amphiboles, 8, 9, 23–24, 42
i-amyl vinyl ether, 194
Analcite, 32, 67, 69
 water-argon system, 32, 33
Anatectic model, 60–61
Andalusite, 9, 20
Anisotropic,
 crystals, 242
 stress, 219, 255, 260, 269
Annite-phlogopite system, 37
Anorthite-diopside,
 silica system, 22, 40, 58
 solid solution, 21
 water system, 26
Anthophyllite, 24
Antiferromagnetic materials, 301–303
Antimony, 320
Apatite, 36
Aragonite, 321
Argon, 17, 236, 327
 carbon dioxide, 73
 water, 73
 water-analcite, 32–33
Arsenic-iron-sulphur system, 31
Arsenopyrite, 31
Atomic interactions, 267
Austenite-ferrite transition, 282
2 : 2', azo-bis-isobutyronitrile, 175